LIST OF VASCULAR PLANTS
OF THE BRITISH ISLES

LIST OF
VASCULAR PLANTS
OF THE
BRITISH ISLES

D. H. KENT

prepared for the
Botanical Society of the British Isles
from the B.S.B.I. Database (Leicester)

BOTANICAL SOCIETY OF THE BRITISH ISLES
LONDON 1992

Published by the Botanical Society of the British Isles
London

© BSBI 1992

ISBN 0 90115 821 6

Production by Geoff Green and Martin Walters
Silent Books
Cambridge CB4 5RA

Camera-ready copy produced in the
Department of Botany, University of Leicester

Printed in Great Britain by Bell & Bain Ltd,
Glasgow

Contents

Preface

More than thirty years have elapsed since the publication of J.E. Dandy's *List of British vascular plants*(1958), during which time have appeared a second and a third edition of the *Flora of the British Isles* (Clapham, Tutin & Warburg 1962; Clapham, Tutin & Moore 1987), together with the five volumes of *Flora Europaea* (Tutin *et al.* 1964-1980) and, more recently, *New Flora of the British Isles* (Stace 1991). These volumes have introduced many nomenclatural and taxonomic changes, while investigation into hybrid plants, greatly stimulated by the appearance of *Hybridization and the flora of the British Isles* (Stace 1975), has resulted in the recognition of many hybrids new to these islands. In addition there has been a marked increase in the number of established aliens, especially of hortal origin, which have merited interest and study, though there is also the fact that Dandy did not include many that were even in 1958 well established. By contrast, the number of extra native taxa recognized has been very low, but there are a few notable examples, e.g. *Gagea bohemica*, and several of the critical genera, e.g. *Limonium* and *Hieracium*, contain newly described species.

The Dandy *List* was a work of great excellence which served generations of British and Irish botanists very well, but it has been overtaken by time. The need for a revised numbered list treating the vascular plants of the British Isles is thus long overdue, and, sponsored by the Botanical Society of the British Isles, the preparation of the present list was commenced in 1985 and completed in November 1991. Between July 1991 and January 1992 the new list was entered into the BSBI Database at the University of Leicester; this now contains the places and dates of publication of all the taxa in this list as well as many additional synonyms. The information in the database will be kept updated.

June 1992

Douglas H. Kent
75 Adelaide Road
West Ealing
London W13 9ED

Introduction

Scope
The plant taxa included in this list are those which are known at the present time to be native to or introduced and established in the United Kingdom of Great Britain (England, Scotland, Wales) and Northern Ireland, the Republic of Ireland (Eire), the Isle of Man and the Channel Islands, as well as extinct native species.   Casual aliens are excluded, with the exception of species which are repeatedly introduced and hence are common every year, e.g. *Lepidium sativum* and *Triticum aestivum*. Also omitted are native taxa that have been claimed for the British Isles but remain unconfirmed, e.g. *Callitriche palustris* and *C. cophocarpa*, and taxa erroneously reported, e.g. *Orobanche cernua*.   Alien species naturalized or established, often for long periods, in the past but now lost, e.g. *Roemeria hybrida* and *Bupleurum rotundifolium*, are also excluded.

   The qualification for the inclusion of an alien (introduced) species is that it must be naturalized or established, competing with other vegetation where this is present, and with a few exceptions regenerating by seed or suckering.   This includes garden plants which have spread to habitats in the wild often far from their original places of cultivation, as well as foreign weeds and other plants often accidentally introduced and which have become established in at least one locality for a period of five years, and persistent and ineradicable garden weeds (e.g. *Oxalis* species).   Species established as only a single plant in but one locality, even if long known, e.g. *Medicago arborea*, are, however, excluded.

Classification
In Dandy (1958) families, genera and species are arranged in the order of a modification of the Bentham and Hooker classification of 1862-1883 that had been updated by Clapham, Tutin & Warburg (1952).   The arrangement of families in the present list follows, for pteridophytes, Derrick *et al.* (1987); for gymnosperms, Tutin *et al.* 1:29-39 (1964); and for angiosperms, Cronquist (1981).   Within each family the definition and arrangement of the genera, species, subspecies and hybrids follow those of Stace (1991).   In turn, the latter work uses the nomenclature established in this list.   The small number of cases where nomenclatural differences may be detected in the two volumes are instances of changes that were found, or that appeared, too late for incorporation in Stace's

ix

Flora. Families, genera and species are numbered serially throughout the list. Thus *Clematis vitalba* is represented by 28/12/1.

Species

The difficulties in formulating an acceptable species concept in the flora of such a small area as the British Isles was stressed by Dandy (1958), and this still applies especially to such taxa as *Cardamine pratensis/palustris* and *Galium mollugo/erectum* among many others. An attempt has been made here, however, to take into account taxonomic studies in Europe as a whole when determining the status of the British and Irish representatives. There are problems too in the segregates or microspecies of *Limonium, Rubus, Alchemilla, Sorbus, Euphrasia, Taraxacum* and *Hieracium*. Dandy (1958) listed taxa such as these under their appropriate aggregate species as indented entries with serial numbers in italic type. In the present list they are treated as 'orthodox' species and are listed under their genera with normal numbering.

Subspecies

Subspecies are virtually the only infra-specific category adopted in the list and are indented under species and numbered a, b, c, etc. Taxonomically they are problematical, for one man's subspecies may be another man's species, variety or even form. In a very few cases cultivars have been recognized *in lieu* of species where the taxon concerned is a garden plant of uncertain parentage.

Varieties and forms appear only in synonymy, and then only when their citation is necessary to define the scope of the taxa to which they are relegated or when they are basionyms.

Hybrids

Both infrageneric (interspecific) and intergeneric hybrids are included in the list. The former appear under whichever species comes first and is linked to the other parent by the 'x' sign, e.g. *Asplenium ruta-muraria* x *A. septentrionale*. If the hybrid has a binomial name, as does the example used, it is linked to the formula by an equals sign, i.e. = *A. x murbeckii*.

Intergeneric hybrids are treated in a similar manner, following the genus that appears first in the list, e.g. *Phyllitis* x *Asplenium*, and if a generic hybrid name is available, as in this case, it appears as = X *Asplenophyllitis*.

Where a hybrid has originated in the wild in the British Isles between a native and an introduced species, or even between two introduced species, it is regarded as native.

Nomenclature
I have endeavoured to provide the correct names of taxa in accordance with Greuter *et al.* (1988). Considerable time has been spent in checking the original descriptions and places and dates of publication of most of the names presented in the list. Abbreviations of authors' names of taxa follow Meikle (1980) whenever they are covered in that work.

Synonyms
Synonyms are printed in italics. The basionym, where applicable, is placed immediately below the accepted name. Other synonyms appear after this in a separate list in alphabetical order. The list of synonyms is not comprehensive but includes all the accepted names used in all the works listed in the **Bibliography**.

A name in synonymy that has been misapplied in earlier works is cited as auct., e.g. *Asplenium serpentini* auct., non Tausch, but where the original perpetrator of the misapplication is known it appears as sensu, e.g. *Rumex elongatus* sensu Trimen, non Guss.

Census
The number of taxa covered by Dandy (1958) and those included in this list are given in the following table:

	Dandy (1958)			Kent (1992)		
	Native	Alien	Total	Native	Alien	Total
Families	132	21	153	125	37	162
Genera	549	171	720	551	309	860
Hybrid-genera	13	0	13	16	1	17
Species (incl. microspecies)	2179	643	2822	2297	1057	3354
Interspecific hybrids *	523	15	538	639	89	728
Extra subspecies	62	11	73	151	40	191

* including hybrids between species in different genera.

Excluded Taxa
The following is a list of taxa that were included by Dandy (1958) but are excluded from the present list. They fall into the various categories mentioned above under **Scope**. A list of *Rubus* species similarly excluded is given in Edees & Newton (1988, pp. 281-283), but two other species omitted from that list are included here.

15/3 *Asplenium fontanum*
21/1x7 *Dryopteris filix-mas*
       x *D. dilatata*
28/2 *Botrychium lanceolatum*
28/3 *B. matricariifolium*
28/4 *B. multifidum*
52/1 *Epimedium alpinum*
60/1 *Roemeria hybrida*
64/1 *Dicentra spectabilis*
66/8x9 *Fumaria officinalis*
       x *F. vaillantii*
66/8x10 *F. officinalis*
       x *F. parviflora*
72/3 *Diplotaxis erucoides*
73/1 *Eruca sativa*
74/3 *Raphanus sativus*
76/3 *Rapistrum orientale*
78/1 *Conringia orientalis*
85/2 *Teesdalia coronopifolia*
90/1 *Bunias erucago*
110/2 *Camelina microcarpa*
119/1 *Cistus incanus*
123/4 *Silene conoidea*
127/3 *Dianthus carthusianorum*
143/4x5 *Spergularia media*
       x *S. marina*
146/4 *Herniaria cinerea*
150/1 *Claytonia virginica*
153/4 *Amaranthus lividus*
154/4x6 *Chenopodium album*
       x *C. berlandieri*
154/4x7 *C. album*
       x *C. opulifolium*
154/4x9 *C. album*
       x *C. ficifolium*
154/5 *C. suecicum*
154/6 *C. berlandieri*
154/8 *C. hircinum*
154/10 *C. pratericola*
161/1 *Phytolacca americana*
200/4 *Astragalus boeticus*
206/8 *Vicia cassubica*
206/13 *V. hybrida*
206/18 *V. narbonensis*
211/11/200 *Rubus gremlii*

211/11/352 *R. histrix*
212/10 *Potentilla thuringiaca*
225/2 *Rosa sempervirens*
229/4 *Crataegus punctata*
232/2 *Sorbus domestica*
256/4 *Oenothera parviflora*
259/3 *Myriophyllum verrucosum*
259/5 *M. heterophyllum*
260/2 *Gunnera manicata*
274/3 *Anthriscus cerefolium*
278/1 *Caucalis platycarpos*
278/2 *C. latifolia*
283/2 *Bupleurum rotundifolium*
313/1 *Laser trilobum*
319/3 *Euphorbia pilosa*
320/4 *Polygonum cognatum*
328/3 *Urtica pilulifera*
343/3 *Salix babylonica*
366/3 *Armeria pseudarmeria*
379/3 *Vinca herbacea*
398/1 *Nonea rosea*
407/2 *Cuscuta epilinum*
413/2 *Solanum pseudocapsicum*
429/2 *Digitalis lanata*
440/1 *Orobanche ramosa*
445/6 *Mentha longifolia*
450/1 *Satureja montana*
455/3 *Salvia sylvestris*
459/1 *Stachys annua*
464/2 *Phlomis samia*
471/3 *Ajuga genevensis*
472/7 *Plantago sempervirens*
512/3 *Inula britannica*
512/7 *I. graveolens*
528/2 *Achillea tomentosa*
533/3 *Chrysanthemum maximum*
544/4 *Centaurea paniculata*
544/5 *C. jacea*
559/3 *Crepis setosa*
559/7 *C. nicaeensis*
581/2 *Najas graminea*
606/5 *Luzula nivea*
618/3 *Crocus sativus*
618/4 *C. biflorus*
621/3.*Gladiolus segetum*

636/2 *Gymnadenia odoratissima*
X 638/1x2 *Platanthera chlorantha*
        x *P. bifolia*
640/2x3 *Ophrys fuciflora*
        x *O. sphegodes*
663/41 *Carex glacialis*

663/53 *C. bicolor*
663/75 **C. crawfordii*
663/79 *C. capitata*
719/2 **Digitaria sanguinalis*
720/2 **Setaria verticillata*
720/3 **S. lutescens*

In addition the following is a list of 15 *Taraxacum* species that were included by Richards (1972) but whose identity is now uncertain; *Taraxacum* was not dealt with fully by Dandy (1958).

9 *Taraxacum glaucinum*
11 *T. gotlandicum*
12 *T. laetum*
13 *T. laetiforme*
25 *T. pseudolacistophyllum*
40 *T. acrifolium*
44 *T. praestans*
63 *T. litorale*

89 *T. valdedentatum*
95 *T. porrectidens*
97 *T. copidophyllum*
112 *T. christiansenii*
126 *T. reflexilobum*
128 *T. canoviride*
130 *T. privum*

Acknowledgements

During the compilation of the list I have been fortunate to receive advice and comments from many friends and correspondents. Three friends, however, are largely responsible for its appearance: Dick Brummitt, ever patient and ever ready to find time to solve my many, often complex, nomenclatural problems; Arthur Chater, providing a steadying influence to my over-enthusiasm and gently curbing some of my more extreme taxonomic and nomenclatural excesses; and Clive Stace, indefatigable in spotting my numerous errors and spelling mistakes and ever helpful in discussions on systematics — my grateful thanks to them all. Mention must also be made of Peter Sell, who not only made me most welcome on my visits to Cambridge but gave freely of his wide experience in the course of our fruitful discussions.

Thanks are also due to the following specialists who provided invaluable help — John Akeroyd, John Bailey and Ann Conolly (Polygonaceae), Jim Bevan, David McCosh and Peter Sell (*Hieracium* and *Pilosella*), Arthur Chater and Dick David (*Carex*), Tom Cope and Clive Stace (Poaceae), Chris Haworth, John Richards and Andrew Dudman (*Taraxacum*), Keith Ferguson (*Salicornia*), Jeanette Fryer (*Cotoneaster*), Gordon Graham and Tony Primavesi (*Rosa*), Ray Harley (*Mentha*), Charles Jeffrey (Asteraceae), Clive Jermy (pteridophytes), David McClintock (Bambusoideae and Ericaceae), Desmond Meikle (*Viola* and *Salix*), Alan Newton (*Rubus*), Noel Pritchard (*Gentianella*), Alan Radcliffe-Smith (*Euphorbia*), Norman Robson (*Hypericum*), William

Stearn (Liliaceae), Peter Taylor (*Utricularia*), David Webb (*Saxifraga*), and Peter Yeo (*Geranium* and *Euphrasia*).

I am grateful too to Charlie Jarvis and William Stearn for help with nomenclatural problems, to the BSBI Database staff at Leicester, and to Abdul Al-Bermani, Richard Gornall, Peter Hall and Clive Stace for assistance in proof reading.

Bibliography

Bean, W.J. (1970-88). *Trees and shrubs hardy in the British Isles*, 8th ed. (revised by Clarke, D.L.), **1-4** + Suppl. John Murray, London.

Blamey, M. & Grey-Wilson, C. (1989). *The illustrated Flora of Britain and northern Europe*. Hodder & Stoughton, London.

Butcher, R.W. (1961). *A new illustrated British Flora*. Leonard Hill (Books), London.

Clapham, A.R., Tutin, T.G. & Warburg, E.F. (1952). *Flora of the British Isles*. Cambridge University Press, Cambridge. 2nd ed. (1962); 3rd ed. (by Clapham, A.R., Tutin, T.G. & Moore, D.M.) (1987).

Clapham, A.R. Tutin, T.G. & Warburg, E.F. (1959). *Excursion flora of the British Isles*. Cambridge University Press, Cambridge. 2nd ed. (1968); 3rd ed. (1981).

Cronquist, A. (1981). *An integrated system of classification of flowering plants*. Columbia University Press, New York.

Curtis, T.G.F. & McGough, H.N. (1988). *The Irish Red Data Book, 1. Vascular plants*. Stationery Office, Dublin.

Dandy, J.E. (1958). *List of British vascular plants*. British Museum, London.

Derrick, L.N., Jermy, A.C. & Paul, A.M. (1987). Checklist of European pteridophytes. *Sommerfeltia*, **6**.

Edees, E.S. & Newton, A.N. (1988). *Brambles of the British Isles*. Ray Society, London.

Ellis, R.G. (1983). *Flowering plants of Wales*. National Museum of Wales, Cardiff.

Greuter, W., *et al.* (eds) (1988). International code of botanical nomenclature. Adopted by the Fourteenth International Botanical Congress, Berlin, July-Aug. 1987. *Regnum Veg.*, **118.**

Greuter, W., Burdet, H.M. & Long, G. (1984—>). *Med-Checklist*, **1—>**. Conservatoire et jardin botaniques, Geneva.

Hubbard, C.E. (1968). *Grasses*, 2nd ed. Penguin Books, Harmondsworth. 3rd ed. (revised by Hubbard, J.C.E.) (1984).

Hyde, H.A. & Wade, A.E. (1962). *Welsh ferns*, 4th ed. National Museum of Wales, Cardiff. 5th ed. (1969); 6th ed. (revised, expanded and rearranged by Harrison, S.G.) (1978).

Jermy, A.C., Arnold, H.R., Farrell, L. & Perring, F.H. (eds) (1978). *Atlas of ferns of the British Isles*. Botanical Society of the British Isles,

London.

Jermy, A.C. & Camus, J. (1991). *The illustrated field guide to ferns and allied plants of the British Isles*. Natural History Museum, London.

Jermy, A. C., Chater, A.O. & David, R.W. (1982). *Sedges of the British Isles*. Botanical Society of the British Isles, London.

Jermy, A.C. & Tutin, T.G. (1968). *British Sedges*. Botanical Society of the British Isles, London.

Lousley, J.E. & Kent, D.H. (1981). *Docks and knotweeds of the British Isles*. Botanical Society of the British Isles, London.

Mabberley, D.J. (1987). *The plant-book*. Cambridge University Press, Cambridge.

Martin, W.K. (1965). *The concise British Flora in colour*. Ebury Press & Michael Joseph, London. 2nd ed. (1968); 3rd ed. (as *The concise British Flora*) (1982).

Meikle, R.D. (1980). *Draft index of author abbreviations compiled at the Herbarium, Royal Botanic Gardens, Kew*. Royal Botanic Gardens, Kew.

Meikle, R.D. (1984). *Willows and poplars of Great Britain and Ireland*. Botanical Society of the British Isles, London.

Mitchell, A. 1974. *The trees of Britain and northern Europe*. Collins, London. 2nd ed. (1982).

Page, C.N. (1982). *The ferns of Britain and Ireland*. Cambridge University Press, Cambridge.

Perring, F.H.. (ed.) (1968). *Critical supplement to the Atlas of the British flora*. Thomas Nelson, London.

Perring, F.H. & Farrell, L. (1977). *British Red Data Book, 1. Vascular plants*. Society for the Promotion of Nature Conservation, Lincoln. 2nd ed. (1983).

Perring, F.H. & Walters, S.M. (1962). *Atlas of the British flora*. Thomas Nelson, London. 2nd ed. (1976); 3rd ed. (1983).

Rich, T.C.G. (1991). *Crucifers of Great Britain and Ireland*. Botanical Society of the British Isles, London.

Richards, A.J. (1972). The *Taraxacum* flora of the British Isles. *Watsonia*, 9, Suppl.

Scannell, M.J.P. & Synnott, D.M. (1972). *Census catalogue of the flora of Ireland*. Stationery Office, Dublin. 2nd ed. (1987).

Stace, C.A. (ed.) (1975). *Hybridization and the flora of the British Isles*. Academic Press, London.

Stace, C.A. (1991). *New Flora of the British Isles*. Cambridge University Press, Cambridge.

Tutin, T.G. (1980). *Umbellifers of the British Isles*. Botanical Society of the British Isles, London.

Tutin, T.G., *et al.* (eds) (1964-1980). *Flora Europaea*, **1-5.** Cambridge University Press, Cambridge.

Walters, S.M., *et al.* (eds) (1984—>). *The European garden flora*, **1—>.** Cambridge University Press, Cambridge.

The following signs are used in the *List* :

*   Alien
†   Extinct

    These signs are uniquely not applied to the genus *Taraxacum*, where our knowledge is still too fragmentary.

LYCOPODIOPSIDA

1 LYCOPODIACEAE

1 HUPERZIA Bernh.

    1 H. selago (L.) Bernh. ex Schrank & C. Martius
    Lycopodium selago L.

2 LYCOPODIELLA Holub
Lepidotis auct., non P. Beauv. ex Mirbel

    1 L. inundata (L.) Holub
    Lycopodium inundatum L.
    Lepidotis inundata (L.) P. Beauv.

3 LYCOPODIUM L.
Lepidotis P. Beauv. ex Mirbel

    1 L. clavatum L.

    2 L. annotinum L.

4 DIPHASIASTRUM Holub

    1 D. alpinum (L.) Holub
    Lycopodium alpinum L.
    Diphasiastrum complanatum (L.) Holub subsp. *alpinum* (L.)
    Jermy; *Diphasium alpinum* (L.) Rothm.

    2 D. complanatum (L.) Holub
    Lycopodium complanatum L.

        a subsp. **issleri** (Rouy) Jermy
        Lycopodium alpinum L. race *issleri* Rouy

1. LYCOPODIACEAE

Diphasiastrum issleri (Rouy) Holub; *Diphasium issleri* (Rouy) Holub; *Lycopodium issleri* (Rouy) Domin

2 SELAGINELLACEAE

1   SELAGINELLA P. Beauv.

   1   **S. selaginoides** (L.) P. Beauv.
       Lycopodium selaginoides L.

   2   ***S. kraussiana** (Kunze) A. Braun
       Lycopodium kraussianum Kunze

3 ISOETACEAE

1   ISOETES L.

   1   **I. lacustris** L.
       Isoetes morei T. Moore

   1 x 2   **I. lacustris** x **I. echinospora**
       Isoetes x brochonii auct., non Mot.

   2   **I. echinospora** Durieu
       Isoetes ? tenella Léman ex Desv.; *I. setacea* auct., non Lam.

   3   **I. histrix** Bory
       Isoetes durieui auct., non Bory

EQUISETOPSIDA

4 EQUISETACEAE

1   EQUISETUM L.

   1   **E. hyemale** L.

   1 x 2   **E. hyemale** x **E. ramosissimum** = **E. x moorei** Newman

1 x 3   **E. hyemale** x **E. variegatum** = **E. x trachyodon** A. Braun

2   ***E. ramosissimum** Desf.

3   **E. variegatum** Schleicher
Equisetum wilsonii Newman

4   **E. fluviatile** L.
Equisetum limosum L.

4 x 5   **E. fluviatile** x **E. arvense** = **E. x litorale** Kühl. ex Rupr.

4 x 8   **E. fluviatile** x **E. palustre** = **E. x dycei** C. Page

5   **E. arvense** L.

5 x 8   **E. arvense** x **E. palustre** = **E. x rothmaleri** C. Page

6   **E. pratense** Ehrh.

6 x 7   **E. pratense** x **E. sylvaticum** = **E. x mildeanum** Rothm.

7   **E. sylvaticum** L.

7 x 9   **E. sylvaticum** x **E. telmateia** = **E. x bowmanii** C. Page

8   **E. palustre** L.

8 x 9   **E. palustre** x **E. telmateia** = **E. x font-queri** Rothm.

9   **E. telmateia** Ehrh.

PTEROPSIDA

5 OPHIOGLOSSACEAE

1   **OPHIOGLOSSUM** L.

1   **O. vulgatum** L.

2   **O. azoricum** C. Presl
Ophioglossum polyphyllum auct., non A. Braun; *O. vulgatum*

L. subsp. *ambiguum* (Cosson & Germ.) E. Warb.; *O. vulgatum* L. subsp. *polyphyllum* sensu E. Warb., non (A. Braun) E. Warb.; *O. vulgatum* L. var. *islandicum* Á. Löve & D. Löve, nom. nud.

3   **O. lusitanicum** L.

2   **BOTRYCHIUM** Sw.

    1   **B. lunaria** (L.) Sw.
       Osmunda lunaria L.

6 OSMUNDACEAE

1   **OSMUNDA** L.

    1   **O. regalis** L.

7 ADIANTACEAE
Cryptogrammaceae; Gymnogrammaceae

1   **CRYPTOGRAMMA** R. Br.

    1   **C. crispa** (L.) R. Br. ex Hook.
       Osmunda crispa L.

2   **ANOGRAMMA** Link

    1   **A. leptophylla** (L.) Link
       Polypodium leptophyllum L.

3   **ADIANTUM** L.

    1   **A. capillus-veneris** L.

8 *PTERIDACEAE

1 *PTERIS L.

    1 *P. cretica L.

9 MARSILEACEAE

1 PILULARIA L.

    1 P. globulifera L.

10 HYMENOPHYLLACEAE

1 HYMENOPHYLLUM Smith

    1 H. tunbrigense (L.) Smith
    Trichomanes tunbrigense L.

    2 H. wilsonii Hook.
    Hymenophyllum peltatum auct., non (Poiret) Desv.; *H.*
    unilaterale auct., non Bory

2 TRICHOMANES L.

    1 T. speciosum Willd.
    Trichomanes radicans auct., non Sw.; *Vandenboschia speciosa*
    (Willd.) Kunkel

11 POLYPODIACEAE

1 POLYPODIUM L.

    1 P. vulgare L.

    1 x 2 P. vulgare x **P. interjectum = P. x mantoniae** Rothm. & U.
    Schneider

1 x 3   **P. vulgare** x **P. cambricum** = **P. x font-queri** Rothm.

2   **P. interjectum** Shivas
Polypodium australe auct., non Fée; *P. serratum* auct., non
(Willd.) Sauter nec Aublet; *P. vulgare* L. subsp. *prionodes*
(Asch.) Rothm.; *P. vulgare* auct., non L.

2 x 3   **P. interjectum** x **P. cambricum** = **P. x shivasiae** Rothm.
Polypodium x rothmaleri Shivas, nom. illegit.

3   **P. cambricum** L.
Polypodium australe Fée; *P. australe* Fée var. *cambricum* (L.)
Kunkel; *P. cambricum* L. subsp. *australe* (Fée) Greuter &
Burdet; *P. cambricum* L. subsp. *serrulatum* (F. Schultz ex
Arcang.) Pichi Serm.; *P. vulgare* L. subsp. *serrulatum* F.
Schultz ex Arcang.; *P. vulgare* L. var. *cambricum* (L.) Light.

2 *PHYMATODES C. Presl

1 *P. diversifolia (Willd.) Pichi Serm.
Polypodium diversifolium Willd.
Microsorum diversifolium (Willd.) Copel.

12 *DICKSONIACEAE

1 *DICKSONIA L'Hér.

1 *D. antarctica Labill.

13 DENNSTAEDTIACEAE

1   **PTERIDIUM** Gled. ex Scop.

1   **P. aquilinum** (L.) Kuhn
Pteris aquilina L.
Pteridium aquilinum (L.) Kuhn subsp. *atlanticum* C. Page; *P.
aquilinum* (L.) Kuhn subsp. *latiusculum* C. Page, nom. inval.;
Pteris latiuscula sensu C. Page, non Desv.

14 THELYPTERIDACEAE

1 **THELYPTERIS** Schmidel

    1 **T. palustris** Schott
    Dryopteris thelypteris (L.) A. Gray; *Thelypteris thelypteroides*
    (Michaux) Holub subsp. *glabra* Holub

2 **PHEGOPTERIS** (C. Presl) Fée
Polypodium sect. *Phegopteris* C. Presl

    1 **P. connectilis** (Michaux) Watt
    Polypodium connectile Michaux
    Dryopteris phegopteris (L.) C. Chr.; *Phegopteris polypodioides* Fée;
    Thelypteris phegopteris (L.) Slosson

3 **OREOPTERIS** Holub

    1 **O. limbosperma** (Bellardi ex All.) Holub
    Polypodium limbosperma Bellardi ex All.
    Dryopteris limbosperma (Bellardi ex All.) Bech.; *D. oreopteris*
    (Ehrh.) Maxon; *Lastrea limbosperma* (Bellardi ex All.) Holub
    & Pouzar; *Thelypteris limbosperma* (Bellardi ex All.) H.P.
    Fuchs; *T. oreopteris* (Ehrh.) Slosson

15 ASPLENIACEAE

1 **PHYLLITIS** Hill

    1 **P. scolopendrium** (L.) Newman
    Asplenium scolopendrium L.

1 x 2 **PHYLLITIS** x **ASPLENIUM** = **X ASPLENOPHYLLITIS** Alston

    1 x 1 **P. scolopendrium** x **A. adiantum-nigrum** = **X A. jacksonii**
    Alston
    Asplenium x jacksonii (Alston) Lawalrée

1 × 3   **P. scolopendrium** × **A. obovatum** = **X A. microdon** (T. Moore) Alston
Asplenium marinum L. var. *microdon* T. Moore
Asplenium x microdon (T. Moore) Lovis & Vida

1 × 5   **P. scolopendrium** × **A. trichomanes** = **X A. confluens** (T. Moore ex Lowe) Alston
Asplenium trichomanes L. var. *confluens* T. Moore ex Lowe
Asplenium x confluens (T. Moore ex Lowe) Lawalrée

2   ASPLENIUM L.

     1   **A. adiantum-nigrum** L.
Asplenium cuneifolium sensu R.H. Roberts & Stirling et auct., non Viv.; *A. serpentini* auct., non Tausch

1 × 2   **A. adiantum-nigrum** × **A. onopteris** = **A. x ticinense** D. Meyer

1 × 3   **A. adiantum-nigrum** × **A. obovatum** = **A. x sarniense** Sleep
Asplenium x obovatum auct., non Viv.

1 × 8   **A. adiantum-nigrum** × **A. septentrionale** = **A. x contrei** Callé, Lovis & Reichst.
Asplenium x souchei auct., non Litard.

     2   **A. onopteris** L.
Asplenium adiantum-nigrum L. subsp. *onopteris* (L.) Heufler

     3   **A. obovatum** Viv.

         a   subsp. **lanceolatum** (Fiori) Pinto da Silva
Asplenium fontanum (L.) Bernh. subsp. *lanceolatum* Fiori
Asplenium billotii F. Schultz; *A. lanceolatum* Hudson, non Forsskål; *A. obovatum* Viv. subsp. *billotii* (F. Schultz) O. Bolòs, Vigo, Masalles & Ninot

     4   **A. marinum** L.

     5   **A. trichomanes** L.

         a   subsp. **trichomanes**

    b   subsp. **quadrivalens** D. Meyer
         Asplenium trichomanes L. subsp. *lovisii* Rothm.

    c   subsp. **pachyrachis** (Christ) Lovis & Reichst.
         Asplenium trichomanes L. sublusus *pachyrachis* Christ

5 x 7   **A. trichomanes** x **A. ruta-muraria** = **A. x clermontiae** Syme

5 x 8   **A. trichomanes** x **A. septentrionale** = **A. x alternifolium**
       Wulfen
       Asplenium x breynii auct., non Retz.; *A. x germanicum* auct., non
       Asch. & Graebner

    6   **A. trichomanes-ramosum** L.
       Asplenium viride Hudson

    7   **A. ruta-muraria** L.

7 x 8   **A. ruta-muraria** x **A. septentrionale** = **A. x murbeckii**
       Doerfler
       Asplenium x suevicum Bertsch ex D. Meyer

    8   **A. septentrionale** (L.) Hoffm.
       Acrostichum septentrionale L.

3   CETERACH Willd.

    1   **C. officinarum** Willd.
       Asplenium ceterach L.

16 WOODSIACEAE
Athyriaceae

1 *MATTEUCCIA Tod.

    1   *M. struthiopteris** (L.) Tod.
       Osmunda struthiopteris L.

2 *ONOCLEA L.

    1   *O. sensibilis** L.

3 **ATHYRIUM** Roth

1 **A. filix-femina** (L.) Roth
Polypodium filix-femina L.

2 **A. distentifolium** Tausch ex Opiz
Athyrium alpestre (Hoppe) Ryl. ex T. Moore, non Clairv.

3 **A. flexile** (Newman) Druce
Pseudathyrium flexile Newman
Athyrium alpestre Clairv. var. *flexile* (Newman) Milde; *A. distentifolium* Tausch ex Opiz var. *flexile* (Newman) Jermy

4 **GYMNOCARPIUM** Newman
Carpogymnia (H.P. Fuchs) Á. Löve & D. Löve

1 **G. dryopteris** (L.) Newman
Polypodium dryopteris L.
Carpogymnia dryopteris (L.) Á. Löve & D. Löve; *Gymnocarpium disjunctum* (Rupr.) R.-C. Ching; *Phegopteris dryopteris* (L.) Fée; *Thelypteris dryopteris* (L.) Slosson

2 **G. robertianum** (Hoffm.) Newman
Polypodium robertianum Hoffm.
Carpogymnia robertiana (Hoffm.) Á. Löve & D. Löve; *Dryopteris robertiana* (Hoffm.) C.Chr.; *Gymnocarpium dryopteris* (L.) Newman var. *pumilum* (DC.) Boivin; *Phegopteris robertiana* (Hoffm.) A. Braun ex Asch.; *Thelypteris robertiana* (Hoffm.) Slosson

5 **CYSTOPTERIS** Bernh.

1 **C. fragilis** (L.) Bernh.
Polypodium fragile L.
Cystopteris alpina auct., non (Lam.) Desv.; *C. regia* (L.) Desv.

2 **C. dickieana** Sim
Cystopteris fragilis auct., non (L.) Bernh.

3 **C. montana** (Lam.) Desv.
Polypodium montanum Lam.

6 WOODSIA R. Br.

> **1 W. ilvensis** (L.) R. Br.
> *Acrostichum ilvense* L.

> **2 W. alpina** (Bolton) Gray
> *Acrostichum alpinum* Bolton

17 DRYOPTERIDACEAE

1 POLYSTICHUM Roth

> **1 P. setiferum** (Forsskål) Moore ex Woynar
> *Polypodium setiferum* Forsskål

> **1 x 2 P. setiferum** x **P. aculeatum** = **P. x bicknellii** (Christ) Hahne
> *Aspidium x bicknellii* Christ

> **1 x 3 P. setiferum** x **P. lonchitis** = **P. x lonchitiforme** (Hal.) Bech.
> *Aspidium x lonchitiforme* Hal.

> **2 P. aculeatum** (L.) Roth
> *Polypodium aculeatum* L.

> **2 x 3 P. aculeatum** x **P. lonchitis** = **P. x illyricum** (Borbás) Hahne
> *Aspidium x illyricum* Borbás
> *Polystichum x eberlei* D. Meyer

> **3 P. lonchitis** (L.) Roth
> *Polypodium lonchitis* L.

2 *CYRTOMIUM C. Presl
Phanerophlebia C. Presl

> **1 *C. falcatum** (L.f.) C. Presl
> *Polypodium falcatum* L.f.
> *Polystichum falcatum* (L.f.) Diels; *Phanerophlebia falcata* (L.f.) Copel.

3   DRYOPTERIS Adans.

1   D. oreades Fomin
Dryopteris abbreviata Newman ex Manton, non DC. nec
(Schrader) Kuntze; *D. filix-mas* (L.) Schott subsp. *oreades*
(Fomin) O. Bolòs & Vigo

1 x 2   D. oreades x **D. filix-mas** = **D. x mantoniae** Fraser-Jenkins &
Corley

1 x 5   D. oreades x **D. aemula** = **D. x pseudoabbreviata** Jermy

2   D. filix-mas (L.) Schott
Polypodium filix-mas L.

2 x 3   D. filix-mas x **D. affinis** = **D. x complexa** Fraser-Jenkins
Dryopteris x tavelii auct., non Rothm.

2 x 8   D. filix-mas x **D. carthusiana** = **D. x brathaica** Fraser-Jenkins
& Reichst.
Dryopteris x remota auct., non (A. Braun ex Doell) Druce;
Lastrea x remota sensu T. Moore, non (A. Braun ex Doell) T.
Moore

3   D. affinis (Lowe) Fraser-Jenkins
Nephrodium affine Lowe
Aspidium affine auct., non Blume nec Fischer & C. Meyer

a   subsp. **affinis**
Dryopteris pseudomas (Wollaston) Holub & Pouzar;
Lastrea pseudomas Wollaston

b   subsp. **cambrensis** Fraser-Jenkins
Dryopteris affinis (Lowe) Fraser-Jenkins subsp.
stilluppensis sensu Fraser-Jenkins, non (Sabr.) Fraser-
Jenkins; *D. cambrensis* (Fraser-Jenkins) Beitel & Buck;
D. stilluppensis sensu Holub, non (Sabr.) Holub

c   subsp. **borreri** (Newman) Fraser-Jenkins
Dryopteris filix-mas (L.) Schott var. *borreri* Newman
Dryopteris affinis (Lowe) Fraser-Jenkins subsp. *robusta*
Fraser-Jenkins, nom. nud., non Sabr.; *D. affinis*
(Lowe) Fraser-Jenkins subsp. *stilluppensis* (Sabr.)
Fraser-Jenkins; *D. affinis* (Lowe) Fraser-Jenkins var.
robusta Oberholzer & Tavel ex Fraser-Jenkins &

Salvo; *D. borreri* (Newman) Newman ex Oberholzer
& Tavel; *D. filix-mas* (L.) Schott subsp. *abbreviata*
(DC.) Schidlay; *D. mediterranea* sensu Holub et auct.,
non Fomin; *D. mediterranea* sensu Holub et auct., non
Fomin var. *robusta* (Oberholzer & Tavel ex Fraser-
Jenkins) Holub; *D. paleacea* auct., non (Sw.) Hand.-
Mazz. nec (Sw.) C. Chr.; *D. pseudomas* (Wollaston)
Holub & Pouzar subsp. *robusta* (Oberholzer & Tavel
ex Fraser-Jenkins) Holub; *D. pseudomas* (Wollaston)
Holub & Pouzar, pro parte excl. typ.; *D. tavelii*
Rothm.; *D. woynarii* auct., non Rothm.

4 †**D. remota** (A. Braun ex Doell) Druce
Aspidium rigidum Sw. var. *remotum* A. Braun ex Doell
Dryopteris woynarii Rothm.

5 **D. aemula** (Aiton) Kuntze
Polypodium aemulum Aiton

6 **D. submontana** (Fraser-Jenkins & Jermy) Fraser-Jenkins
Dryopteris villarii (Bellardi) Woynar ex Schinz & Thell. subsp.
submontana Fraser-Jenkins & Jermy
Dryopteris villarii auct., non (Bellardi) Woynar ex Schinz &
Thell.

7 **D. cristata** (L.) A. Gray
Polypodium cristatum L.

7 x 8 **D. cristata** x **D. carthusiana** = **D. x uliginosa** (A. Braun ex
Doell) Kuntze ex Druce
Aspidium spinulosum Sw., nom. illegit. var. *uliginosum* A.
Braun ex Doell

8 **D. carthusiana** (Villars) H.P. Fuchs
Polypodium carthusianum Villars
Dryopteris lanceolatocristata (Hoffm.) Alston; *D. spinulosa*
Kuntze

8 x 9 **D. carthusiana** x **D. dilatata** = **D. x deweveri** (J. Jansen)
Wachter
Aspidium x deweveri J. Jansen

8 x 10 **D. carthusiana** x **D. expansa** = **D. x sarvelae** Fraser-Jenkins &
Jermy

9 **D. dilatata** (Hoffm.) A. Gray
Polypodium dilatatum Hoffm.
Aspidium dilatatum (Hoffm.) Smith; *Dryopteris austriaca* sensu
Woynar ex Schinz & Thell. et auct., non Jacq.; *D. carthusiana*
(Villars) H.P. Fuchs subsp. *dilatata* (Hoffm.) O. Bolòs, Vigo,
Massales & Ninot; *Lastrea dilatata* (Hoffm.) C. Presl

9 x 10 **D. dilatata x D. expansa = D. x ambroseae** Fraser-Jenkins &
Jermy

10 **D. expansa** (C. Presl) Fraser-Jenkins & Jermy
Nephrodium expansum C. Presl
Dryopteris assimilis S. Walker; *D. carthusiana* (Villars) H.P.
Fuchs subsp. *assimilis* (S. Walker) O. Bolòs, Vigo, Massales
& Ninot; *D. expansa* (C. Presl) Fraser-Jenkins & Jermy var.
alpina (T. Moore) Vigne; *D. spinulosa* Kuntze subsp. *assimilis*
(S. Walker) Schidlay

18 BLECHNACEAE

1 **BLECHNUM** L.
Lomaria Willd.

1 **B. spicant** (L.) Roth
Osmunda spicant L.

2 ***B. cordatum** (Desv.) Hieron.
Lomaria cordata Desv.
Blechnum capense auct., non (L.) Schldl.; *B. chilense* (Kaulf.)
Mett.; *B. magellanicum* auct., non Mett.; *B. tabulare* sensu
Druce et auct., non (Thunb.) Kuhn

19 *AZOLLACEAE

1 ***AZOLLA** Lam.

1 ***A. filiculoides** Lam.
Azolla caroliniana Willd.

PINOPSIDA

20 PINACEAE

1 *ABIES Miller

1 *A. alba Miller

2 *A. grandis (Douglas ex D. Don) Lindley
Pinus grandis Douglas ex D. Don

3 *A. procera Rehder
Abies nobilis (Douglas ex D. Don) Lindley, non A. Dietr.

2 *PSEUDOTSUGA Carrière

1 *P. menziesii (Mirbel) Franco
Abies menziesii Mirbel
Pseudotsuga taxifolia Britton, nom. illegit.

3 *TSUGA (Antoine) Carrière
Pinus sect. *Tsuga* Antoine

1 *T. heterophylla (Raf.) Sarg.
Abies heterophylla Raf.

4 *PICEA A. Dietr.

1 *P. sitchensis (Bong.) Carrière
Pinus sitchensis Bong.

2 *P. abies (L.) Karsten
Pinus abies L.

5 *LARIX Miller

1 *L. decidua Miller

1 x 2 *L. decidua x L. kaempferi = L. x marschlinsii Coaz
Larix x eurolepis A. Henry, nom. illegit.; *L. x henryana* Rehder

2 ***L. kaempferi** (Lindley) Carrière
Abies kaempferi Lindley
Larix leptolepis (Siebold & Zucc.) Endl.

6 *CEDRUS Trew

1 ***C. deodara** (Roxb. ex D. Don) Don
Pinus deodara Roxb. ex D. Don
Cedrus libani A. Rich. subsp. *deodara* (Roxb. ex D. Don) Sell

2 ***C. atlantica** (Endl.) Carrière
Pinus atlantica Endl.
Cedrus libani A. Rich. subsp. *atlantica* (Endl.) Battand. & Trabut

7 PINUS L.

1 **P. sylvestris** L.
Pinus sylvestris L. subsp. *scotica* (P.K. Schott) E. Warb.

2 ***P. nigra** Arnold

a *subsp. **nigra**
Pinus nigricans Host

b *subsp. **laricio** Maire
Pinus nigra Arnold var. *maritima* (Aiton) Melville

3 ***P. contorta** Douglas ex Loudon

4 ***P. pinaster** Aiton
Pinus pinaster Aiton subsp. *atlantica* Villar

5 ***P. radiata** D. Don

6 ***P. strobus** L.

21 CUPRESSACEAE

1 *CUPRESSUS L.

1 ***C. macrocarpa** Hartweg ex Gordon

2 *CHAMAECYPARIS Spach
Retinispora Siebold & Zucc.

    1 *C. lawsoniana (A. Murray) Parl.
    Cupressus lawsoniana A. Murray

    2 *C. pisifera (Siebold & Zucc.) Siebold & Zucc.
    Retinispora pisifera Siebold & Zucc.

3 *THUJA L.

    1 *T. plicata Donn ex D. Don

4 JUNIPERUS L.

    1 J. communis L.

        a subsp. **communis**

        b subsp. **alpina** Celak.
        Juniperus communis L. subsp. *nana* (Willd.) Syme; *J. nana*
        Willd.; *J. sibirica* Lodd. ex Burgsd.

22 *ARAUCARIACEAE

1 *ARAUCARIA A.L. Juss.

    1 *A. araucana (Molina) K. Koch
    Pinus araucana Molina
    Araucaria imbricata Pavón

23 TAXACEAE

1 TAXUS L.

    1 T. baccata L.

MAGNOLIOPSIDA

MAGNOLIIDAE

24 *LAURACEAE

1 *LAURUS L.

　　1 *L. nobilis L.

25 *ARISTOLOCHIACEAE

1 *ASARUM L.

　　1 *A. europaeum L.

2 *ARISTOLOCHIA L.

　　1 *A. clematitis L.

　　2 *A. rotunda L.

26 NYMPHAEACEAE

1 NYMPHAEA L.

　　1 N. alba L.

　　　　a subsp. **alba**

　　　　b subsp. **occidentalis** (Ostenf.) N. Hylander
　　　　Nymphaea alba L. var. *occidentalis* Ostenf.
　　　　Nymphaea occidentalis (Ostenf.) Moss

2 NUPHAR Smith

　　1 N. lutea (L.) Smith
　　Nymphaea lutea L.

1 x 2   N. lutea x **N. pumila = N. x spenneriana** Gaudin
Nymphaea x intermedia Ledeb.

2   N. pumila (Timm) DC.
Nymphaea lutea L. var. *pumila* Timm

3   *N. advena (Aiton) W.T. Aiton
Nymphaea advena Aiton
Nuphar lutea (L.) Smith subsp. *advena* (Aiton) Kartesz &
Gandhi

27 CERATOPHYLLACEAE

1   CERATOPHYLLUM L.

   1   C. demersum L.

   2   C. submersum L.

28 RANUNCULACEAE

1   CALTHA L.

   1   C. palustris L.
   Caltha minor sensu Clapham, non Miller; *C. palustris* L. subsp.
   minor sensu Graebner et auct., non (Miller) Graebner; *C.*
   palustris L. var. *flabellifolia* (Pursh) Torrey & A. Gray; *C.*
   radicans T. Forster

2   TROLLIUS L.

   1   T. europaeus L.

3   HELLEBORUS L.

   1   H. foetidus L.

   2   H. viridis L.

    a   subsp. **occidentalis** (Reuter) Schiffner
          Helleborus occidentalis Reuter

3 *H. orientalis Lam.

4 *ERANTHIS Salisb.

    1 *E. hyemalis (L.) Salisb.
        Helleborus hyemalis L.

5 *NIGELLA L.

    1 *N. damascena L.

6 ACONITUM L.

    1 A. napellus L.

        a subsp. **napellus**
           Aconitum anglicum Stapf

        b subsp. **vulgare** (DC.) Rouy & Fouc.
           Aconitum vulgare DC.
           Aconitum compactum (Reichb.) Gayer

1 x var *A. napellus x A. variegatum L. = A. x cammarum L.
        Aconitum x bicolor auct., non Schultes; *A. x variegatum* auct.,
        non L.

    2 *A. vulparia Reichb.
        Aconitum lycoctonum L. subsp. *vulparia* (Reichb.) Nyman

7 *CONSOLIDA (DC.) Gray
  Delphinium sect. *Consolida* DC.

    1 *C. ajacis (L.) Schur
        Delphinium ajacis L.
        Consolida ambigua auct., non (L.) P. Ball & Heyw.; *C. gayanum*
        (Wilm.) Laínz; *Delphinium ambiguum* auct., non L.; *D.*
        gayanum Wilm.

8 ACTAEA L.

    1 A. spicata L.

9 ANEMONE L.

    1 A. nemorosa L.

    2 *A. apennina L.

    3 *A. ranunculoides L.

hup x **vit** *A. hupehensis** (Lemoine) Lemoine x **A. vitifolia** Buch.-Ham.
    ex DC. = **A. x hybrida** Paxton
    Anemone x japonica hort., non (Thunb.) Siebold & Zucc.

10 *HEPATICA Miller

    1 *H. nobilis Schreber
    Anemone hepatica L.

11 PULSATILLA Miller
Anemone subgen. *Pulsatilla* (Miller) Thome

    1 P. vulgaris Miller
    Anemone pulsatilla L.

12 CLEMATIS L.

    1 C. vitalba L.

    2 *C. flammula L.

    3 *C. tangutica (Maxim.) Korsh
    Clematis orientalis L. var. *tangutica* Maxim.

    4 *C. montana Buch.-Ham. ex DC.

    5 *C. viticella L.

13 RANUNCULUS L.
Batrachium (DC.) Gray; *Ficaria* Schaeffer

1   **R. acris** L.

2   **R. repens** L.

3   **R. bulbosus** L.
    Ranunculus bulbosus L. subsp. *bulbifer* (Jordan) P. Fourn.

4   **R. sardous** Crantz

5   ***R. marginatus** Urv.
    Ranunculus marginatus Urv. subsp. *trachycarpus* (Fischer & C. Meyer) Hayek

6   ***R. muricatus** L.

7   **R. parviflorus** L.

8   **R. arvensis** L.

9   **R. paludosus** Poiret

10   **R. auricomus** L.

11   **R. sceleratus** L.

12   **R. lingua** L.

13   **R. flammula** L.

    a   subsp. **flammula**

    b   subsp. **minimus** (A. Bennett) Padm.
    Ranunculus flammula L. forma *minimus* A. Bennett

    c   subsp. **scoticus** (E. Marshall) Clapham
    Ranunculus scoticus E. Marshall

13 x 14   **R. flammula** x **R. reptans** = **R. x levenensis** Druce ex Gornall

14   **R. reptans** L.

15   **R. ophioglossifolius** Villars

16 *R. aconitifolius* L.

17 **R. ficaria** L.
Ficaria verna Hudson

    a   subsp. **ficaria**
       Ranunculus ficaria L. var. *fertilis* Clapham, nom. inval.

    b   subsp. **bulbilifer** Lambinon
       Ficaria bulbifera Holub; *F. verna* Hudson agsp. *bulbifer* Á.
       Löve & D. Löve; *F. verna* Hudson subsp. *bulbilifer*
       (Lambinon) Dostál; *Ranunculus ficaria* L. subsp.
       bulbifer Lawalrée, nom. illegit.; *R. ficaria* L. var.
       bulbifera Marsden-Jones, non Albert

    c   subsp. **ficariiformis** (F. Schultz) Rouy & Fouc.
       Ranunculus ficariiformis F. Schultz

18 **R. hederaceus** L.

19 **R. omiophyllus** Ten.
Ranunculus lenormandi F. Schultz

19 x 20 **R. omiophyllus** x **R. tripartitus** = **R. x novae-forestae** S.
Webster
Ranunculus x lutarius auct., non (Revel) Bouvet

19 x 24 **R. omiophyllus** x **R. peltatus** = **R. x hiltonii** Groves & J.
Groves

20 **R. tripartitus** DC.
Ranunculus lutarius (Revel) Bouvet

20 x 23 **R. tripartitus** x **R. aquatilis**

21 **R. baudotii** Godron
Ranunculus peltatus Schrank subsp. *baudotii* (Godron) Meikle
ex C. Cook

21 x 22 **R. baudotii** x **R. trichophyllus** = **R. x segretii** A. Félix

21 x 23 **R. baudotii** x **R. aquatilis** = **R. x lambertii** A. Félix

21 x 24 **R. baudotii** x **R. peltatus**

22 **R. trichophyllus** Chaix
Ranunculus drouetii F. Schultz; *R. trichophyllus* Chaix subsp.
drouetii (F. Schultz) Clapham

22 x 23 **R. trichophyllus** x **R. aquatilis** = **R. x lutzii** A. Félix

22 x 24 **R. trichophyllus** x **R. peltatus**

22 x 26 **R. trichophyllus** x **R. fluitans** = **R. x bachii** Wirtgen
Ranunculus x pseudofluitans auct., non (Syme) Newbould ex
Baker & Foggitt

22 x 27 **R. trichophyllus** x **R. circinatus**
Ranunculus x glueckii A. Félix, nom. inval.

23 **R. aquatilis** L.
Ranunculus aquatilis L. subsp. *heterophyllus* (Wigg.) Syme; *R.
aquatilis* L. subsp. *radians* (Revel) Clapham; *R. heterophyllus*
Wigg.

23 x 24 **R. aquatilis** x **R. peltatus** = **R. x virzionensis** A. Félix

23 x 26 **R. aquatilis** x **R. fluitans**
Ranunculus x bachii auct., non Wirtgen; *R. x pseudofluitans*
auct., non (Syme) Newbould ex Baker & Foggitt

24 **R. peltatus** Schrank
Ranunculus aquatilis L. subsp. *peltatus* (Schrank) Syme; *R.
aquatilis* L. subsp. *sphaerospermus* sensu Clapham, non
(Boiss. & Blanche) Clapham; *R. floribundus* Bab.; *R.
sphaerospermus* sensu Druce, non Boiss. & Blanche

24 x 26 **R. peltatus** x **R. fluitans** = **R. x kelchoensis** S. Webster

25 **R. penicillatus** (Dumort.) Bab.
Batrachium penicillatum Dumort.

a subsp. **penicillatus**

b subsp. **pseudofluitans** (Syme) S. Webster
Ranunculus aquatilis L. var. *pseudofluitans* Syme
Ranunculus aquatilis L. subsp. *pseudofluitans* (Syme)
Clapham; *R. calcareus* Butcher; *R. peltatus* Schrank
subsp. *pseudofluitans* (Syme) C. Cook, nom. inval.; *R.
penicillatus* (Dumort.) Bab. var. *calcareus* (Butcher) C.

Cook; *R. penicillatus* (Dumort.) Bab. var. *vertumnus*
C. Cook; *R. pseudofluitans* (Syme) Newbould ex
Baker & Foggitt

26   R. fluitans Lam.
Ranunculus aquatilis auct., non L.

26 x 27   R. fluitans x **R. circinatus**

27   R. circinatus Sibth.
Ranunculus aquatilis auct., non L.

14 *ADONIS L.

1 *A. annua L.

15 MYOSURUS L.

1   M. minimus L.

16 AQUILEGIA L.

1   A. vulgaris L.

2 *A. pyrenaica DC.
Aquilegia alpina auct., non L.

17 THALICTRUM L.

1 *T. aquilegiifolium L.

2 *T. delavayi Franchet

3   T. flavum L.

4   T. minus L.
Thalictrum arenarium Butcher; *T. babingtonii* Butcher; *T.*
capillare Reichb.; *T. collinum* auct., non Wallr.; *T. dunense*
auct., non Dumort.; *T. expansum* Jordan; *T. majus* Crantz; *T.*
minus L. subsp. *arenarium* (Butcher) Clapham; *T. minus* L.
subsp. *elatum* (Jacq.) Kerguélen; *T. minus* L. subsp. *majus*

(Crantz) J.D. Hook.; *T. montanum* Wallr.; *T. umbrosum* Butcher

5   **T. alpinum** L.

29 BERBERIDACEAE

1   **BERBERIS** L.

1   **B. vulgaris** L.

2   ***B. thunbergii** DC.

3   ***B. glaucocarpa** Stapf
Berberis aristata auct., non DC.

4   ***B. wilsoniae** Hemsley

5   ***B. aggregata** C. Schneider

6   ***B. gagnepainii** C. Schneider

7   ***B. julianae** C. Schneider

8   ***B. buxifolia** Lam.

9   ***B. darwinii** Hook.

9 x emp   ***B. darwinii** x **B. empetrifolia** Lam. = **B. x stenophylla** Lindley

2   ***MAHONIA** Nutt.

1   ***M. aquifolium** (Pursh) Nutt.
Berberis aquifolium Pursh

1 x rep   ***M. aquifolium** x **M. repens** (Lindley) G. Don = **M. x decumbens** Stace
Mahonia x repens auct., non (Lindley) G. Don

30 PAPAVERACEAE

1 PAPAVER L.

1 **P. orientale* L.

2 **P. atlanticum* (Ball) Cosson
Papaver rupifragum Boiss. & Reuter var. *atlanticum* Ball
Papaver lateritium sensu Robbins et auct., non Koch

3 **P. somniferum* L.

    a subsp. **somniferum**
    Papaver somniferum L. subsp. *hortense* (Hussenot) Syme

    b subsp. **setigerum** (DC.) Arcang.
    Papaver setigerum DC.

4 **P. rhoeas** L.

4 x 5 **P. rhoeas** x **P. dubium** = **P. x hungaricum** Borbás
Papaver x expectatum Fedde; *P. x strigosum* auct., non (Boenn.)
Schur

5 **P. dubium** L.

    a subsp. **dubium**

    b subsp. **lecoqii** (Lamotte) Syme
    Papaver lecoqii Lamotte

6 **P. hybridum** L.

7 **P. argemone** L.

2 MECONOPSIS Viguier

    1 **M. cambrica** (L.) Viguier
    Papaver cambricum L.

3 *ARGEMONE L.

    1 **A. mexicana* L.

4   GLAUCIUM Miller

    1   G. flavum Crantz

5   CHELIDONIUM L.

    1   C. majus L.

6   *ESCHSCHOLZIA Cham.

    1   *E. californica Cham.

7   *MACLEAYA R. Br.

cor x mic   *M. cordata (Willd.) R. Br. x **M. microcarpa** (Maxim.) Fedde =
    M. x kewensis Turrill
        Bocconia x cordata sensu G.C. Brown ex Druce et auct., non
        Willd.; *Macleaya x cordata* auct., non (Willd.) R. Br.

31 FUMARIACEAE

1   *DICENTRA Bernh.

    1   *D. formosa (Andrews) Walp.
        Fumaria formosa Andrews

2   *CORYDALIS DC.

    1   *C. solida (L.) Clairv.
        Fumaria bulbosa L. var. *solida* L.
        Corydalis bulbosa (L.) DC., nom. illegit.

    2   *C. cava (L.) Schweigger & Koerte
        Fumaria bulbosa L. var. *cava* L.
        Corydalis bulbosa auct., non (L.) DC.

    3   *C. cheilanthifolia Hemsley

3 *PSEUDOFUMARIA Medikus

    1 *P. lutea (L.) Borkh.
      Fumaria lutea L.
      Corydalis lutea (L.) DC.

    2 *P. alba (Miller) Lidén
      Fumaria alba Miller
      Corydalis ochroleuca Koch, nom. illegit.

4 CERATOCAPNOS Durieu

    1 C. claviculata (L.) Lidén
      Fumaria claviculata L.
      Corydalis claviculata (L.) DC.

5 FUMARIA L.

    1 F. capreolata L.

      a subsp. **capreolata**

      b subsp. **babingtonii** (Pugsley) Sell
        Fumaria capreolata L. var. *babingtonii* Pugsley

    2 F. occidentalis Pugsley

    3 F. bastardii Boreau

  3 x 5 F. bastardii x **F. muralis**

    4 F. reuteri Boiss.
      Fumaria martinii Clavaud; *F. reuteri* Boiss. subsp. *martinii*
      (Clavaud) A. Soler

    5 F. muralis Sonder ex Koch

      a subsp. **muralis**

      b subsp. **boraei** (Jordan) Pugsley
        Fumaria boraei Jordan

      c subsp. **neglecta** Pugsley

5 x 7   F. muralis x F. officinalis = F. x painteri Pugsley

6   F. purpurea Pugsley

7   F. officinalis L.

    a   subsp. officinalis

    b   subsp. wirtgenii (Koch) Arcang.
       Fumaria wirtgenii Koch

7 x 8   F. officinalis x F. densiflora

7 x 9   F. officinalis x F. parviflora

8   F. densiflora DC.
    Fumaria micrantha Lagasca

9   F. parviflora Lam.

10   F. vaillantii Lois.

32 *PLATANACEAE

1 *PLATANUS L.

occ x ori   *P. occidentalis L. x P. orientalis L. = P. x hispanica Miller ex
    Muenchh.
    Platanus x acerifolia (Aiton) Willd.; *P. x hybrida* Brot.

33 ULMACEAE

1   **ULMUS** L.

    1   U. glabra Hudson

        a   subsp. glabra
           Ulmus glabra Hudson subsp. *scabra* (Miller) Dostál

        b   subsp. montana N. Hylander

1 x 2   **U. glabra** x **U. procera**

1 x 3   **U. glabra** x **U. minor** = **U. x vegeta** (Loudon) Ley
Ulmus glabra Hudson var. *vegeta* Loudon

1 x 3 x 4   **U. glabra** x **U. minor** x **U. plotii** = **U. x hollandica** Miller
Ulmus x minor auct., non Miller

1 x 4   **U. glabra** x **U. plotii** = **U. ? x elegantissima** Horw.

2   **U. procera** Salisb.
Ulmus minor Miller var. *vulgaris* (Aiton) Richens; *U. minor*
auct., non Miller

2 x 3   **U. procera** x **U. minor**

2 x 4   **U. procera** x **U. plotii**

3   **U. minor** Miller

    a   subsp. **minor**
Ulmus ? diversifolia Melville; *U. angustifolia* (Weston)
Weston var. *cornubiensis* (Weston) Melville; *U.
carpinifolia* auct., non Gled.; *U. coritana* Melville; *U.
minor* Miller var. *cornubiensis* (Weston) Richens; *U.
minor* Miller var. *suberosa* (Moench) Dostál; *U. stricta*
(Aiton) Lindley

    b   subsp. **angustifolia** (Weston) Stace
Ulmus campestris L. var. *angustifolia* Weston
Ulmus angustifolia (Weston) Weston

    c   subsp. **sarniensis** (C. Schneider) Stace
Ulmus glabra Hudson forma *sarniensis* C. Schneider
Ulmus minor auct., non Miller; *U. sarniensis* (C.
Schneider) Bancroft

3 x 4   **U. minor** x **U. plotii** = **U. x viminalis** Lodd. ex Loudon

4   **U. plotii** Druce
Ulmus carpinifolia Gled. var. *plotii* (Druce) Tutin, nom. inval.;
U. lockii auct., non Druce; *U. minor* Miller var. *lockii* (Druce)
Richens; *U. minor* auct., non Miller

34 CANNABACEAE

1 *CANNABIS L.

    1 *C. sativa L.

2 HUMULUS L.

    1 H. lupulus L.

35 *MORACEAE

1 *MORUS L.

    1 *M. nigra L.

2 *FICUS L.

    1 *F. carica L.

36 URTICACEAE

1 URTICA L.

    1 U. dioica L.

    2 U. urens L.

2 PARIETARIA L.

    1 P. judaica L.
    Parietaria diffusa Mert. & Koch

3 *SOLEIROLIA Gaudich.
Helxine Req.

1 *S. soleirolii (Req.) Dandy
Helxine soleirolii Req.

37 *JUGLANDACEAE

1 *JUGLANS L.

1 *J. regia L.

2 *PTEROCARYA Kunth

1 *P. fraxinifolia (Poiret) Spach
Juglans fraxinifolia Poiret

38 MYRICACEAE

1 MYRICA L.

1 M. gale L.

2 *M. cerifera L.
Myrica caroliniensis sensu Wangenh., non Miller; *M. pensylvanica* Lois. ex Duhamel, nom. illegit.

39 FAGACEAE

1 FAGUS L.

1 F. sylvatica L.

2 *NOTHOFAGUS Blume

1 *N. obliqua (Mirbel) Blume
Fagus obliqua Mirbel

1 x 2 *N. obliqua x N. nervosa

2 *N. nervosa (Philippi) Dmitri & Milano
  Fagus nervosa Philippi
  Fagus procera Poeppig & Endl., non Salisb.; *Nothofagus procera* Oersted

3 *CASTANEA Miller

  1 *C. sativa Miller

4 QUERCUS L.

  1 *Q. castaneaefolia C. Meyer

  2 *Q. cerris L.

  2 x 6   Q. cerris x Q. robur

  2 x sub   *Q. cerris x Q. suber L. = Q. x pseudosuber Santi
  Quercus x hispanica auct., non Lam.

  3 *Q. ilex L.

  4 *Q. canariensis Willd.

  5   Q. petraea (Mattuschka) Liebl.
  Quercus robur L. var. *petraea* Mattuschka

  5 x 6   Q. petraea x Q. robur = Q. x rosacea Bechst.

  6   Q. robur L.

  7 *Q. rubra L.
  Quercus borealis Michaux f. var. *maxima* (Marshall) Ashe

40 BETULACEAE
Corylaceae

1 BETULA L.

  1   B. pendula Roth
  Betula alba L., pro parte; *B. verrucosa* Ehrh.

1 x 2   **B. pendula** x **B. pubescens** = **B. x aurata** Borkh.

2   **B. pubescens** Ehrh.
Betula alba L., pro parte

   a   subsp. **pubescens**

   b   subsp. **tortuosa** (Ledeb.) Nyman
   Betula tortuosa Ledeb.
   Betula carpatica Willd.; *B. odorata* auct., non Bechst.; *B. pubescens* Ehrh. subsp. *carpatica* (Willd.) Asch. & Graebner; *B. pubescens* Ehrh. subsp. *odorata* sensu E. Warb., non (Bechst.) E. Warb.

2 x 3   **B. pubescens** x **B. nana** = **B. x intermedia** Thomas ex Gaudin

3   **B. nana** L.

2   **ALNUS** Miller

1   **A. glutinosa** (L.) Gaertner
Betula alnus L. var. *glutinosa* L.

1 x 2   *****A. glutinosa** x **A. incana** = **A. x pubescens** Tausch

2   *****A. incana** (L.) Moench
Betula alnus L. var. *incana* L.

3   *****A. cordata** (Lois.) Duby
Betula cordata Lois.

3   **CARPINUS** L.

1   **C. betulus** L.

4   **CORYLUS** L.

1   **C. avellana** L.

1 x 2   **C. avellana** x **C. maxima**

2   *****C. maxima** Miller

41 *PHYTOLACCACEAE

1 *PHYTOLACCA L.

1 *P. acinosa Roxb.
Phytolacca americana auct., non L.; *P. decandra* auct., non L.

42 *AIZOACEAE

1 *APTENIA N.E. Br.

1 *A. cordifolia (L.f.) Schwantes
Mesembryanthemum cordifolium L.f.

2 *RUSCHIA Schwantes

1 *R. caroli (L. Bolus) Schwantes
Mesembryanthemum caroli L. Bolus

3 *LAMPRANTHUS N.E. Br.

1 *L. falciformis (Haw.) N.E. Br.
Mesembryanthemum falciforme Haw.

2 *L. roseus (Willd.) Schwantes
Mesembryanthemum roseum Willd.

4 *OSCULARIA Schwantes

1 *O. deltoides (L.) Schwantes
Mesembryanthemum deltoides L.
Lampranthus deltoides (L.) Glen; *Oscularia caulescens* auct., non
(Miller) Schwantes

5 *DISPHYMA N.E. Br.

1 *D. crassifolium (L.) L. Bolus
Disphyma australe auct., non (Sol. ex G. Forster) N.E. Br.

6 *DROSANTHEMUM Schwantes

   1 *D. floribundum (Haw.) Schwantes
     Mesembryanthemum floribundum Haw.
     Drosanthemum candens auct., non (Haw.) Schwantes

7 *EREPSIA N.E. Br.

   1 *E. heteropetala (Haw.) Schwantes
     Mesembryanthemum heteropetalum Haw.

8 *CARPOBROTUS N.E. Br.

   1 *C. acinaciformis (L.) L. Bolus
     Mesembryanthemum acinaciforme L.

   2 *C. edulis (L.) N.E. Br.
     Mesembryanthemum edule L.
     Carpobrotus acinaciformis sensu Lousley et auct., non (L.) L.
       Bolus; *C. aequilaterus* auct., non (Haw.) N.E. Br.; *C. chilensis*
       auct., non (Molina) N.E. Br.

   3 *C. glaucescens (Haw.) Schwantes
     Mesembryanthemum glaucescens Haw.
     Carpobrotus chilensis auct., non (Molina) N.E. Br.; *C. edulis*
       auct., non (L.) N.E. Br.

43 CHENOPODIACEAE

1 CHENOPODIUM L.
Blitum L.

   1 *C. ambrosioides L.
     Chenopodium anthelminticum auct., non L.

   2 *C. pumilio R. Br.
     Chenopodium carinatum auct., non R. Br.

   3 *C. capitatum (L.) Asch.
     Blitum capitatum L.

4 *C. bonus-henricus L.

5 *C. glaucum L.

6 C. rubrum L.

7 C. chenopodioides (L.) Aellen
   Blitum chenopodioides L.
   Chenopodium botryodes Smith

8 C. polyspermum L.

9 C. vulvaria L.

10 C. hybridum L.

11 C. urbicum L.

12 C. murale L.

13 C. ficifolium Smith

14 *C. opulifolium Schrader ex Koch & Ziz

15 C. album L.
   Chenopodium album L. subsp. *reticulatum* (Aellen) Beauge ex
   Greuter & Burdet; *C. reticulatum* Aellen

2 *BASSIA All.
   Kochia Roth

   1 *B. scoparia (L.) A.J. Scott
      Chenopodium scoparia L.
      Kochia scoparia (L.) Schrader

3 ATRIPLEX L.
   Halimione Aellen

   1 *A. hortensis L.

   2 A. prostrata Boucher ex DC.
      Atriplex calotheca auct., non (Rafn) Fries; *A. hastata* sensu
      L.(1754), non L.(1753); *A. patula* L. var. *triangularis* (Willd.)

Thorne & Welsh; *A. prostrata* Boucher ex DC. subsp. *deltoidea* (Bab.) Rauschert; *A. prostrata* Boucher ex DC. subsp. *triangularis* (Willd.) Rauschert

2 x 3   **A. prostrata** x **A. glabriuscula**

2 x 4   **A. prostrata** x **A. longipes** = **A. x gustafssoniana** Taschereau
Atriplex longipes Drejer subsp. *kattegatensis* Turesson

2 x 6   **A. prostrata** x **A. littoralis** = **A. x hulmeana** Taschereau

3   **A. glabriuscula** Edmondston
Atriplex babingtonii J. Woods

3 x 4   **A. glabriuscula** x **A. longipes** = **A. x taschereaui** Stace

3 x 5   **A. glabriuscula** x **A. praecox**

4   **A. longipes** Drejer
Atriplex prostrata Boucher ex DC. var. *longipes* (Drejer) Meijden

5   **A. praecox** Hülph.
Atriplex ? nudicaulis Boguslaw

6   **A. littoralis** L.
Atriplex laciniata auct., non L.

6 x 7   **A. littoralis** x **A. patula**

7   **A. patula** L.

8   **A. laciniata** L.
Atriplex rosea L. subsp. *arenaria* Dostál; *A. sabulosa* Rouy

9   *****A. halimus** L.

10   **A. portulacoides** L.
Halimione portulacoides (L.) Aellen

11   **A. pedunculata** L.
Halimione pedunculata (L.) Aellen

4   BETA L.

  1   B. vulgaris L.

    a   subsp. **maritima** (L.) Arcang.
        Beta maritima L.

    b   *subsp. **cicla** (L.) Arcang.
        Beta vulgaris L. var. *cicla* L.

    c   *subsp. **vulgaris**

  2   *B. trigyna** Waldst. & Kit.

5   SARCOCORNIA A.J. Scott

  1   S. perennis (Miller) A.J. Scott
      Salicornia perennis Miller
      Arthrocnemum perenne (Miller) Moss; *Salicornia lignosa* J.
      Woods

6   SALICORNIA L.

  1   S. pusilla J. Woods
      Salicornia disarticulata Moss

  1 x 2   S. pusilla x S. ramosissima

  2   S. ramosissima J. Woods
      Salicornia appressa Dumort.; *S. gracillima* (F. Towns.) Moss; *S.
      prostrata* auct., non Pallas; *S. smithiana* Moss; *S. stricta*
      Dumort.

  3   S. europaea L.

  4   S. obscura P. Ball & Tutin

  5   S. nitens P. Ball & Tutin
      Salicornia ? emerici Duval-Jouve; *S. ? intermedia* J. Woods; *S.
      ramosissima* sensu Dalby et auct., non J. Woods

  6   S. fragilis P. Ball & Tutin
      Salicornia ? procumbens Smith; *S. herbacea* auct., non L.;

S. lutescens P. Ball & Tutin; *S. stricta* auct., non Dumort.

7   S. dolichostachya Moss
Salicornia ? oliveri Moss; *S. stricta* sensu D. Koenig, non Dumort.

7   SUAEDA Forsskål ex J. Gmelin
Dondia Adans.

   1   S. vera Forsskål ex J. Gmelin
   Dondia fruticosa auct., non (Forsskål) Druce; *Suaeda fruticosa* auct., non Forsskål

   2   S. maritima (L.) Dumort.
   Chenopodium maritimum L.

8   SALSOLA L.

   1   S. kali L.

     a subsp. **kali**

     b *subsp. **ruthenica** (Iljin) Soó
       Salsola ruthenica Iljin
       Salsola australis R. Br.; *S. pestifer* Nelson; *S. tragus* auct., non L.

44 *AMARANTHACEAE

1 *AMARANTHUS L.

   1 *A. retroflexus L.

   2 *A. hybridus L.
   Amaranthus hypochondriacus L.; *A. patulus* Bertol.; *A. powellii* S. Watson

   3 *A. cruentus L.
   Amaranthus hybridus L. subsp. *cruentus* (L.) Thell.; *A. hybridus* L. subsp. *incurvatus* (Timeroy ex Gren. & Godron) Brenan

4 *A. bouchonii Thell.
   Amaranthus hybridus L. subsp. *bouchonii* (Thell.) O. Bolòs & Vigo

5 *A. deflexus L.

6 *A. albus L.

45 PORTULACACEAE

1 *PORTULACA L.

   1 *P. oleracea L.

2 *CLAYTONIA L.

   1 *C. perfoliata Donn ex Willd.
      Montia perfoliata (Donn ex Willd.) Howell

   2 *C. sibirica L.
      Claytonia alsinoides Sims; *Montia sibirica* (L.) Howell

3 MONTIA L.

   1 M. fontana L.

      a subsp. **fontana**
         Montia lamprosperma Cham.; *M. rivularis* auct., non C. Gmelin

      b subsp. **variabilis** Walters
         Montia rivularis auct., non C. Gmelin

      c subsp. **amporitana** Sennen
         Montia fontana L. subsp. *intermedia* (Beeby) Walters; *M. lusitanica* Samp.; *M. rivularis* auct., non C. Gmelin

      d subsp. **minor** Hayw.
         Montia fontana L. subsp. *chondrosperma* (Fenzl) Walters; *M. verna* Necker, nom. illegit.

2 *M. parvifolia (Mociño) E. Greene
   Claytonia parviflora Mociño

46 CARYOPHYLLACEAE
Illecebraceae

1 ARENARIA L.

   1 A. serpyllifolia L.

      a subsp. **serpyllifolia**

      b subsp. **lloydii** (Jordan) Bonnier
         Arenaria lloydii Jordan
         Arenaria serpyllifolia L. subsp. *macrocarpa* Perring & Sell

      c subsp. **leptoclados** (Reichb.) Nyman
         Arenaria serpyllifolia L. var. *leptoclados* Reichb.
         Arenaria leptoclados (Reichb.) Guss.; *A. leptoclados*
            (Reichb.) Guss. subsp. *viscidula* (Rouy & Fouc.)
            Holub

   2 A. norvegica Gunnerus

      a subsp. **norvegica**

      b subsp. **anglica** Halliday
         Arenaria gothica auct., non Fries

   3 A. ciliata L.
      Arenaria ciliata L. subsp. *hibernica* Ostenf. & O. Dahl

   4 *A. balearica L.

   5 *A. montana L.

2 MOEHRINGIA L.

   1 M. trinervia (L.) Clairv.
      Arenaria trinervia L.

3 HONCKENYA Ehrh.

1 H. peploides (L.) Ehrh.
Arenaria peploides L.

4 MINUARTIA L.
Cherleria L.

1 M. recurva (All.) Schinz & Thell.
Arenaria recurva All.

2 M. verna (L.) Hiern
Arenaria verna L.

3 M. rubella (Wahlenb.) Hiern
Alsine rubella Wahlenb.
Arenaria rubella (Wahlenb.) Smith

4 M. stricta (Sw.) Hiern
Spergula stricta Sw.
Arenaria uliginosa Schleicher ex DC.

5 M. hybrida (Villars) Schischkin
Arenaria hybrida Villars
Arenaria tenuifolia L.; *Minuartia tenuifolia* (L.) Hiern, non Nees
ex Mart.

6 M. sedoides (L.) Hiern
Cherleria sedoides L.
Arenaria sedoides (L.) F. Hanb.

5 STELLARIA L.

1 S. nemorum L.

    a subsp. **nemorum**

    b subsp. **montana** (Pierrat) Berher
    Stellaria montana Pierrat
    Stellaria nemorum L. subsp. *glochidisperma* Murb.

2 S. media (L.) Villars
Alsine media L.

3 S. pallida (Dumort.) Piré
Alsine pallida Dumort.
Stellaria apetala auct., non Ucria ex Roemer; *S. boraeana* Jordan

4 S. neglecta Weihe
Alsine neglecta (Weihe) Á. Löve & D. Löve; *Stellaria umbrosa*
auct., non Opiz & Rupr.

5 S. holostea L.

6 S. palustris Retz.
Stellaria dilleniana Moench, non Leers; *S. glauca* With.

7 S. graminea L.

8 S. uliginosa Murray
Stellaria alsine Grimm, nom. inval.

6 †HOLOSTEUM L.

1 †H. umbellatum L.

7 CERASTIUM L.

1 C. cerastoides (L.) Britton
Stellaria cerastoides L.
Arenaria trigyna (Villars) Shinners

2 C. arvense L.

2 x 3 C. arvense x **C. tomentosum** = **C. x maueri** Schulze
Cerastium x decalvens auct., non Schlosser Klek. & Vukot.

2 x 7 C. arvense x **C. fontanum** = **C. x pseudoalpinum** Murr

3 *C. tomentosum L.
Cerastium biebersteinii auct., non DC.; *C. columnae* Ten.; *C.
decalvens* auct., non Schlosser Klek. & Vukot.; *C. lanigerum*
auct., non Clemente

4 C. alpinum L.

a   subsp. **lanatum** (Lam.) Gremli
    Cerastium lanatum Lam.

4 x 5   **C. alpinum x C. arcticum**
    Cerastium x blyttii auct., non Baenitz

4 x 7   **C. alpinum x C. fontanum = C. x symei** Druce
    Cerastium x laestedianum auct., non Samz.

5   **C. arcticum** Lange
    Cerastium nigrescens (H. Watson) Edmondston ex H. Watson
    subsp. *arcticum* (Lange) Lusby

5 x 7   **C. arcticum x C. fontanum = C. x richardsonii** Druce

6   **C. nigrescens** (H. Watson) Edmondston ex H. Watson
    Cerastium latifolium L. var. *nigrescens* H. Watson
    Cerastium arcticum Lange subsp. *edmondstonii* (Edmondston)
    Á. Löve & D. Löve; *C. arcticum* Lange var. *nigrescens* (H.
    Watson) Á. Löve & D. Löve, nom. inval.; *C. edmondstonii*
    (Edmondston) Murb. & Ostenf., nom. illegit.; *C.
    edmondstonii* (Edmondston) Murb. & Ostenf., nom. illegit.
    var. *nigrescens* (H. Watson) Clapham

7   **C. fontanum** Baumg.
    Cerastium vulgatum sensu L.(1759), non L.(1755)

    a   subsp. **vulgare** (Hartman) Greuter & Burdet
        Cerastium fontanum Baumg. subsp. *triviale* (Murb.) Jalas;
        C. vulgare Hartman

    b   subsp. **holosteoides** (Fries) Salman, van Ommering &
        de Voogd
        Cerastium holosteoides Fries
        Cerastium fontanum Baumg. subsp. *glabrescens* (G.
        Meyer) Salman, van Ommering & de Voogd; *C.
        fontanum* Baumg. var. *holosteoides* (Fries) Jalas; *C.
        holosteoides* Fries var. *glabrescens* (G. Meyer) N.
        Hylander

    c   subsp. **scoticum** Jalas & Sell
        Cerastium triviale Link, nom. illegit. var. *alpinum* auct.,
        non Mert. & Koch

8   **C. glomeratum** Thuill.
Cerastium viscosum L.

9   ***C. brachypetalum** Pers.
Cerastium brachypetalum Pers. subsp. *tenoreanum* auct., non
(Ser.) Soó

10   **C. diffusum** Pers.
Cerastium atrovirens Bab.; *C. subtetrandrum* sensu Druce, non
(Lange) Murb.; *C. tetrandrum* Curtis, nom. illegit.

11   **C. pumilum** Curtis

12   **C. semidecandrum** L.

8   **MYOSOTON** Moench

1   **M. aquaticum** (L.) Moench
Cerastium aquaticum L.
Stellaria aquatica (L.) Scop.

9   **MOENCHIA** Ehrh.

1   **M. erecta** (L.) P. Gaertner, Meyer & Scherb.
Sagina erecta L.

10   **SAGINA** L.

1   **S. nodosa** (L.) Fenzl
Spergula nodosa L.

2   **S. nivalis** (Lindblad) Fries
Sagina saginoides (L.) Karsten var. *nivalis* Lindblad
Sagina intermedia Fenzl

3   **S. subulata** (Sw.) C. Presl
Spergula subulata Sw.
Sagina glabra sensu Lousley et auct., non (Willd.) Fenzl; *S.
pilifera* auct., non (DC.) Fenzl

3 x 5   **S. subulata** x **S. procumbens** = **S. x micrantha** Boreau ex É.
Martin

4   **S. saginoides** (L.) Karsten
Spergula saginoides L.

4 x 5   **S. saginoides** x **S. procumbens** = **S. x normaniana** Lagerh.
Sagina saginoides (L.) Karsten subsp. *scotica* (Druce) Clapham;
S. x media Bruegger; *S. x scotica* (Druce) Druce

5   **S. procumbens** L.

6   †**S. boydii** F.B. White

7   **S. apetala** Ard.

    a   subsp. **apetala**
       Sagina ciliata Fries; *S. filicaulis* auct., non Jordan; *S.*
       reuteri Boiss.

    b   subsp. **erecta** F. Herm.
       Sagina apetala auct., non Ard.; *S. micropetala* Rauschert

8   **S. maritima** G. Don
Sagina procumbens auct., non L.

11   SCLERANTHUS L.

    1   **S. perennis** L.

       a   subsp. **perennis**

       b   subsp. **prostratus** Sell

    2   **S. annuus** L.

       a   subsp. **annuus**

       b   subsp. **polycarpos** (L.) Bonnier & Layens
          Scleranthus polycarpos L.

12   CORRIGIOLA L.

    1   **C. litoralis** L.

13 HERNIARIA L.

    1 H. glabra L.
    Herniaria hirsuta auct., non L.

    2 H. ciliolata Meld.
    Herniaria ciliata Bab., non Clairv.

        a subsp. **ciliolata**

        b subsp. **subciliata** (Bab.) Chaudhri
        Herniaria glabra L. var. *subciliata* Bab.

    3 *H. hirsuta L.
    Corrigiola cinerea DC.

14 ILLECEBRUM L.

    1 I. verticillatum L.

15 POLYCARPON L.

    1 P. tetraphyllum (L.) L.
    Mollugo tetraphylla L.
    Polycarpon diphyllum Cav.; *P. tetraphyllum* (L.) L. subsp.
      diphyllum (Cav.) O. Bolòs & Font Quer

16 SPERGULA L.

    1 S. arvensis L.
    Spergula sativa Boenn., nom. illegit.

    2 *S. morisonii Boreau
    Spergula vernalis sensu Pugsley et auct., non Willd.

17 SPERGULARIA (Pers.) J.S. Presl & C. Presl
Arenaria sect. *Spergularia* Pers.

    1 S. rupicola Lebel ex Le Jolis
    Spergularia rupestris Lebel, non Cambess.

1 x 3   S. rupicola x S. marina

   2   **S. media** (L.) C. Presl
Arenaria media L.
Spergularia marginata Kittel, nom. illegit.; *S. maritima* (All.) Chiov.

   3   **S. marina** (L.) Griseb.
Arenaria rubra L. var. *marina* L.
Spergularia salina J.S. Presl & C. Presl

   4   **S. rubra** (L.) J.S. Presl & C. Presl
Arenaria rubra L.

   5   **S. bocconei** (Scheele) Graebner
Alsine bocconei Scheele

18   LYCHNIS L.
Steris Adans.; *Viscaria* Roehl.

   1   ***L. coronaria** (L.) Murray
Agrostemma coronaria L.
Silene coronaria (L.) Clairv.

   2   **L. flos-cuculi** L.
Silene flos-cuculi (L.) Clairv.

   3   **L. viscaria** L.
Silene viscaria (L.) Jessen; *Steris viscosa* (L.) Raf.; *Viscaria vulgaris* Bernh.

   4   **L. alpina** L.
Silene suecica (Lodd.) Greuter & Burdet; *Steris alpina* (L.) Sourk., nom. inval.; *Viscaria alpina* (L.) Don

19   *AGROSTEMMA L.

   1   ***A. githago** L.
Lychnis githago (L.) Scop.

20 SILENE L.
Melandrium Roehl.

1 **S. italica* (L.) Pers.
Cucubalus italicus L.

2 **S. nutans** L.
Silene dubia auct., non Herbich; *S. nutans* L. subsp. *smithiana*
(Moss) Jeanm. & Bocq.; *S. salmoniana* (Hepper) Butcher,
nom. inval.

3 **S. otites** (L.) Wibel
Cucubalus otites L.

4 **S. vulgaris** Garcke

    a subsp. **vulgaris**
       Silene angustifolia auct., non (DC.) Guss.; *S. cucubalus*
       Wibel, nom. illegit.

    b *subsp. **macrocarpa** Turrill
       Silene angustifolia auct., non (DC.) Guss.; *S. linearis*
       sensu Clapham et auct., non Sweet

4 x 5 S. vulgaris x **S. uniflora**

5 **S. uniflora** Roth
Silene maritima With.; *S. vulgaris* Garcke subsp. *alpina* (Lam.)
Nyman; *S. vulgaris* Garcke subsp. *maritima* (With.) Á. Löve
& D. Löve, nom. illegit.

6 **S. acaulis** (L.) Jacq.
Cucubalus acaulis L.

7 **S. armeria* L.

8 **S. noctiflora** L.
Melandrium noctiflorum (L.) Fries

9 **S. latifolia** Poiret

    a subsp. **alba** (Miller) Greuter & Burdet
       Lychnis alba Miller

Melandrium album (Miller) Garcke; *Silene alba* (Miller)
E.H.L. Krause, non Muhlenb. ex Britton; *S. pratensis*
(Rafn) Godron & Gren.

9 x 10 **S. latifolia** x **S. dioica** = **S. x hampeana** Meusel & K. Werner
Silene x dubia (Hampe) Guinochet & Vilmorin, non Herbich
nec E.H.L. Krause; *S. x intermedia* (Schur) Philp, non
(Lange) Bocq.

10 **S. dioica** (L.) Clairv.
Lychnis dioica L.
Melandrium dioicum (L.) Cosson & Germ.; *Silene dioica* (L.)
Clairv. subsp. *zetlandica* (Compton) Clapham, nom. inval.

11 **S. gallica** L.
Silene anglica L.; *S. quinquevulnera* L.

12 **S. conica** L.

21 ***CUCUBALUS** L.

1 ***C. baccifer** L.

22 **SAPONARIA** L.

1 **S. officinalis** L.

2 ***S. ocymoides** L.

23 ***VACCARIA** Wolf

1 ***V. hispanica** (Miller) Rauschert
Saponaria hispanica Miller
Saponaria vaccaria L.; *Vaccaria pyramidata* Medikus; *V. segetalis*
(Necker) Garcke, nom. illegit.

24 **PETRORHAGIA** (Ser. ex DC.) Link
Gypsophila sect. *Petrorhagia* Ser. ex DC.
Kohlrauschia Kunth

1 **P. nanteuilii** (Burnat) P. Ball & Heyw.

Dianthus nanteuilii Burnat
Dianthus prolifer sensu L.(1754), non L.(1753); *Kohlrauschia
nanteuilii* (Burnat) P. Ball & Heyw.; *K. prolifera* (L.) Kunth
subsp. *nanteuilii* (Burnat) Laínz; *K. prolifera* auct., non (L.)
Kunth; *Petrorhagia prolifera* (L.) P. Ball & Heyw. subsp.
nanteuilii (Burnat) O. Bolòs & Vigo

2   **P. prolifera** (L.) P. Ball & Heyw.
    Dianthus prolifer L.
    Kohlrauschia prolifera (L.) Kunth

3   ***P. saxifraga** (L.) Link
    Dianthus saxifragus L.
    Kohlrauschia saxifraga (L.) Dandy

25 **DIANTHUS** L.

1   **D. gratianopolitanus** Villars

1 x 3   ***D. gratianopolitanus** x **D. plumarius**

2   ***D. caryophyllus** L.

2 x 3   ***D. caryophyllus** x **D. plumarius**

3   ***D. plumarius** L.

4   ***D. gallicus** Pers.

5   **D. deltoides** L.

6   ***D. barbatus** L.

7   **D. armeria** L.

47 POLYGONACEAE

1   **PERSICARIA** Miller
    Aconogonum Reichb.; *Bistorta* (L.) Adans.

1   ***P. alpina** (All.) Gross
    Polygonum alpinum All.

Aconogonum alpinum (All.) Schur; *Persicaria angustifolia* (Pallas) Ronse Decraene, nom. illegit.

2 *P. campanulata** (J.D. Hook.) Ronse Decraene
Polygonum campanulatum J.D. Hook.

3 *P. wallichii** Greuter & Burdet
Aconogonum polystachyum (Wallich ex Meissner) M. Král;
Persicaria polystachya (Wallich ex Meissner) Gross, non
Opiz; *Polygonum polystachyum* Wallich ex Meissner

4 *P. weyrichii** (F. Schmidt ex Maxim.) Ronse Decraene
Polygonum weyrichii F. Schmidt ex Maxim.
Aconogonum weyrichii (F. Schmidt ex Maxim.) H. Hara

5 *P. mollis** (D. Don) Gross
Polygonum molle D. Don
Aconogonum molle (D. Don) H. Hara; *A. paniculatum* (Blume)
Haraldson; *Polygonum paniculatum* Blume; *P. rude* Meissner

6 P. bistorta (L.) Samp.
Polygonum bistorta L.
Bistorta major Gray

7 *P. amplexicaulis** (D. Don) Ronse Decraene
Polygonum amplexicaule D. Don
Bistorta amplexicaulis (D. Don) E. Greene

8 P. vivipara (L.) Ronse Decraene
Polygonum viviparum L.
Bistorta vivipara (L.) Gray

9 P. amphibia (L.) Gray
Polygonum amphibium L.

10 *P. nepalensis** (Meissner) Gross
Polygonum nepalense Meissner

11 P. maculosa Gray
Persicaria maculata (Raf.) Á. Löve & D. Löve, non Gray;
Polygonum persicaria L.

11 x 12 P. maculosa x P. lapathifolia = P. x lenticularis (Hy) Soják
Polygonum x lenticulare Hy

11 x 14   **P. maculosa** x **P. hydropiper** = **P. x intercedens** (G. Beck)
Soják
Polygonum x intercedens G. Beck
Polygonum x hybridum auct., non Chaub. ex St.-Amans

11 x 15   **P. maculosa** x **P. laxiflora** = **P. x condensata** (F. Schultz) Soják
Polygonum mite Schrank var. *condensatum* F. Schultz
Polygonum x condensatum (F. Schultz) F. Schultz

11 x 16   **P. maculosa** x **P. minor** = **P. x brauniana** (F. Schultz) Soják
Polygonum x braunianum F. Schultz

12   **P. lapathifolia** (L.) Gray
Polygonum lapathifolium L.
Polygonum nodosum Pers.

12 x 14   **P. lapathifolia** x **P. hydropiper** = **P. x figertii** (G. Beck) Soják
Polygonum x figertii G. Beck
Polygonum x metschii G. Beck

13   *P. pensylvanica** (L.) M. Gómez
Polygonum pensylvanicum L.

14   **P. hydropiper** (L.) Spach
Polygonum hydropiper L.

14 x 15   **P. hydropiper** x **P. laxiflora** = **P. x hybrida** (Chaub. ex St.-Amans) Soják
Polygonum x hybridum Chaub. ex St.-Amans
Polygonum x oleraceum Schur

14 x 16   **P. hydropiper** x **P. minor** = **P. x subglandulosa** (Borbás) Soják
Polygonum x subglandulosum Borbás

15   **P. laxiflora** (Weihe) Opiz
Polygonum laxiflorum Weihe
Persicaria mitis (Schrank) Holub, non Gilib.; *Polygonum hydropiper* L. subsp. *mite* (Schrank) Munshi & Javeid; *P. mite* Schrank

15 x 16   **P. laxiflora** x **P. minor** = **P. x wilmsii** (G. Beck) Soják
Polygonum x wilmsii G. Beck

16   **P. minor** (Hudson) Opiz
Polygonum minus Hudson

17 *P. sagittata (L.) Gross ex Nakai
Polygonum sagittatum L.

2 KOENIGIA L.

1 K. islandica L.

3 *FAGOPYRUM Miller

1 *F. esculentum Moench
Fagopyrum sagittatum Gilib., nom. illegit.

2 *F. dibotrys (D. Don) H. Hara
Polygonum dibotrys D. Don

4 POLYGONUM L.

1 P. maritimum L.

2 P. oxyspermum C. Meyer & Bunge ex Ledeb.

    a subsp. **raii** (Bab.) D. Webb & Chater
    Polygonum raii Bab.
    Polygonum robertii Lois.

3 P. arenastrum Boreau
Polygonum aequale Lindman; *P. aviculare* L. subsp. *aequale*
(Lindman) Asch. & Graebner; *P. calcatum* Lindman

4 P. aviculare L.
Polygonum heterophyllum Lindman, nom. illegit.; *P. littorale*
sensu Gren. & Godron et auct., non Link ex Pers.

5 P. boreale (Lange) Small
Polygonum aviculare L. var. *boreale* Lange
Polygonum arenastrum Boreau subsp. *boreale* (Lange) Á. Löve

6 P. rurivagum Jordan ex Boreau
Polygonum aviculare L. subsp. *rurivagum* (Jordan ex Boreau)
Berher

5   **FALLOPIA** Adans.
Bilderdykia Dumort.; *Reynoutria* Houtt.

1   **F. japonica* (Houtt.) Ronse Decraene
Reynoutria japonica Houtt.
Polygonum compactum J.D. Hook.; *P. cuspidatum* Siebold &
Zucc.

1 x 2   **F. japonica** x **F. sachalinensis** = **F. x bohemica** (Chrtek &
Chrtková) J. Bailey
Reynoutria x bohemica Chrtek & Chrtková
Reynoutria x vivax auct., non J. Schmitz & Strank

1 x 3   **F. japonica** x **F. baldschuanica**

2   **F. sachalinensis* (F. Schmidt ex Maxim.) Ronse Decraene
Polygonum sachalinense F. Schmidt ex Maxim.
Polygonum vivax J. Schmitz & Strank, nom. inval.; *Reynoutria
sachalinensis* (F. Schmidt ex Maxim.) Nakai; *R. vivax* J.
Schmitz & Strank

3   **F. baldschuanica* (Regel) Holub
Polygonum baldschuanicum Regel
Bilderdykia aubertii (L. Henry) Mold.; *B. baldschuanica* (Regel)
D. Webb; *Fallopia aubertii* (L. Henry) Holub; *Polygonum
aubertii* L. Henry; *Reynoutria baldschuanica* (Regel) Shinners

4   **F. convolvulus** (L.) Á. Löve
Polygonum convolvulus L.
Bilderdykia convolvulus (L.) Dumort.; *Reynoutria convolvulus* (L.)
Shinners

5   **F. dumetorum** (L.) Holub
Polygonum dumetorum L.
Bilderdykia dumetorum (L.) Dumort.; *Reynoutria scandens* (L.)
Shinners var. *dumetorum* (L.) Shinners

6   **MUEHLENBECKIA* Meissner

1   **M. complexa* (Cunn.) Meissner
Polygonum complexum Cunn.

7 *RHEUM L.

rha x pal *R. rhaponticum L. x R. palmatum L. = R. x hybridum Murray
Rheum x cultorum Thorsrud & Reis., nom. nud.; *R. x rhabarbarum* auct., non L.; *R. x rhaponticum* auct., non L.

8 RUMEX L.
Acetosa Miller; *Acetosella* (Meissner) Fourr.

1 R. acetosella L.

    a subsp. **acetosella**
        Acetosella multifida (L.) Á. Löve; *Rumex acetosella* L.
          subsp. *tenuifolius* (Wallr.) O. Schwarz; *R. tenuifolius*
          (Wallr.) Á. Löve

    b subsp. **pyrenaicus** (Pourret) Akeroyd
        Rumex pyrenaicus Pourret
        Acetosella vulgaris (Koch) Fourr. subsp. *pyrenaica*
          (Pourret) Á. Löve; *Rumex acetosella* L. subsp.
          angiocarpus auct., non (Murb.) Murb.; *R. angiocarpus*
          auct., non Murb.

2 *R. scutatus L.

3 R. acetosa L.

    a subsp. **acetosa**

    b subsp. **hibernicus** (K.H. Rech.) Akeroyd
        Rumex hibernicus K.H. Rech.
        Acetosa hibernica (K.H. Rech.) Holub

    c subsp. **biformis** (Lange) Valdes-Berm. & Castroviejo
        Rumex biformis Lange

    d *subsp. **ambiguus** (Gren.) Á. Löve
        Rumex ambiguus Gren.
        Rumex rugosus Campderá

4 *R. salicifolius Weinm.
Rumex salicifolius Weinm. subsp. *triangulivalvis* Danser; *R. triangulivalvis* (Danser) K.H. Rech.

5 *R. frutescens Thouars
   Rumex cuneifolius Campderá

5 x 14   R. frutescens x R. conglomeratus = R. x wrightii Lousley

6 *R. pseudoalpinus Hoefft
   Rumex alpinus sensu L.(1759), non L.(1753)

7   R. aquaticus L.

7 x 13   R. aquaticus x R. crispus = R. x conspersus Hartman

7 x 15   R. aquaticus x R. sanguineus = R. x dumulosus Hausskn.

7 x 19   R. aquaticus x R. obtusifolius = R. x platyphyllos Aresch.
         Rumex x schmidtii Hausskn.

8   R. longifolius DC.
    Rumex aquaticus auct., non L.; *R. domesticus* Hartman; *R.
    pseudonatronatus* sensu Lousley, non Borbás

8 x 13   R. longifolius x R. crispus = R. x propinquus Aresch.

8 x 19   R. longifolius x R. obtusifolius = R. x hybridus Kindb.
         Rumex x arnottii Druce; *R. x conspersus* sensu Syme et auct.,
         non Hartman

9 *R. confertus Willd.
   Rumex pseudoalpinus auct., non Hoefft

9 x 13   R. confertus x R. crispus = R. x skofitzii Blocki

9 x 19   R. confertus x R. obtusifolius = R. x borbasii Blocki
         Rumex x kerneri Blocki, non Borbás

10   R. hydrolapathum Hudson

10 x 13   R. hydrolapathum x R. crispus = R. x schreberi Hausskn.

10 x 14   R. hydrolapathum x R. conglomeratus = R. x digeneus G.
          Beck
          Rumex x hybridus Hausskn., non Kindb.

10 x 19   R. hydrolapathum x R. obtusifolius = R. x lingulatus Jungn.
          Rumex x maximus auct.; *R. x weberi* Fischer-Benzon

11 *****R. cristatus** DC.
Rumex patientia auct., non L.

11 x 13   **R. cristatus** x **R. crispus** = **R. x dimidiatus** Hausskn.

11 x 19   **R. cristatus** x **R. obtusifolius** = **R. x lousleyi** D.H. Kent

11 x 20   **R. cristatus** x **R. palustris**

12 *****R. patientia** L.

    a *****subsp. **orientalis** Danser
    Rumex orientalis Bernh., non Campderá

12 x 13   **R. patientia** x **R. crispus** = **R. x confusus** Simonkai

12 x 14   **R. patientia** x **R. conglomeratus**

12 x 19   **R. patientia** x **R. obtusifolius** = **R. x erubescens** Simonkai

    13   **R. crispus** L.

    a   subsp. **crispus**

    b   subsp. **littoreus** (J. Hardy) Akeroyd
    Rumex crispus L. var. *littoreus* J. Hardy

    c   subsp. **uliginosus** (Le Gall) Akeroyd
    Rumex crispus L. var. *uliginosus* Le Gall
    Rumex elongatus sensu Trimen et auct., non Guss.

13 x 14   **R. crispus** x **R. conglomeratus** = **R. x schulzei** Hausskn.

13 x 15   **R. crispus** x **R. sanguineus** = **R. x sagorskii** Hausskn.

13 x 16   **R. crispus** x **R. rupestris**

13 x 18   **R. crispus** x **R. pulcher** = **R. x pseudopulcher** Hausskn.

13 x 19   **R. crispus** x **R. obtusifolius** = **R. x pratensis** Mert. & Koch
Rumex x acutus auct., non L.

13 x 20   **R. crispus** x **R. palustris** = **R. x heteranthos** Borbás
Rumex x areschougii G. Beck

14 R. conglomeratus Murray

14 x 15 R. conglomeratus x R. sanguineus = R. x ruhmeri Hausskn.

14 x 18 R. conglomeratus x R. pulcher = R. x muretii Hausskn.

14 x 19 R. conglomeratus x R. obtusifolius = R. x abortivus Ruhmer

14 x 20 R. conglomeratus x R. palustris = R. x wirtgenii G. Beck

14 x 21 R. conglomeratus x R. maritimus = R. x knafii Celak.

15 R. sanguineus L.
Rumex condylodes M. Bieb.

15 x 18 R. sanguineus x R. pulcher = R. x mixtus Lambert

15 x 19 R. sanguineus x R. obtusifolius = R. x dufftii Hausskn.

16 R. rupestris Le Gall

16 x 18 R. rupestris x R. pulcher = R. x trimenii Camus

17 *R. brownii Campderá

18 R. pulcher L.

18 x 19 R. pulcher x R. obtusifolius = R. x ogulinensis Borbás

19 R. obtusifolius L.
Rumex obtusifolius L. subsp. *sylvestris* (Wallr.) Celak.; *R. obtusifolius* L. subsp. *transiens* (Simonkai) K.H. Rech.

19 x 20 R. obtusifolius x R. palustris = R. x steinii A. Becker

19 x 21 R. obtusifolius x R. maritimus = R. x callianthemus Danser

20 R. palustris Smith

21 R. maritimus L.

9 **OXYRIA** Hill

1 O. digyna (L.) Hill
Rumex digynus L.

48 PLUMBAGINACEAE

1 LIMONIUM Miller
Statice auct., non L.

> **1 L. vulgare** Miller
> *Statice limonium* L.

1 x 2 L. vulgare x **L. humile** = **L. x neumanii** Salmon

> **2 L. humile** Miller

> **3 L. bellidifolium** (Gouan) Dumort.
> *Statice limonium* L. var. *bellidifolia* Gouan

> **4 L. auriculae-ursifolium** (Pourret) Druce
> *Statice auriculae-ursifolium* Pourret
> *Limonium lychnidifolium* Kuntze, nom. illegit.

> **5 L. normannicum** Ingrouille
> *Limonium lychnidifolium* Kuntze, nom. illegit. var. *corymbosum*
> (Boiss.) Salmon; *Statice lychnidifolia* Girard, nom. illegit. var.
> *corymbosa* Boiss., pro parte

> **6 *L. hyblaeum** Brullo
> *Limonium companyonis* sensu Ingrouille et auct., non (Gren. &
> Billot) Kuntze

> **7 L. binervosum** (G.E. Smith) Salmon
> *Statice auriculaefolia* auct., non Vahl; *S. binervosa* G.E. Smith

>> **a** subsp. **binervosum**

>> **b** subsp. **cantianum** Ingrouille

>> **c** subsp. **anglicum** Ingrouille

>> **d** subsp. **saxonicum** Ingrouille

>> **e** subsp. **mutatum** Ingrouille

>> **f** subsp. **sarniense** Ingrouille

> **8 L. paradoxum** Pugsley

9 L. procerum (Salmon) Ingrouille
Limonium occidentale (Lloyd) Kuntze var. *procerum* Salmon

    a   subsp. **procerum**

    b   subsp. **devoniense** Ingrouille

    c   subsp. **cambrense** Ingrouille

10 L. britannicum Ingrouille

    a   subsp. **britannicum**

    b   subsp. **coombense** Ingrouille

    c   subsp. **transcanalis** Ingrouille

    d   subsp. **celticum** Ingrouille

11 L. parvum Ingrouille

12 L. loganicum Ingrouille

13 L. transwallianum (Pugsley) Pugsley
Statice transwalliana Pugsley

14 L. dodartiforme Ingrouille

15 L. recurvum Salmon

    a   subsp. **recurvum** Salmon

    b   subsp. **portlandicum** Ingrouille

    c   subsp. **pseudotranswallianum** Ingrouille

    d   subsp. **humile** (Girard) Ingrouille
        Statice dodartii Girard var. *humilis* Girard

2 ARMERIA Willd.
Statice L.

    1   **A. maritima** (Miller) Willd.
        Statice maritima Miller

a   subsp. **maritima**
Armeria maritima (Miller) Willd. subsp. *planifolia* (Syme)
Á. Löve & D. Löve; *A. pubescens* Link

b   subsp. **elongata** (Hoffm.) Bonnier
Statice elongata Hoffm.
Armeria elongata (Hoffm.) Koch

1 x 2   A. maritima x **A. arenaria**

2   A. arenaria (Pers.) Schultes
Armeria alliacea (Cav.) Hoffsgg. & Link subsp. *plantaginea* O.
Bolòs & Vigo; *A. alliacea* auct., non (Cav.) Hoffsgg. & Link;;
Statice arenaria Pers.; *S. ? plantaginea* All.

49 *PAEONIACEAE

1 *PAEONIA L.

1 *P. mascula (L.) Miller
Paeonia officinalis L. var. *mascula* L.
Paeonia corallina Retz.

50 ELATINACEAE

1   ELATINE L.

1   E. hexandra (Lapierre) DC.
Tillaea hexandra Lapierre

2   E. hydropiper L.

51 CLUSIACEAE
Guttiferae; Hypericaceae

1   HYPERICUM L.

1   *H. calycinum L.

2 *H. pseudohenryi N. Robson

3 H. androsaemum L.

3 x 4 *H. androsaemum x H. hircinum = H. x inodorum Miller
Hypericum x elatum Aiton

4 *H. hircinum L.

    a *subsp. majus (Aiton) N. Robson
        Hypericum hircinum L. var. *majus* Aiton

5 *H. xylosteifolium (Spach) N. Robson
Androsaemum xylosteifolium Spach
Hypericum inodorum Willd., non Miller

6 H. perforatum L.

6 x 7 H. perforatum x H. maculatum = H. x desetangsii Lamotte

7 H. maculatum Crantz
Hypericum quadrangulum sensu L.(1754), non L.(1753)

    a subsp. maculatum

    b subsp. obtusiusculum (Tourlet) Hayek
        Hypericum quadrangulum L. subsp. *obtusiusculum*
        Tourlet
        Hypericum dubium Leers

8 H. undulatum Schousboe ex Willd.
Hypericum quadrangulum auct., non L.

9 H. tetrapterum Fries
Hypericum quadrangulum L.

10 H. humifusum L.

10 x 11 H. humifusum x H. linariifolium

11 H. linariifolium Vahl

12 H. pulchrum L.

13 *H. nummularium L.

14 H. hirsutum L.

15 H. montanum L.

16 H. elodes L.

17 *H. canadense L.

52 TILIACEAE

1 TILIA L.

1 T. platyphyllos Scop.

1 x 2 T. platyphyllos x T. cordata = T. x vulgaris Hayne
Tilia x europaea auct., non L.

2 T. cordata Miller

53 MALVACEAE

1 MALVA L.

1 M. moschata L.

2 *M. alcea L.

3 M. sylvestris L.

4 *M. nicaeensis All.

5 *M. parviflora L.

6 *M. pusilla Smith
Malva rotundifolia L.

7 M. neglecta Wallr.
Malva rotundifolia sensu L.(1754) et auct., non L.(1753)

8 *M. verticillata L.

2 LAVATERA L.

    1 L. arborea L.

    2 L. cretica L.

    3 *L. olbia L.

3 ALTHAEA L.

    1 A. officinalis L.

    2 *A. hirsuta L.

4 *ALCEA L.

    1 *A. rosea L.
      Alcea ? ficifolia L.; *Althaea rosea* (L.) Cav.

5 *SIDALCEA A. Gray ex Benth.

    1 *S. malvaeflora (DC.) A. Gray ex Benth.
      Sida malvaeflora DC.

6 *ABUTILON Miller

    1 *A. theophrasti Medikus
      Abutilon avicennae Gaertner, nom. illegit.

54 *SARRACENIACEAE

1 *SARRACENIA L.

    1 *S. purpurea L.

55 DROSERACEAE

1 DROSERA L.

    1 D. rotundifolia L.

    1 x 2 D. rotundifolia x **D. longifolia** = **D. x obovata** Mert. & Koch

    1 x 3 D. rotundifolia x **D. intermedia** = **D. x beleziana** Camus

    2 D. longifolia L.
       Drosera anglica Hudson

    3 D. intermedia Hayne
       Drosera longifolia auct., non L.

56 CISTACEAE

1 TUBERARIA (Dunal) Spach
   Helianthemum sect. *Tuberaria* Dunal

    1 T. guttata (L.) Fourr.
       Cistus guttatus L.
       Helianthemum guttatum (L.) Miller; *H. guttatum* (L.) Miller
         subsp. *breweri* (Planchon) Syme; *Tuberaria guttata* (L.) Fourr.
         subsp. *breweri* (Planchon) E. Warb.

2 HELIANTHEMUM Miller

    1 H. nummularium (L.) Miller
       Cistus nummularius L.
       Helianthemum chamaecistus Miller; *H. vulgare* Gaertner, nom.
       illegit.

    1 x 2 H. nummularium x **H. apenninum** = **H. x sulphureum** Willd.
       ex Schldl.

    2 H. apenninum (L.) Miller
       Cistus apenninus L.
       Helianthemum polifolium Miller

3   **H. canum** (L.) Hornem.
Cistus canus L.
Helianthemum oelandicum (L.) DC. subsp. *canum* (L.) Bonnier

    a   subsp. **canum**

    b   subsp. **piloselloides** (Lapeyr.) M. Proctor
      Cistus piloselloides Lapeyr.
      Helianthemum oelandicum (L.) DC. subsp. *piloselloides*
      (Lapeyr.) Greuter & Burdet

    c   subsp. **levigatum** M. Proctor

57   VIOLACEAE

1   **VIOLA** L.

    1   **V. odorata** L.

1 x 2   **V. odorata** x **V. hirta** = **V. x scabra** F. Braun
    Viola ? x suavis M. Bieb.; *V. x permixta* Jordan

    2   **V. hirta** L.
      Viola calcarea (Bab.) Gregory; *V. hirta* L. subsp. *calcarea* (Bab.)
      E. Warb.

    3   **V. rupestris** F.W. Schmidt
      Viola rupestris F.W. Schmidt subsp. *arenaria* (DC.) Rothm.

3 x 4   **V. rupestris** x **V. riviniana** = **V. x burnatii** Gremli

    4   **V. riviniana** Reichb.
      Viola riviniana Reichb. subsp. *minor* (Murb. ex Gregory)
      Valent.

4 x 5   **V. riviniana** x **V. reichenbachiana** = **V. x bavarica** Schrank
    Viola x intermedia Reichb., non Krocker

4 x 6   **V. riviniana** x **V. canina** = **V. x intersita** G. Beck
    Viola x weinhartii W. Becker

4 x 7   **V. riviniana** x **V. lactea**

5   **V. reichenbachiana** Jordan ex Boreau

5 x 6   **V. reichenbachiana** x **V. canina** = **V. x mixta** A. Kerner
Viola x borussica (Borbás) W. Becker

6   **V. canina** L.

    a   subsp. **canina**

    b   subsp. **montana** (L.) Hartman
        Viola montana L.
        Viola canina L. subsp. *elatior* (Fries) Kirschl.

6 x 7   **V. canina** x **V. lactea** = **V. x militaris** Savouré

6 x 8   **V. canina** x **V. persicifolia** = **V. x ritschliana** W. Becker

7   **V. lactea** Smith

8   **V. persicifolia** Schreber
Viola stagnina Kit.

9   **V. palustris** L.

    a   subsp. **palustris**

    b   subsp. **juressi** (Link ex Wein) P. Fourn.
        Viola juressi Link ex Wein

10   *****V. cornuta** L.

11   **V. lutea** Hudson

11 x 12   **V. lutea** x **V. tricolor**

11 x 12 x alt   *****V. lutea** x **V. tricolor** x **V. altaica** Ker Gawler = **V. x
wittrockiana** Gams ex Kappert
Viola x hortensis auct., non Schur

12   **V. tricolor** L.

    a   subsp. **tricolor**
        Viola lepida sensu E.G. Baker et auct., non Jordan

b subsp. **curtisii** (E. Forster) Syme
Viola curtisii E. Forster
Viola saxatilis F.W. Schmidt subsp. *curtisii* (E. Forster)
Kirschner & Skalicky

12 x 13 **V. tricolor** x **V. arvensis** = **V. x contempta** Jordan
Viola tricolor L. subsp. *saxatilis* auct., non (F.W. Schmidt)
Simonkai

13 **V. arvensis** Murray
Viola arvatica sensu Drabble et auct., non Jordan; *V. obtusifolia*
sensu Drabble et auct., non Jordan

14 **V. kitaibeliana** Schultes
Viola nana (DC.) Godron

58 *TAMARICACEAE

1 *TAMARIX* L.

1 *T. gallica* L.
Tamarix anglica Webb

59 FRANKENIACEAE

1 FRANKENIA L.

1 F. laevis L.

60 CUCURBITACEAE

1 BRYONIA L.

1 B. dioica Jacq.
Bryonia cretica L. subsp. *dioica* (Jacq.) Tutin

2 *ECBALLIUM A. Rich.

 1 *E. elaterium (L.) A. Rich.
  Momordica elaterium L.

61 SALICACEAE

1 POPULUS L.

 1 *P. alba L.

 1 x 2 *P. alba x **P. tremula** = **P. x canescens** (Aiton) Smith
  Populus alba L. var. *canescens* Aiton
  Populus x hybrida M. Bieb.

 2 P. tremula L.

 3 P. nigra L.

  a subsp. **betulifolia** (Pursh) W. Wettst.
   Populus betulifolia Pursh

3 x 5 x del **P. nigra** x **P. candicans** x **P. deltoides** Marshall

 3 x del *P. nigra x **P. deltoides** Marshall = **P. x canadensis** Moench
  Populus x deltoides auct., non Marshall; *P. x euroamericana*
  (Dode) Guinier ex Piccarolo, nom. illegit.; *P. x serotina*
  Hartig

 4 *P. trichocarpa Torrey & A. Gray ex Hook.
  Populus balsamifera L. subsp. *trichocarpa* (Torrey & A. Gray ex
  Hook.) Brayshaw

 5 *P. candicans Aiton
  Populus balsamifera auct., non L.; *P. gileadensis* Roul.; *P.*
  tacamahacca auct., non Miller

2 SALIX L.

 1 S. pentandra L.

 1 x 2 S. pentandra x **S. fragilis** = **S. x meyeriana** Rostkov ex Willd.

1 x 3   S. pentandra x S. alba = S. x ehrhartiana Smith

2   S. fragilis L.

2 x 3   S. fragilis x S. alba = S. x rubens Schrank
Salix x basfordiana Scal. ex J. Salter

2 x 4   S. fragilis x S. triandra = S. x alopecuroides Tausch
Salix x speciosa Host

2 x bab   *S. fragilis x S. babylonica L. = S. x pendulina Wender.
Salix x babylonica auct., non L.; *S. x blanda* Andersson

3   S. alba L.
Salix alba L. subsp. *caerulea* (Smith) K.H. Rech.; *S. alba* L.
subsp. *vitellina* (L.) Arcang.

3 x bab   *S. alba x S. babylonica L. = S. x sepulcralis Simonkai
Salix x babylonica auct., non L.; *S. x pendulina* Wender. var.
elegantissima (Koch) Meikle

4   S. triandra L.

4 x 5   S. triandra x S. purpurea
Salix x leiophylla auct., non Camus & A. Camus

4 x 9   S. triandra x S. viminalis = S. x mollissima Hoffm. ex Elwert

5   S. purpurea L.
Salix purpurea L. subsp. *lambertiana* (Smith) Macreight

5 x 9   S. purpurea x S. viminalis = S. x rubra Hudson
Salix ? x helix L.

5 x 9 x 10 x 11   S. purpurea x S. viminalis x S. caprea x S. cinerea = S. x
taylorii K.H. Rech.

5 x 9 x 11   S. purpurea x S. viminalis x S. cinerea = S. x forbyana Smith

5 x 11   S. purpurea x S. cinerea = S. x pontederiana Willd.
Salix x sordida A. Kerner

5 x 11 x 12   S. purpurea x S. cinerea x S. aurita = S. x confinis Camus &
A. Camus

5 x 12   **S. purpurea** x **S. aurita** = **S. x dichroa** Doell

5 x 12 x 15   **S. purpurea** x **S. aurita** x **S. phylicifolia** = **S. x sesquitertia** F.B. White

5 x 14   **S. purpurea** x **S. myrsinifolia** = **S. x beckiana** Beck

5 x 15   **S. purpurea** x **S. phylicifolia** = **S. x secerneta** F.B. White

5 x 16   **S. purpurea** x **S. repens** = **S. x doniana** G. Anderson ex Smith

6   ***S. daphnoides** Villars

7   ***S. acutifolia** Willd.

8   ***S. udensis** Trautv. & C. Meyer

9   **S. viminalis** L.

9 x 10   **S. viminalis** x **S. caprea** = **S. x sericans** Tausch ex A. Kerner
Salix x laurina auct., non Smith; *S. x smithiana* auct., non Willd.

9 x 10 x 11   **S. viminalis** x **S. caprea** x **S. cinerea** = **S. x calodendron** Wimmer
Salix x dasyclados auct., non Wimmer

9 x 10 x 12   **S. viminalis** x **S. caprea** x **S. aurita** = **S. x stipularis** Smith

9 x 11   **S. viminalis** x **S. cinerea** = **S. x smithiana** Willd.
Salix ? x holosericea Willd.

9 x 11 x 16   **S. viminalis** x **S. cinerea** x **S. repens** = **S. x angusensis** K.H. Rech.

9 x 12   **S. viminalis** x **S. aurita** = **S. x fruticosa** Doell

9 x 14   **S. viminalis** x **S. myrsinifolia** = **S. x seminigricans** Camus & A. Camus

9 x 16   **S. viminalis** x **S. repens** = **S. x friesiana** Andersson

10   **S. caprea** L.

a   subsp. **caprea**

b subsp. **sphacelata** (Smith) Macreight
Salix sphacelata Smith
Salix caprea L. subsp. *sericea* (Andersson) Flod.; *S. coaetanea* (Hartman) Flod.

10 x 11 S. caprea x S. cinerea = S. x reichardtii A. Kerner

10 x 12 S. caprea x S. aurita = S. x capreola J. Kerner ex Andersson

10 x 14 S. caprea x S. myrsinifolia = S. x latifolia Forbes

10 x 15 S. caprea x S. phylicifolia

10 x 16 S. caprea x S. repens = S. x laschiana Zahn

10 x 17 S. caprea x S. lapponum = S. x laestadiana Hartman

10 x 20 S. caprea x S. myrsinites = S. x lintonii Camus & A. Camus

11 S. cinerea L.

a subsp. **cinerea**

b subsp. **oleifolia** Macreight
Salix atrocinerea Brot.; *S. cinerea* L. subsp. *atrocinerea* (Brot.) Silva & Sobrinho; *S. oleifolia* Smith, non Villars

11 x 12 S. cinerea x S. aurita = S. x multinervis Doell

11 x 12 x 14 S. cinerea x S. aurita x S. myrsinifolia = S. x forbesiana Druce
Salix x waldsteiniana auct., non Willd.

11 x 14 S. cinerea x S. myrsinifolia
Salix x strepida Forbes, non Schleicher

11 x 15 S. cinerea x S. phylicifolia = S. x laurina Smith
Salix x wardiana Leefe ex F.B. White

11 x 16 S. cinerea x S. repens = S. x subsericea Doell

12 S. aurita L.

12 x 14 S. aurita x S. myrsinifolia = S. x coriacea Forbes

12 x 14 x 15   S. aurita x S. myrsinifolia x S. phylicifolia = **S. x saxetana**
F.B. White

12 x 15   S. aurita x S. phylicifolia = **S. x ludificans** F.B. White

12 x 16   S. aurita x S. repens = **S. x ambigua** Ehrh.

12 x 16 x 21   S. aurita x S. repens x S. herbacea = **S. x grahamii** Borrer ex
Baker

12 x 17   S. aurita x S. lapponum = **S. x obtusifolia** Willd.

12 x 21   S. aurita x S. herbacea = **S. x margarita** F.B. White

13   *****S. eriocephala** Michaux
Salix acutidens Rydb.; *S. cordata* Muhlenb., non Michaux; *S.
rigida* Muhlenb.

14   **S. myrsinifolia** Salisb.
Salix ? spadicea Chaix; *S. nigricans* Smith

14 x 15   **S. myrsinifolia** x S. phylicifolia = **S. x tetrapla** Walker

14 x 15 x 20   **S. myrsinifolia** x S. phylicifolia x S. myrsinites
Salix x myrsinitoides Druce, nom. nud.

14 x 16   **S. myrsinifolia** x S. repens = **S. x felina** Buser ex Camus & A.
Camus

14 x 20   **S. myrsinifolia** x S. myrsinites = **S. x punctata** Wahlenb.

14 x 21   **S. myrsinifolia** x S. herbacea = **S. x semireticulata** F.B. White

15   **S. phylicifolia** L.
Salix hibernica K.H. Rech.

15 x 16   **S. phylicifolia** x S. repens
Salix x schraderiana auct., non Willd.

15 x 17   **S. phylicifolia** x S. lapponum = **S. x gillotii** Camus & A.
Camus

15 x 20   **S. phylicifolia** x S. myrsinites = **S. x notha** Andersson

16 **S. repens** L.
Salix arenaria L.; *S. repens* L. subsp. *argentea* (Smith) Camus &
A. Camus

16 x 17 **S. repens** x **S. lapponum** = **S. x pithoensis** Rouy

16 x 21 **S. repens** x **S. herbacea** = **S. x cernua** E.F. Linton

17 **S. lapponum** L.

17 x 19 **S. lapponum** x **S. arbuscula** = **S. x pseudospuria** Rouy

17 x 21 **S. lapponum** x **S. herbacea** = **S. x sobrina** F.B. White

17 x 22 **S. lapponum** x **S. reticulata** = **S. x boydii** E.F. Linton
Salix ? x sybillina F.B. White

18 **S. lanata** L.

18 x 21 **S. lanata** x **S. herbacea** = **S. x sadleri** Syme

19 **S. arbuscula** L.

19 x 21 **S. arbuscula** x **S. herbacea** = **S. x simulatrix** F.B. White

19 x 22 **S. arbuscula** x **S. reticulata** = **S. x ganderi** Huter ex Zahn

20 **S. myrsinites** L.

21 **S. herbacea** L.

22 **S. reticulata** L.

62 BRASSICACEAE
Cruciferae

1 **SISYMBRIUM** L.

1 *****S. strictissimum** L.

2 *****S. irio** L.

3 *S. loeselii L.
Sisymbrium irio auct., non L.

4 *S. volgense M. Bieb. ex Fourn.

5 *S. altissimum L.

6 *S. orientale L.
Sisymbrium irio auct., non L.

7 S. officinale (L.) Scop.
Erysimum officinale L.

2 *DESCURAINIA Webb & Berth.

1 *D. sophia (L.) Webb ex Prantl
Sisymbrium sophia L.

3 ALLIARIA Heister ex Fabr.

1 A. petiolata (M. Bieb.) Cavara & Grande
Arabis petiolata M. Bieb.

4 ARABIDOPSIS (DC.) Heynh.
Sisymbrium sect. *Arabidopsis* DC.

1 A. thaliana (L.) Heynh.
Arabis thaliana L.
Sisymbrium thaliana (L.) Gay

5 *ISATIS L.

1 *I. tinctoria L.

6 *BUNIAS L.

1 *B. orientalis L.

7 *ERYSIMUM L.
Cheiranthus L.

    1 *E. cheiranthoides L.

    2 *E. cheiri (L.) Crantz
    Cheiranthus cheiri L.

8 *HESPERIS L.

    1 *H. matronalis L.

9 *MALCOLMIA R. Br.

    1 *M. maritima (L.) R. Br.
    Cheiranthus maritimus L.

10 MATTHIOLA R. Br.

    1 M. incana (L.) R. Br.
    Cheiranthus incanus L.

    2 M. sinuata (L.) R. Br.
    Cheiranthus sinuatus L.

11 BARBAREA R. Br.

    1 B. vulgaris R. Br.
    Barbarea arcuata (Opiz ex J.S. Presl & C. Presl) Reichb.

    2 B. stricta Andrz.

    3 *B. intermedia Boreau

    4 *B. verna (Miller) Asch.
    Erysimum vernum Miller

12 RORIPPA Scop.
Nasturtium R. Br.

1 R. nasturtium-aquaticum (L.) Hayek
Sisymbrium nasturtium-aquaticum L.
Nasturtium officinale R. Br.

1 x 2 R. nasturtium-aquaticum x **R. microphylla** = **R. x sterilis**
Airy Shaw
Nasturtium x sterile (Airy Shaw) Oefel.

2 R. microphylla (Boenn.) N. Hylander ex Á. Löve & D. Löve
Nasturtium officinale R. Br. var. *microphyllum* Boenn.
Nasturtium microphyllum (Boenn.) Reichb.; *N. uniseriatum*
Howard & Manton

3 R. islandica (Oeder ex Murray) Borbás
Sisymbrium islandicum Oeder ex Murray
Rorippa palustris auct., non (L.) Besser

4 R. palustris (L.) Besser
Sisymbrium amphibium L. var. *palustre* L.

4 x 6 R. palustris x **R. amphibia** = **R. x erythrocaulis** Borbás

5 R. sylvestris (L.) Besser
Sisymbrium sylvestre L.

5 x 6 R. sylvestris x **R. amphibia** = **R. x anceps** (Wahlenb.) Reichb.
Sisymbrium x anceps Wahlenb.
Rorippa x prostrata auct., ?an (Bergeret) Schinz & Thell.

5 x 7 R. sylvestris x **R. austriaca** = **R. x armoracioides** (Tausch)
Fuss
Nasturtium x armoracioides Tausch

6 R. amphibia (L.) Besser
Sisymbrium amphibium L.

6 x 7 R. amphibia x **R. austriaca** = **R. x hungarica** Borbás

7 *R. austriaca (Crantz) Besser
Nasturtium austriacum Crantz

13 *ARMORACIA P. Gaertner, Meyer & Scherb.

    1 *A. rusticana P. Gaertner, Meyer & Scherb.
       Armoracia lapathifolia Gilib., nom. illegit.; *Cochlearia armoracia* L.

14 CARDAMINE L.
Dentaria L.

    1 C. bulbifera (L.) Crantz
       Dentaria bulbifera L.

    2 *C. trifolia L.

    3 C. amara L.

    4 *C. raphanifolia Pourret
       Cardamine chelidonia Lam., non L.; *C. latifolia* Vahl

    5 C. pratensis L.
       Cardamine crassifolia Pourret; *C. hayneana* (Reichb.) Fritsch; *C. matthioli* Moretti; *C. nymanii* Gand.; *C. palustris* (Wimmer & Grab.) Peterm.; *C. rivularis* Schur

  5 x 7 C. pratensis x **C. flexuosa** = **C. x fringsii** Wirtgen f.
       Cardamine x haussknechtiana O. Schulz; *C. x keckii* sensu D.H. Kent ex R.M. Burton, non A. Kerner

    6 C. impatiens L.

    7 C. flexuosa With.

  7 x 8 C. flexuosa x **C. hirsuta** = **C. x zahlbruckneriana** O. Schulz

    8 C. hirsuta L.

15 ARABIS L.
Cardaminopsis (C. Meyer) Hayek; *Turritis* L.

    1 A. petraea (L.) Lam.
       Cardamine petraea L.
       Cardaminopsis petraea (L.) Hiit.

2 **A. glabra** (L.) Bernh.
  Turritis glabra L.

3 ***A. turrita** L.

4 **A. alpina** L.

5 ***A. caucasica** Willd. ex Schldl.
  Arabis albida Steven ex M. Bieb.

6 **A. hirsuta** (L.) Scop.
  Turritis hirsuta L.
  Arabis brownii Jordan

7 ***A. collina** Ten.
  Arabis muralis Bertol., non Salisb.; *A. muricola* Jordan

8 **A. scabra** All.
  Arabis stricta Hudson, nom. illegit.

16 ***AUBRIETA** Adans.

  1 ***A. deltoidea** (L.) DC.
    Alyssum deltoideum L.

17 ***LUNARIA** L.

  1 ***L. annua** L.

18 ***ALYSSUM** L.
   Aurinia Desv.

  1 ***A. alyssoides** (L.) L.
    Clypeola alyssoides L.

  2 ***A. saxatile** L.
    Aurinia saxatilis (L.) Desv.

19 *BERTEROA DC.

> **1 *B. incana** (L.) DC.
> *Alyssum incanum* L.

20 *LOBULARIA Desv.

> **1 *L. maritima** (L.) Desv.
> *Clypeola maritima* L.
> *Alyssum maritimum* (L.) Lam.

21 DRABA L.

> **1 D. aizoides** L.
>
> **2 D. norvegica** Gunnerus
> *Draba rupestris* R. Br.
>
> **3 D. incana** L.
>
> **4 D. muralis** L.

22 EROPHILA DC.

> **1 E. majuscula** Jordan
> *Erophila simplex* Winge
>
> **2 E. verna** (L.) DC.
> *Draba verna* L.
> *Erophila conferta* Wilm.; *E. praecox* (Steven) DC.; *E. spathulata*
> Láng; *E. verna* (L.) DC. subsp. *praecox* (Steven) Walters; *E.*
> *verna* (L.) DC. subsp. *spathulata* (Láng) Vollm.
>
> **3 E. glabrescens** Jordan
> *Erophila quadriplex* Winge; *E. verna* (L.) DC. var. *glabrescens*
> (Jordan) Diklic

23 COCHLEARIA L.

> **1 C. anglica** L.
> *Cochlearia officinalis* L. subsp. *anglica* (L.) Hartman

1 x 3   C. anglica x **C. officinalis** = **C. x hollandica** Henrard

2   C. pyrenaica DC.
Cochlearia alpina (Bab.) H. Watson, pro parte excl. typ.

2 x 3   C. pyrenaica x **C. officinalis**

3   C. officinalis L.
Cochlearia alpina (Bab.) H. Watson; *C. atlantica* Pobed.; *C. groenlandica* L. subsp. *scotica* (Druce) Á. Löve & D. Löve; *C. islandica* Pobed.; *C. officinalis* L. subsp. *scotica* (Druce) P. Wyse Jackson; *C. pyrenaica* DC. subsp. *alpina* (Bab.) Dalby; *C. scotica* Druce

3 x 5   C. officinalis x **C. danica**

4   C. micacea E. Marshall
Cochlearia groenlandica auct., non L. nec Gunnerus

5   C. danica L.

24 *CAMELINA Crantz

1 *C. sativa (L.) Crantz
Myagrum sativum L.

25 CAPSELLA Medikus

1   C. bursa-pastoris (L.) Medikus
Thlaspi bursa-pastoris L.

1 x 2   C. bursa-pastoris x **C. rubella** = **C. x gracilis** Gren.

2 *C. rubella Reuter

26 HORNUNGIA Reichb.
Hutchinsia R. Br., nom. illegit.

1   H. petraea (L.) Reichb.
Lepidium petraeum L.
Hutchinsia petraea (L.) R. Br., nom. illegit.

27   TEESDALIA R. Br.

    1   T. nudicaulis (L.) R. Br.
       Iberis nudicaulis L.

28   THLASPI L.
Pachyphragma (DC.) Reichb.

    1   T. arvense L.

    2   *T. alliaceum L.

    3   T. perfoliatum L.

    4   T. caerulescens J.S. Presl & C. Presl
       Thlaspi alpestre L., non Jacq.; *T. calaminare* auct., non (Lej.) Lej.
       & Court.

    5   *T. macrophyllum Hoffm.
       Pachyphragma macrophyllum (Hoffm.) N. Busch

29   IBERIS L.

    1   *I. sempervirens L.

    2   I. amara L.

30   LEPIDIUM L.
Cardaria Desv.

    1   *L. sativum L.

    2   L. campestre (L.) R. Br.
       Thlaspi campestre L.

    3   L. heterophyllum Benth.
       Lepidium smithii Hook.

    4   *L. virginicum L.
       Lepidium densiflorum Schrader; *L. neglectum* Thell.

    5   L. ruderale L.

6   **L. latifolium** L.

7   *****L. graminifolium** L.

8   *****L. draba** L.
Cardaria draba (L.) Desv.

   a   *subsp. **draba**

   b   *subsp. **chalepense** (L.) Thell.
Lepidium draba L. var. *chalepensis* L.
Cardaria draba (L.) Desv. subsp. *chalepensis* (L.) O.
Schulz

31   **CORONOPUS** Zinn

   1   **C. squamatus** (Forsskål) Asch.
Lepidium squamatum Forsskål

   2   *****C. didymus** (L.) Smith
Lepidium didymum L.

32   **SUBULARIA** L.

   1   **S. aquatica** L.

33   **DIPLOTAXIS** DC.

   1   **D. tenuifolia** (L.) DC.
Sisymbrium tenuifolium L.

   2   *****D. muralis** (L.) DC.
Sisymbrium murale L.

34   **BRASSICA** L.

   1   **B. oleracea** L.

   2   *****B. napus** L.

    a *subsp. **oleifera** (DC.) Metzger
       Brassica napus L. var. *oleifera* DC.

    b *subsp. **rapifera** Metzger
       Brassica napus L. subsp. *napobrassica* (L.) O. Schwarz

2 x 3 *B. napus x B. rapa = B. x harmsiana** O. Schulz

  3 *B. rapa** L.

    a *subsp. **rapa**

    b *subsp. **campestris** (L.) Clapham
       Brassica campestris L.
       Brassica rapa L. subsp. *sylvestris* (Lam.) Janchen

    c *subsp. **oleifera** (DC.) Metzger
       Brassica rapa L. var. *oleifera* DC.

  4 *B. juncea** (L.) Czernj.
    Sinapis juncea L.

  5 **B. nigra** (L.) Koch
    Sinapis nigra L.

35 SINAPIS L.

  1 **S. arvensis** L.
    Brassica arvensis (L.) Rabenh., non L.; *B. kaber* (DC.) Wheeler;
    B. sinapis Vis., nom. illegit.

  2 *S. alba** L.
    Brassica alba (L.) Rabenh.; *B. hirta* Moench

36 *ERUCASTRUM C. Presl

  1 *E. gallicum** (Willd.) O. Schulz
    Sisymbrium gallicum Willd.

37 COINCYA Rouy
Brassicella Fourr. ex O. Schulz; *Hutera* Porta; *Rhynchosinapis* Hayek

1 C. monensis (L.) Greuter & Burdet
Sisymbrium monense L.
Brassica monensis (L.) Hudson; *Brassicella monensis* (L.) O.
Schulz; *Hutera monensis* (L.) Gómez-Campo; *Rhynchosinapis monensis* (L.) Dandy ex Clapham

   a subsp. **monensis**

   b *subsp. **recurvata** (All.) Leadlay
     Sinapis recurvata All.
     Brassica cheiranthos Villars; *Brassicella erucastrum* O.
       Schulz, pro parte; *Coincya cheiranthos* (Villars)
       Greuter & Burdet; *Hutera cheiranthos* (Villars)
       Gómez-Campo; *Rhynchosinapis cheiranthos* (Villars)
       Dandy; *R. erucastrum* sensu Clapham, non (L.)
       Dandy

2 C. wrightii (O. Schulz) Stace
Brassicella wrightii O. Schulz
Brassica wrightii (O. Schulz) Sikka; *Hutera wrightii* (O. Schulz)
Gómez-Campo; *Rhynchosinapis cheiranthos* (Villars) Dandy
subsp. *wrightii* (O. Schulz) Malagarriga; *R. wrightii* (O.
Schulz) Dandy ex Clapham

38 *HIRSCHFELDIA Moench

1 *H. incana (L.) Lagr.-Fossat
Sinapis incana L.
Brassica incana (L.) Meigen, non Ten.

39 CAKILE Miller

1 C. maritima Scop.

   a subsp. **integrifolia** (Hornem.) N. Hylander ex Greuter
     & Burdet
     Cakile maritima Scop. var. *integrifolia* Hornem.
     Cakile edentula sensu D. Allen et auct., non (Bigelow)
       Hook.

40 *RAPISTRUM Crantz

   1 *R. rugosum (L.) Bergeret
      Myagrum rugosum L.

      a *subsp. **linnaeanum** (Cosson) Rouy & Fouc.
         Rapistrum rugosum (L.) Bergeret var. *linnaeanum* Cosson
         Rapistrum linnaeanum Boiss. & Reuter, nom. illegit.; *R.
         orientale* auct., non (L.) Crantz; *R. rugosum* (L.)
         Bergeret subsp. *orientale* auct., non (L.) Arcang.

   2 *R. perenne (L.) All.

41 CRAMBE L.

   1 C. maritima L.

   2 *C. cordifolia Steven

42 RAPHANUS L.

   1 R. raphanistrum L.

      a *subsp. **raphanistrum**

      b subsp. **maritimus** (Smith) Thell.
         Raphanus maritimus Smith

63 RESEDACEAE

1 RESEDA L.

   1 R. luteola L.

   2 *R. alba L.

   3 R. lutea L.

   4 *R. phyteuma L.

64 EMPETRACEAE

1 EMPETRUM L.

    1 E. nigrum L.

        a subsp. **nigrum**

        b subsp. **hermaphroditum** (Hagerup) Böcher
          Empetrum hermaphroditum Hagerup
          Empetrum eamesii Fern. & Wieg. subsp. *hermaphroditum*
          (Hagerup) D. Löve

65 ERICACEAE

1 *LEDUM L.

    1 *L. palustre L.

        a *subsp. **groenlandicum** (Oeder) Hultén
          Ledum groenlandicum Oeder

2 *RHODODENDRON L.

    1 *R. ponticum L.

    2 *R. luteum Sweet

3 LOISELEURIA Desv.

    1 L. procumbens (L.) Desv.
        Azalea procumbens L.

4 *KALMIA L.

    1 *K. polifolia Wangenh.

    2 *K. angustifolia L.

5 PHYLLODOCE Salisb.

    1 P. caerulea (L.) Bab.
       Andromeda caerulea L.

6 DABOECIA D. Don

    1 D. cantabrica (Hudson) K. Koch
       Vaccinium cantabricum Hudson

7 ANDROMEDA L.

    1 A. polifolia L.

8 GAULTHERIA L.
X Gaulnettya W. Marchant; *X Gaulthettya* Camp; *Pernettya* Gaudich.
ex Mirbel

    1 *G. shallon Pursh
       Gaultheria procumbens auct., non L.

    1 x 3 G. shallon x **G. mucronata**
       X Gaulnettya wisleyensis W. Marchant, nom. nud.

    2 *G. procumbens L.

    3 *G. mucronata (L.f.) Hook. & Arn.
       Arbutus mucronata L.f.
       Pernettya mucronata (L.f.) Gaudich. ex Sprengel

9 ARBUTUS L.

    1 A. unedo L.

10 ARCTOSTAPHYLOS Adans.
Arctous (A. Gray) Niedenzu

    1 A. uva-ursi (L.) Sprengel
       Arbutus uva-ursi L.

2   **A. alpinus** (L.) Sprengel
Arbutus alpina L.
Arctous alpina (L.) Niedenzu

11   **CALLUNA** Salisb.

1   **C. vulgaris** (L.) Hull
Erica vulgaris L.

12   **ERICA** L.

1   **E. ciliaris** L.

1 x 3   **E. ciliaris** x **E. tetralix** = **E. x watsonii** Benth.

2   **E. mackaiana** Bab.

2 x 3   **E. mackaiana** x **E. tetralix** = **E. x stuartii** E.F. Linton
Erica x praegeri Ostenf.

3   **E. tetralix** L.

3 x 8   **E. tetralix** x **E. vagans** = **E. x williamsii** Druce

4   ***E. terminalis** Salisb.

5   **E. cinerea** L.

6   ***E. lusitanica** Rudolphi

7   **E. erigena** R. Ross
Erica carnea L. subsp. *occidentalis* (Benth.) Laínz; *E. herbacea* L.
subsp. *occidentalis* (Benth.) Laínz; *E. herbacea* auct., non L.; *E. hibernica* (Hook. & Arn.) Syme, non Utinet; *E. mediterranea* L. var. *hibernica* Hook. & Arn.

7 x her   ***E. erigena** x **E. herbacea** L. = **E. x darleyensis** Bean

8   **E. vagans** L.

13 VACCINIUM L.
Oxycoccus Hill

    1 V. oxycoccos L.
    Oxycoccus oxycoccos (L.) Adolphi; *O. quadripetalus* Gilib., nom.
    illegit.

    2 V. microcarpum (Turcz. ex Rupr.) Schmal.
    Oxycoccus microcarpus Turcz. ex Rupr.

    3 *V. macrocarpon Aiton

    4 V. vitis-idaea L.

  4 x 6 V. vitis-idaea x **V. myrtillus** = **V. x intermedium** Ruthe

    5 V. uliginosum L.

    6 V. myrtillus L.

    7 *V. corymbosum L.

66 PYROLACEAE

1 PYROLA L.

    1 P. minor L.

    2 P. media Sw.

    3 P. rotundifolia L.

      a subsp. **rotundifolia**

      b subsp. **maritima** (Kenyon) E. Warb.
      Pyrola maritima Kenyon

2 ORTHILIA Raf.
Ramischia Opiz ex Garcke

    1 O. secunda (L.) House
    Pyrola secunda L.

66. PYROLACEAE

Ramischia secunda (L.) Garcke

3 MONESES Salisb. ex Gray

    1 M. uniflora (L.) A. Gray
    Pyrola uniflora L.

67 MONOTROPACEAE

1 MONOTROPA L.

    1 M. hypopitys L.

        a subsp. **hypopitys**

        b subsp. **hypophegea** (Wallr.) Holmboe
        Monotropa hypophegea Wallr.
        Monotropa hypopitys L. var. *glabra* Roth

68 DIAPENSIACEAE

1 DIAPENSIA L.

    1 D. lapponica L.

69 PRIMULACEAE

1 PRIMULA L.

    1 P. vulgaris Hudson
    Primula veris L. var. *acaulis* L.; *P. acaulis* (L.) Hill

  1 x 2 P. vulgaris x **P. elatior** = **P. x digenea** A. Kerner

1 x 2 x 3 P. vulgaris x **P. elatior** x **P. veris** = **P. x murbeckii** Lindq.

  1 x 3 P. vulgaris x **P. veris** = **P. x polyantha** Miller
    Primula x tommasinii Gren. & Godron;

P. x variabilis Goupil, non Bast.

2   P. elatior (L.) Hill
Primula veris L. var. *elatior* L.

2 x 3   P. elatior x **P. veris** = **P. x media** Peterm.

3   P. veris L.

4   P. farinosa L.

5   P. scotica Hook.

6   *P. auricula L.

7   *P. florindae Kingdon-Ward

8   *P. sikkimensis J.D. Hook.

9   *P. japonica A. Gray

2   HOTTONIA L.

1   H. palustris L.

3   *CYCLAMEN L.

1   *C. hederifolium Aiton

2   *C. coum Miller

4   LYSIMACHIA L.
Naumbergia Moench

1   L. nemorum L.

2   L. nummularia L.

3   L. vulgaris L.

4   *L. ciliata L.
Lysimachia punctata auct., non L.

5 ***L. punctata** L.
  Lysimachia ciliata auct., non L.

6 ***L. terrestris** (L.) Britton
  Viscum terrestre L.

7 **L. thyrsiflora** L.
  Naumbergia thyrsiflora (L.) Reichb.

5 TRIENTALIS L.

1 **T. europaea** L.

6 ANAGALLIS L.
Centunculus L.

1 **A. tenella** (L.) L.
  Lysimachia tenella L.

2 **A. arvensis** L.

  a subsp. **arvensis**
    Anagallis phoenicia Scop., nom. illegit.

  b subsp. **caerulea** Hartman
    Anagallis arvensis L. subsp. *foemina* (Miller) Schinz &
      Thell.; *A. caerulea* Schreber, non L.; *A. foemina* Miller

3 **A. minima** (L.) E.H. Krause
  Centunculus minimus L.

7 GLAUX L.

1 **G. maritima** L.

8 SAMOLUS L.

1 **S. valerandi** L.

70 *PITTOSPORACEAE

1 *PITTOSPORUM Banks ex Gaertner

    1 *P. crassifolium Sol. ex Putterl.

    2 *P. tenuifolium Gaertner

71 *HYDRANGEACEAE

1 *PHILADELPHUS L.

    1 *P. coronarius L.

x mic x pub *P. coronarius x P. microphyllus A. Gray x P. pubescens Lois.
    = P. x virginalis Rehder

72 GROSSULARIACEAE
Escalloniaceae

1 *ESCALLONIA Mutis ex L.f.

    1 *E. macrantha Hook. & Arn.
      Escallonia rubra (Ruíz-Lopez & Pavón) Pers. var. *macrantha*
      (Hook. & Arn.) Reiche; *E. sanguinea* hort.

2 RIBES L.

    1 R. rubrum L.
      Ribes sylvestre (Lam.) Mert. & Koch

    2 R. spicatum Robson

    3 R. nigrum L.

    4 *R. sanguineum Pursh

    5 *R. odoratum H.L. Wendl.
      Ribes aureum Lindley, non Pursh

6   R. alpinum L.

7   R. uva-crispa L.
Grossularia uva-crispa (L.) Miller subsp. *reclinata* (L.) Dostál;
Ribes grossularia L.

73 CRASSULACEAE

1   CRASSULA L.
Tillaea L.

    1   C. tillaea Lester-Garl.
    Tillaea muscosa L.

    2   C. aquatica (L.) Schönl.
    Tillaea aquatica L.

    3   *C. helmsii (Kirk) Cockayne
    Tillaea helmsii Kirk
    Crassula recurva (J.D. Hook.) Ostenf., non N.E. Br.; *Tillaea*
    recurva (J.D. Hook.) J.D. Hook.

    4   *C. decumbens Thunb.

    5   *C. pubescens Thunb.

        a   *subsp. radicans (Haw.) Tolken
        Globulea radicans Haw.
        Crassula radicans (Haw.) D. Dietr.

2   UMBILICUS DC.

    1   U. rupestris (Salisb.) Dandy
    Cotyledon rupestris Salisb.
    Umbilicus pendulinus DC., nom. illegit.

3   *SEMPERVIVUM L.

    1   *S. tectorum L.

4 *AEONIUM Webb & Berth.

    1 *A. cuneatum Webb & Berth.

5 SEDUM L.
Rhodiola L.

    1 S. rosea (L.) Scop.
    Rhodiola rosea L.
    Sedum rhodiola DC., nom. illegit.

    2 *S. praealtum A. DC.
    Sedum dendroideum Mociño & Sessé subsp. *praealtum* (A. DC.)
      R.T. Clausen

    3 *S. confusum Hemsley
    Sedum hybridum sensu P. Ryan et auct., non L.

    4 *S. spectabile Boreau

    5 S. telephium L.

      a subsp. **telephium**
      Sedum purpurascens Koch, nom. illegit.; *S. telephium* L.
        subsp. *purpurascens* Syme

      b subsp. **fabaria** (Koch) Kirschl.
      Sedum fabaria Koch

    6 *S. anacampseros L.

    7 *S. spurium M. Bieb.
    Sedum stoloniferum auct., non S. Gmelin

    8 *S. stoloniferum S. Gmelin

    9 *S. nicaeense All.
    Sedum sediforme (Jacq.) Pau ex Pau, non (Schweinf.) Hamet

    10 *S. rupestre L.
    Sedum reflexum L.

    11 S. forsterianum Smith
    Sedum elegans Lej.; *S. forsterianum* Smith subsp. *elegans*

(Lej.) E. Warb.; *S. rupestre* auct., non L.

12   S. acre L.

13   *S. sexangulare L.

14   S. album L.
   Sedum album L. subsp. *micranthum* (Bast.) Syme; *S. micranthum*
   Bast.

15   *S. lydium Boiss.

16   S. anglicum Hudson

17   *S. dasyphyllum L.

18   S. villosum L.

19   *S. hispanicum L.
   Sedum lydium auct., non Boiss.

74 SAXIFRAGACEAE
Parnassiaceae

1   *ASTILBE Buch.-Ham. ex D. Don

   1   *A. japonica (Morren & Decne.) A. Gray
      Hoteia japonica Morren & Decne.

1 x **ros** x **chi   *A. japonica** x **A. rosea** Arends x **A. chinensis** (Maxim.)
      Franchet & Savat. = **A. x arendsii** Arends
      Astilbe x rosea auct., non Arends

   2   *A. rivularis Buch.-Ham. ex D. Don

2   *RODGERSIA A. Gray

   1   *R. podophylla A. Gray

3 *BERGENIA Moench

    1 *B. crassifolia (L.) Fritsch
    Saxifraga crassifolia L.

4 *DARMERA Voss ex Post & Kuntze
Peltiphyllum (Engl.) Engl., nom. illegit.; *Peltophyllum* auct., non
Gardner

    1 *D. peltata (Torrey ex Benth.) Voss ex Post & Kuntze
    Saxifraga peltata Torrey ex Benth.
    Peltiphyllum peltatum (Torrey ex Benth.) Engl., nom. illegit.

5 SAXIFRAGA L.

    1 S. hirculus L.

    2 *S. cymbalaria L.

    3 S. nivalis L.

    4 S. stellaris L.

    5 *S. stolonifera Curtis
    Saxifraga sarmentosa L.f.

    6 *S. rotundifolia L.

    7 *S. cuneifolia L.

    8 *S. umbrosa L.

 8 x 9 *S. umbrosa x **S. spathularis** = **S. x urbium** D. Webb

8 x 10 *S. umbrosa x **S. hirsuta** = **S. x geum** L.

    9 S. spathularis Brot.
    Saxifraga umbrosa auct., non L.

9 x 10 S. spathularis x **S. hirsuta** = **S. x polita** (Haw.) Link
    Robertsonia x polita Haw.
    Saxifraga x hirsuta auct., non L.

10   S. hirsuta L.
Saxifraga geum sensu L.(1762), non L.(1753); *S. lactiflora* Pugsley

11   S. oppositifolia L.

12   S. aizoides L.

13   S. rivularis L.

14   S. cernua L.

15   S. granulata L.

16   S. hypnoides L.
Saxifraga platypetala Smith

16 x 17   S. hypnoides x **S. rosacea**

16 x 19   S. hypnoides x **S. tridactylites**

17   S. rosacea Moench

    a   subsp. **rosacea**
Saxifraga decipiens Ehrh. subsp. *sternbergii* (Willd.) Kerguélen, nom. illegit.; *S. decipiens* Ehrh., nom. nud.; *S. drucei* E. Marshall; *S. hirta* Donn ex Smith, non Haw.; *S. incurvifolia* D. Don

    b   subsp. **hartii** (D. Webb) D. Webb
Saxifraga hartii D. Webb

18   S. cespitosa L.

19   S. tridactylites L.

6 *HEUCHERA L.

    1 *H. sanguinea Engelm.

7 *TOLMIEA Torrey & A. Gray

    1 *T. menziesii (Pursh) Torrey & A. Gray

Tiarella menziesii Pursh

8 *TELLIMA R. Br.

1 *T. grandiflora** (Pursh) Douglas ex Lindley
Mitella grandiflora Pursh

9 CHRYSOSPLENIUM L.

1 C. oppositifolium L.

2 C. alternifolium L.

10 PARNASSIA L.

1 P. palustris L.

75 ROSACEAE

1 *SORBARIA (Ser. ex DC.) A. Braun
Spiraea sect. *Sorbaria* Ser. ex DC.

1 *S. sorbifolia** (L.) A. Braun
Spiraea sorbifolia L.

2 *S. tomentosa** (Lindley) Rehder
Schizonotus tomentosus Lindley
Sorbaria aitchisonii (Hemsley) Hemsley ex Rehder

3 *S. kirilowii** (Regel) Maxim.
Spiraea kirilowii Regel
Sorbaria arborea C. Schneider; *S. assurgens* Vilm. & Bois

2 *PHYSOCARPUS (Cambess.) Maxim.
Spiraea sect. *Physocarpus* Cambess.

1 *P. opulifolius** (L.) Maxim.
Spiraea opulifolia L.

3 *SPIRAEA L.

    1 *S. salicifolia L.

    1 x 2 *S. salicifolia x **S. alba = S. x rosalba** Dippel
        Spiraea x rubella Dippel

    1 x 3 *S. salicifolia x **S. douglasii = S. x pseudosalicifolia** Silverside
        Spiraea x billardii auct., non Hérincq; *S. x eximia* W. Koch, non
        Regel

    2 *S. alba Duroi
        Spiraea latifolia (Aiton) Borkh.; *S. salicifolia* L. var. *latifolia* Aiton

    2 x 3 *S. alba x **S. douglasii = S. x billardii** Hérincq

    3 *S. douglasii Hook.
        Spiraea fulvescens auct., non Dippel

        a *subsp. **douglasii**

        b *subsp. **menziesii** (Hook.) Calder & R.L. Taylor
            Spiraea menziesii Hook.

    3 x 6 *S. douglasii x **S. canescens = S. x brachybotrys** Lange

    4 *S. tomentosa L.

    5 *S. japonica L.f.

    6 *S. canescens D. Don

    7 *S. chamaedryfolia L.

        a *subsp. **ulmifolia** (Scop.) J. Duvign.
            Spiraea ulmifolia Scop.

can x tri *S. cantoniensis Lour. x **S. trilobata** L. = **S. x vanhouttei**
        (Briot) Zabel
        Spiraea aquilegifolia Pallas var. *vanhouttei* Briot

4 *ARUNCUS L.

    1 *A. dioicus (Walter) Fern.

Actaea dioica Walter
Aruncus sylvester Kostel; *A. vulgaris* Raf.

5 *HOLODISCUS (K. Koch) Maxim.
Spiraea sect. *Holodiscus* K. Koch

1 *H. discolor (Pursh) Maxim.
Spiraea discolor Pursh

6 FILIPENDULA Miller

1 F. vulgaris Moench
Filipendula hexapetala Gilib., nom. illegit.; *Spiraea filipendula* L.

2 F. ulmaria (L.) Maxim.
Spiraea ulmaria L.

3 *F. kamtschatica (Pallas) Maxim.
Spiraea kamtschatica Pallas
Filipendula purpurea auct., non Maxim.

7 *KERRIA DC.

1 *K. japonica (L.) DC.
Rubus japonicus L.

8 RUBUS L.

1 R. chamaemorus L.

2 *R. tricolor Focke
Rubus polytrichus Franchet, non Progel

3 R. saxatilis L.

4 †R. arcticus L.

5 *R. odoratus L.

6 *R. parviflorus Nutt.
Rubus nutkanus Mociño ex DC.

7   R. idaeus L.

7 x 321   **R. idaeus** x **R. caesius** = **R. x pseudoidaeus** (Weihe) Lej.
Rubus caesius L. var. *pseudoidaeus* Weihe
Rubus x idaeoides Ruthe ex Focke

7 x fru   **R. idaeus** x **R. fruticosus** L.

8   *****R. phoenicolasius** Maxim.

9   *****R. spectabilis** Pursh

10   *****R. loganobaccus** L. Bailey

11   *****R. cockburnianus** Hemsley
Rubus thibetianus auct., non Franchet

sect. **Rubus**

subsect. **Rubus**

12   **R. accrescens** Newton

13   *****R. allegheniensis** Porter

14   **R. arrheniiformis** W.C.R. Watson

15   **R. bertramii** G. Braun
Rubus opacus Bertram, non Focke

16   **R. briggsianus** (Rogers) Rogers
Rubus affinis Weihe & Nees, nom. illegit. var. *briggsianus*
Rogers

17   *****R. canadensis** L.

18   **R. daltrii** Edees & Rilstone

19   **R. divaricatus** P.J. Mueller

20   **R. fissus** Lindley
Rubus fastigiatus sensu Lindley, non Weihe & Nees; *R. rogersii*
E.F. Linton

21   **R. glanduliger** W.C.R. Watson

22　**R. integribasis** P.J. Mueller ex Boulay

23　**R. nessensis** W. Hall

24　**R. nitidiformis** Sudre
　　Rubus nitidoides W.C.R. Watson, non Neuman

25　**R. nobilissimus** (W.C.R. Watson) Pearsall
　　Rubus opacus Focke subsp. *nobilissimus* W.C.R. Watson

26　*R. pergratus** Blanchard

27　**R. plicatus** Weihe & Nees

28　**R. scissus** W.C.R. Watson

29　**R. subopacus** Sudre

30　**R. sulcatus** Vest

31　**R. trelleckensis** Edees & Newton
　　Rubus orthocladus Ley, non Boulay

32　**R. vigorosus** P.J. Mueller & Wirtgen
　　Rubus affinis Weihe & Nees, pro parte, nom. illegit.

subsect. **Hiemales** E.H.L. Krause

　ser. **Sylvatici** (P.J. Mueller) Focke
　Rubus sect. *Sylvatici* P.J. Mueller

33　**R. adspersus** Weihe ex H.E. Weber
　　Rubus carpinifolius Weihe & Nees, non C. Presl & J.S. Presl

34　**R. albionis** W.C.R. Watson
　　Rubus schlechtendalii Weihe ex Link var. *anglicus* Sudre

35　**R. averyanus** W.C.R. Watson

36　**R. boulayi** (Sudre) W.C.R. Watson
　　Rubus macrophyllus Weihe & Nees var. *boulayi* Sudre

37　**R. calvatus** Lees ex Bloxam

38　**R. cambrensis** W.C.R. Watson

39   R. canterburiensis Edees

40   R. castrensis Wolley-Dod

41   R. chloophyllus Sudre
Rubus rhodanthus sensu W.C.R. Watson(1958), non W.C.R.
   Watson(1933)

42   R. chrysoxylon (Rogers) Rogers
Rubus mercicus Bagnall var. *chrysoxylon* Rogers

43   R. confertiflorus W.C.R. Watson

44   R. crespignyanus W.C.R. Watson
Rubus similatus sensu W.C.R. Watson, non P.J. Mueller

45   R. crudelis W.C.R. Watson

46   R. cumbrensis Newton

47   R. dasycoccus W.C.R. Watson
Rubus lasiocarpus W.C.R. Watson, non Smith

48   R. dobuniensis Sudre & Ley

49   R. durescens W.R. Linton

50   R. ebudensis Newton

51   R. errabundus W.C.R. Watson
Rubus scheutzii sensu Sudre, non Lindeb.

52   R. gratus Focke

53   R. hesperius Rogers

54   R. imbricatus F.J.A. Hort

55   *R. laciniatus Willd.

56   R. lacustris Rogers

57   R. lentiginosus Lees

58   **R. leptothyrsos** G. Braun
      Rubus danicus (Focke) Focke

59   **R. leucandriformis** Edees & Newton
      Rubus leucandrus sensu W.C.R. Watson, non Focke

60   **R. lindleianus** Lees

61   **R. ludensis** W.C.R. Watson
      Rubus sciaphilus sensu W.C.R. Watson, non Lange

62   **R. macrophyllus** Weihe & Nees

63   †**R. mercicus** Bagnall

64   **R. mollissimus** Rogers

65   **R. monensis** W.C. Barton & Riddelsd.
      Rubus laetus W.C.R. Watson, non Progel

66   **R. obesifolius** W.C.R. Watson

67   **R. oxyanchus** Sudre

68   **R. perdigitatus** Newton
      Rubus digitatus Newton, non Sprengel

69   **R. platyacanthus** P.J. Mueller & Lef.

70   **R. pliocenicus** (W.C.R. Watson) Edees & Newton
      Rubus egregius Focke var. *pliocenicus* W.C.R. Watson

71   **R. plymensis** (Focke) Edees & Newton
      Rubus egregius Focke var. *plymensis* Focke

72   **R. poliodes** W.C.R. Watson

73   **R. polyoplus** W.C.R. Watson
      Rubus perarmatus W.C.R. Watson, non Boulay ex Malbr.

74   **R. pullifolius** W.C.R. Watson

75   **R. purbeckensis** W.C. Barton & Riddelsd.

76   **R. pyramidalis** Kaltenb.

77   R. questieri Lef. & P.J. Mueller

78   R. riparius W.C. Barton ex Newton

79   R. robiae (W.C.R. Watson) Newton
Rubus muenteri Marsson var. *robiae* W.C.R. Watson

80   R. salteri Bab.

81   R. sciocharis (Sudre) W.C.R. Watson
Rubus gratus Focke subsp. *sciocharis* Sudre

82   R. silurum (Ley) Ley
Rubus nemoralis P.J. Mueller var. *silurum* Ley

83   R. silvaticus Weihe & Nees

84   R. sneydii Edees

85   R. subintegribasis Druce

86   R. varvicensis Edees
Rubus mercicus Bagnall var. *bracteatus* Bagnall

87   R. viridescens (Rogers) T.A.W. Davis
Rubus thyrsoideus Wimmer var. *viridescens* Rogers

ser. **Rhamnifolii** (Bab.) Focke
Rubus group *Rhamnifolii* Bab.

88   R. acclivitatum W.C.R. Watson
Rubus argentatus P.J. Mueller var. *clivicola* Ley

89   R. altiarcuatus W.C. Barton & Riddelsd.
Rubus rotundatus sensu W.C.R. Watson, non P.J. Mueller ex
Genev.; *R. cariensis* sensu Rogers, non Rip. ex Genev.

90   R. amplificatus Lees

91   R. bakerianus W.C. Barton & Riddelsd.

92   R. boudiccae A.L. Bull & Edees

93   R. cardiophyllus Lef. & P.J. Mueller

94 **R. carnkiefensis** Rilstone

95 **R. cissburiensis** W.C. Barton & Riddelsd.

96 **R. cordatifolius** (Rogers ex Riddelsd.) D. Allen
Rubus dumnoniensis Bab. var. *cordatifolius* Rogers ex Riddelsd.

97 **R. cornubiensis** (Rogers ex Riddelsd.) Rilstone
Rubus nemoralis P.J. Mueller taxon *cornubiensis* Rogers ex Riddelsd.

98 **R. curvispinosus** Edees & Newton
Rubus curvispinis W.C.R. Watson, non A. Förster

99 **R. daveyi** Rilstone

100 **R. diversiarmatus** W.C.R. Watson

101 **R. dumnoniensis** Bab.
Rubus rotundatus sensu W.C.R. Watson, non P.J. Mueller ex Genev.

102 ***R. elegantispinosus** (A. Schum.) H.E. Weber
Rubus argenteus Weihe & Nees subsp. *elegantispinosus* A. Schum.
Rubus elegans Utsch, non P.J. Mueller

103 **R. furnarius** W.C. Barton & Riddelsd.

104 **R. herefordensis** Sudre

105 **R. incurvatiformis** Edees

106 **R. incurvatus** Bab.

107 **R. iricus** Rogers

108 **R. lasiodermis** Sudre

109 **R. lindebergii** P.J. Mueller

110 **R. londinensis** (Rogers) W.C.R. Watson
Rubus imbricatus F.J.A. Hort var. *londinensis* Rogers

111 **R. milfordensis** Edees
Rubus broensis auct., non W.C.R. Watson; *R. villicaulis* sensu
Rogers, non Köhler ex Weihe & Nees; *R. holerythros* sensu
W.C.R. Watson, non Focke ex Rogers

112 **R. nemoralis** P.J. Mueller
Rubus selmeri Lindeb.

113 **R. pampinosus** Lees
Rubus favonii W.C.R. Watson; *R. buttii* W.C. Barton &
Riddelsd.

114 **R. patuliformis** Sudre

115 **R. pervalidus** Edees & Newton
Rubus atrocaulis sensu W.C.R. Watson, non P.J. Mueller

116 **R. pistoris** W.C. Barton & Riddelsd.

117 **R. polyanthemus** Lindeb.
Rubus pulcherrimus Neuman, non Hook.

118 **R. prolongatus** Boulay & Letendre ex Corbière
Rubus griseoviridis W.C. Barton & Riddelsd.

119 **R. ramosus** Bloxam ex Briggs

120 **R. rhombifolius** Weihe ex Boenn.
Rubus incurvatus Bab. var. *subcarpinifolius* (Rogers) Riddelsd.

121 **R. riddelsdellii** Rilstone

122 **R. rubritinctus** W.C.R. Watson
Rubus cryptadenes Sudre, non Dumort.

123 **R. septentrionalis** W.C.R. Watson
Rubus insularis sensu W.C.R. Watson, non Aresch.; *R. confinis*
Lindeb., non P.J. Mueller

124 **R. stanneus** W.C. Barton & Riddelsd.

125 **R. subinermoides** Druce
Rubus pubescens Weihe var. *subinermis* Rogers

126   **R. tavensis** Newton & M. Porter
Rubus godronii Lecoq & Lamotte var. *foliolatus* Rogers & Ley

127   **R. tresidderi** Rilstone

128   **R. villicauliformis** Newton
Rubus villicaulis sensu Rilstone, non Köhler ex Weihe & Nees

ser. **Sprengeliani** Focke

129   **R. arrhenii** (Lange) Lange
Rubus sprengelii Weihe var. *arrhenii* Lange

130   **R. brevistaminosus** Edees & Newton
Rubus braeuckeri sensu W.C.R. Watson, non G. Braun

131   **R. permundus** W.C.R. Watson
Rubus mundiflorus W.C.R. Watson, non Sudre

132   **R. sprengelii** Weihe

ser. **Discolores** (P.J. Mueller) Focke
Rubus sect. *Discolores* P.J. Mueller

133   **R. anglocandicans** Newton
Rubus falcatus auct., non Kaltenb.

134   **R. armeniacus** Focke
Rubus procerus auct. brit., non P.J. Mueller ex Boulay

135   **R. armipotens** W.C. Barton ex Newton
Rubus pseudobifrons sensu W.C.R. Watson, non Sudre ex
   Bouvet

136   **R. hylophilus** Rip. ex Genev.
Rubus brittonii W.C. Barton & Riddelsd.

137   **R. lamburnensis** Rilstone

138   **R. neomalacus** Sudre
Rubus incarnatus sensu W.C.R. Watson, non P.J. Mueller

139   **R. pydarensis** Rilstone

140   **R. rossensis** Newton
Rubus propinquus auct., non P.J. Mueller; *R. crassifolius* sensu
W.C.R. Watson, non Genev.

141   **R. stenopetalus** Lef. & P.J. Mueller

142   **R. ulmifolius** Schott
Rubus inermis sensu Beek et auct., non Pourret

143   **R. winteri** P.J. Mueller ex Focke

ser. **Vestiti** (Focke) Focke
Rubus group *Vestiti* Focke

144   **R. adscitus** Genev.

145   **R. andegavensis** Bouvet

146   **R. bartonii** Newton

147   **R. boraeanus** Genev.

148   **R. conspersus** W.C.R. Watson

149   **R. cotteswoldensis** W.C. Barton & Riddelsd.

150   **R. criniger** (E.F. Linton) Rogers
Rubus gelertii Friderichsen var. *criniger* E.F. Linton

151   **R. euanthinus** W.C.R. Watson
Rubus anglosaxonicus Gelert subsp. *vestitiformis* Rogers

152   **R. hirsutissimus** (Sudre & Ley) W.C.R. Watson
Rubus schlechtendalii Weihe ex Link microgene *hirsutissimus*
Sudre & Ley

153   **R. infestisepalus** Edees & Newton
Rubus macrothyrsus sensu W.C.R. Watson, non Lange

154   **R. lanaticaulis** Edees & Newton
Rubus hebecaulis sensu W.C.R. Watson, non Sudre

155   **R. lettii** Rogers

156   **R. leucostachys** Schleicher ex Smith

157   **R. longus** (Rogers & Ley) Newton
Rubus lasioclados Focke var. *longus* Rogers & Ley

158   **R. orbus** W.C.R. Watson
Rubus iricus Rogers var. *minor* Rogers & Riddelsd.

159   **R. ordovicum** Newton

160   **R. painteri** Edees

161   **R. surrejanus** W.C. Barton & Riddelsd.
Rubus hirtior W.C.R. Watson

162   **R. thurstonii** Rilstone

163   **R. vestitus** Weihe

ser. **Mucronati** (Focke) H.E. Weber
Rubus subser. *Mucronati* Focke

164   **R. aquarum** Newton & M. Porter

165   **R. cinerosiformis** Rilstone

166   †**R. devoniensis** (Focke ex Rogers) Rogers
Rubus macrophyllus Weihe & Nees subsp. *devoniensis* Focke ex
Rogers

167   **R. egregius** Focke

168   **R. furvicolor** Focke
Rubus melanoxylon sensu Rogers, non P.J. Mueller & Wirtgen

169   **R. fuscicortex** Sudre

170   **R. melanocladus** (Sudre) Riddelsd.
Rubus pyramidalis Kaltenb. subsp. *melanocladus* Sudre

171   **R. mucronatiformis** (Sudre) W.C.R. Watson
Rubus hypomalacus Focke subsp. *mucronatiformis* Sudre

172   **R. mucronatoides** Ley ex Rogers

173   **R. mucronulatus** Boreau
Rubus mucronatus Bloxam, non Ser.; *R. mucronifer* Sudre

174 **R. wirralensis** Newton

ser. **Micantes** Sudre ex Bouvet

175 **R. acutifrons** Ley

176 **R. aequalidens** Newton
Rubus nigricatus sensu W.C.R. Watson, non P.J. Mueller & Lef.

177 **R. coombensis** Rilstone

178 **R. curvidens** Ley

179 **R. decussatus** W.C. Barton ex Newton
Rubus newbridgensis sensu W.C.R. Watson, non W.C. Barton &
Riddelsd.

180 **R. diversus** W.C.R. Watson

181 **R. erythrops** Edees & Newton
Rubus rosaceus sensu W.C.R. Watson, non Weihe; *R. viridis*
sensu Rogers, non C. Presl ex Ortm.

182 **R. fuscoviridis** Rilstone

183 **R. gallofuscus** Newton & M. Porter

184 **R. glareosus** Rogers

185 **R. griffithianus** Rogers

186 **R. hantonensis** D. Allen

187 **R. hastiformis** W.C.R. Watson
Rubus thyrsiger Bab., non Banning & Focke

188 **R. heterobelus** Sudre
Rubus penhallowensis Rilstone

189 **R. laxatifrons** W.C.R. Watson
Rubus acutifrons Ley var. *amplifrons* Ley

190 **R. leightonii** Lees ex Leighton
Rubus radula Weihe ex Boenn. var. *anglicanus* Rogers

191   **R. lintonii** Focke ex Bab.

192   **R. longifrons** W.C.R. Watson
Rubus longifolius Watson, non Host

193   **R. melanodermis** Focke
Rubus melanoxylon sensu Rogers, non P.J. Mueller & Wirtgen

194   **R. micans** Godron
Rubus anglosaxonicus Gelert

195   **R. moylei** W.C. Barton & Riddelsd.

196   **R. newbouldii** Bab.
Rubus radula Weihe ex Boenn. var. *denticulatus* Bab.

197   **R. norvicensis** A.L. Bull & Edees

198   **†R. powellii** Rogers

199   **R. raduloides** (Rogers) Sudre
Rubus anglosaxonicus Gelert var. *raduloides* Rogers

200   **R. trichodes** W.C.R. Watson
Rubus foliosus sensu W.C.R. Watson, non Weihe & Nees

201   **R. turritus** Edees

202   **R. wedgwoodiae** W.C. Barton & Riddelsd.
Rubus mutabilis Genev. var. *regnorum* W.C.R. Watson

   ser. **Anisacanthi** H.E. Weber

203   **R. adamsii** Sudre

204   **R. ahenifolius** W.C.R. Watson

205   **R. anglofuscus** Edees
Rubus fuscus auct., non Weihe

206   **R. anisacanthos** G. Braun

207   **R. biloensis** Newton & M. Porter

208   **R. cinerosus** Rogers

209 **R. dentatifolius** (Briggs) W.C.R. Watson
Rubus sprengelii Weihe var. *dentatifolius* Briggs
Rubus vectensis W.C.R. Watson

210 **R. distractiformis** Newton

211 **R. drejeri** Jensen ex Lange

212 **R. dunensis** Rogers

213 **R. effrenatus** Newton

214 **R. formidabilis** Lef. & P.J. Mueller

215 **R. hartmanii** Gand.
Rubus horridus Hartman, non Schultz

216 **R. hibernicus** (Rogers) Rogers
Rubus drejeri Jensen ex Lange var. *hibernicus* Rogers

217 **R. infestus** Weihe ex Boenn.
Rubus taeniarum Lindeb.

218 **R. leyanus** Rogers

219 **R. metallorum** Margetts

220 **R. morganwgensis** W.C. Barton & Riddelsd.

221 **R. pascuorum** W.C.R. Watson
Rubus borreri Bell Salter var. *virgultorum* Ley

ser. **Radulae** (Focke) Focke
Rubus group *Radulae* Focke

222 **R. adenanthoides** Newton

223 **R. bloxamianus** Coleman ex Purchas

224 **R. bloxamii** (Bab.) Lees
Rubus babingtonii Bell Salter var. *bloxamii* Bab.

225 **R. botryeros** (Focke ex Rogers) Rogers
Rubus longithyrsiger Lees ex Focke var. *botryeros* Focke ex
Rogers

226 †**R. briggsii** Bloxam

227 **R. cantianus** (W.C.R. Watson) Edees & Newton
     Rubus radula Weihe ex Boenn. var. *cantiana* W.C.R. Watson

228 **R. cavatifolius** P.J. Mueller ex Boulay

229 **R. celticus** Newton
     Rubus obvallatus sensu W.C.R. Watson, non Boulay & Gillot

230 **R. condensatus** P.J. Mueller

231 **R. echinatoides** (Rogers) Dallman
     Rubus radula Weihe ex Boenn. var. *echinatoides* Rogers

232 **R. echinatus** Lindley
     Rubus discerptus P.J. Mueller

233 **R. euryanthemus** W.C.R. Watson
     Rubus pallidus Weihe var. *leptopetalus* Friderichsen ex Rogers

234 **R. flexuosus** P.J. Mueller & Lef.

235 **R. fuscicaulis** Edees
     Rubus fuscus auct., non Weihe

236 **R. fuscus** Weihe

237 **R. hyposericeus** Sudre

238 **R. informifolius** Edees

239 **R. insectifolius** Lef. & P.J. Mueller
     Rubus nuticeps W.C. Barton & Riddelsd.

240 **R. iodnephes** W.C.R. Watson

241 **R. largificus** W.C.R. Watson

242 **R. longithyrsiger** Lees ex Focke
     Rubus pyramidalis (Bab.) Bab., non Kaltenb.

243 **R. malvernicus** Edees

244   **R. newbouldianus** Rilstone
Rubus insericatus P.J. Mueller ex Wirtgen subsp. *newbouldianus*
(Rilstone) W.C.R. Watson

245   **R. pallidus** Weihe

246   **R. peninsulae** Rilstone

247   **R. porphyrocaulis** Newton

248   **R. putneiensis** W.C.R. Watson

249   **R. radula** Weihe ex Boenn.

250   **R. radulicaulis** Sudre

251   **R. regillus** Ley

252   **R. rubristylus** W.C.R. Watson

253   **R. rudis** Weihe

254   **R. rufescens** Lef. & P.J. Mueller
Rubus rosaceus Weihe var. *infecundus* Rogers

255   **R. sagittarius** Riddelsd.

256   **R. scoticus** (Rogers & Ley) Edees
Rubus ericetorum Lef. ex Genev. var. *scoticus* Rogers & Ley

257   **R. sectiramus** W.C.R. Watson

258   **R. spadix** W.C.R. Watson
Rubus podophyllus sensu Rogers pro parte et auct., non P.J.
Mueller

259   **R. subtercanens** W.C.R. Watson
Rubus obscurus P.J. Mueller, non Kaltenb.; *R. thyrsiflorus* sensu
P.J. Mueller, non Weihe

260   **R. troiensis** Newton

261   **R. wolley-dodii** (Sudre) W.C.R. Watson
Rubus macrostachys P.J. Mueller microgene *wolley-dodii* Sudre

ser. **Hystrices** Focke

262 **R. angusticuspis** Sudre
Rubus anglosaxonicus Gelert var. *setulosus* Rogers

263 **R. aristisepalus** (Sudre) W.C.R. Watson
Rubus schleicheri Weihe ex Boenn. var. *aristisepalus* Sudre

264 **R. atrebatum** Newton
Rubus cognatus N.E. Br., pro parte; *R. viridis* sensu Rogers, non
C. Presl ex Ortm.

265 **R. babingtonii** Bell Salter
Rubus ochrodermis Ley

266 **R. bercheriensis** (Druce ex Rogers) Rogers
Rubus rosaceus Weihe var. *bercheriensis* Druce ex Rogers

267 **R. breconensis** W.C.R. Watson

268 **R. dasyphyllus** (Rogers) E. Marshall
Rubus koehleri Weihe subsp. *dasyphyllus* Rogers

269 **R. durotrigum** R. Murray

270 **R. hylocharis** W.C.R. Watson
Rubus rosaceus Weihe var. *silvestris* R. Murray

271 **R. iceniensis** Newton & H.E. Weber
Rubus tereticaulis sensu Rogers, non P.J. Mueller; *R. menkei*
sensu W.C.R. Watson, non Weihe

272 **R. infestior** Edees
Rubus infestus sensu W.C.R. Watson, non Weihe ex Boenn.

273 **R. marshallii** Focke & Rogers

274 **R. merlini** Newton & M. Porter

275 **R. milesii** Newton
Rubus spinulifer sensu W.C.R. Watson, non P.J. Mueller & Lef.

276 **R. murrayi** Sudre
Rubus adornatus sensu Rogers, non P.J. Mueller & Wirtgen

277 **R. naldretti** (J.W. White) W.C.R. Watson
Rubus mutabilis Genev. var. *naldretti* J.W. White

278 **R. newbridgensis** W.C. Barton & Riddelsd.
Rubus horridicaulis sensu W.C.R. Watson, non P.J. Mueller

279 **R. pallidisetus** Sudre

280 **R. phaeocarpus** W.C.R. Watson

281 **R. proiectus** A. Beek
Rubus hirtus auct., non Waldst. & Kit.; *R. anglohirtus* Edees

282 **R. pseudoplinthostylus** W.C.R. Watson

283 **R. purchasianus** Rogers
Rubus obscurus sensu Rogers, non Kaltenb.

284 **R. rilstonei** W.C. Barton & Riddelsd.

285 †**R. rotundifolius** (Bab.) Bloxam
Rubus glandulosus Smith var. *rotundifolius* Bab.
Rubus hiernii Riddelsd.

286 **R. scabripes** Genev.

287 **R. semiglaber** (Rogers) W.C.R. Watson
Rubus marshallii Focke & Rogers var. *semiglaber* Rogers

288 **R. tamarensis** Newton

289 **R. tardus** W.C.R. Watson

290 **R. thyrsigeriformis** (Sudre) D. Allen
Rubus insericatus P.J. Mueller ex Wirtgen var. *thyrsigeriformis* Sudre

291 **R. tumulorum** Rilstone

292 †**R. turneri** W.C.R. Watson

293 **R. vigursii** Rilstone

294 **R. watsonii** Mills

ser. **Glandulosi** (Wimmer & Grab.) Focke
Rubus sect. *Glandulosus* Wimmer & Grab.

295 **R. angloserpens** Edees & Newton
Rubus curtiglandulosus sensu W.C.R. Watson, non Sudre

296 **R. hylonomus** Lef. & P.J. Mueller

297 **R. leptadenes** Sudre
Rubus echinatus P.J. Mueller, non Lindley

298 **R. obscuriflorus** Edees & Newton
Rubus minutiflorus sensu Rogers, pro parte, non P.J. Mueller

299 **R. pedemontanus** Pinkw.
Rubus patulus F. Förster, non P.J. Mueller & Lef.; *R. bellardii*
auct., non Weihe & Nees

300 **R. praetextus** Sudre

301 **R. scaber** Weihe
Rubus dentatus (Bab.) Bloxam

sect. **Corylifolii** Lindley

302 **R. adenoleucus** Chaboiss.

303 **R. babingtonianus** W.C.R. Watson

304 **R. bagnallianus** Edees

305 **R. britannicus** Rogers

306 **R. bucknallii** J.W. White

307 **R. conjungens** (Bab.) Rogers
Rubus corylifolius Smith var. *conjungens* Bab.
Rubus ooliticus W.C.R. Watson; *R. purpureicaulis* W.C.R.
Watson

308 **R. eboracensis** W.C.R. Watson

309 **R. halsteadensis** W.C.R. Watson
Rubus dumetorum Weihe ex Boenn. var. *raduliformis* Ley

310 **R. hebridensis** Edees
Rubus dumetorum Weihe ex Boenn. var. *raduliformis* Ley

311 **R. intensior** Edees

312 **R. latifolius** Bab.

313 **R. nemorosus** Hayne & Willd.
Rubus balfourianus Bloxam ex Bab.

314 **R. pictorum** Edees
Rubus iodnephes auct., non W.C.R. Watson

315 **R. pruinosus** Arrh.
Rubus sublustris Lees

316 **R. rubriflorus** Purchas

317 **R. tenuiarmatus** Lees

318 **R. triangularis** (Ley) Edees
Rubus dumetorum Weihe ex Boenn. var. *triangularis* Ley

319 **R. tuberculatus** Bab.
Rubus myriacanthus sensu W.C.R. Watson, non P.J. Mueller; *R. dumetorum* Weihe ex Boenn. var. *diversifolius* Warren

320 **R. warrenii** Sudre
Rubus dumetorum Weihe ex Boenn. var. *concinnus* Baker ex Warren

sect. **Caesii** Lej. & Courtois

321 **R. caesius** L.

9 **POTENTILLA** L.
Comarum L.

1 **P. fruticosa** L.

2 **P. palustris** (L.) Scop.
Comarum palustre L.

3 **P. anserina** L.

4   P. rupestris L.

5   P. argentea L.

6   *P. inclinata Villars

7   *P. recta L.

8   *P. intermedia L.

9   *P. norvegica L.

10   *P. rivalis Nutt. ex Torrey & A. Gray

11   P. crantzii (Crantz) G. Beck ex Fritsch
     Fragaria crantzii Crantz
     Potentilla verna L., pro parte

11 x 12   P. crantzii x P. neumanniana = P. x beckii Murr

12   P. neumanniana Reichb.
     Potentilla tabernaemontani Asch., nom. illegit.; *P. verna* L., pro
     parte

13   P. erecta (L.) Räusch
     Tormentilla erecta L.

     a   subsp. erecta

     b   subsp. strictissima (Zimm.) A. Richards
         Potentilla strictissima Zimm.
         Potentilla erecta (L.) Räusch var. *strictissima* (Zimm.)
         Druce

13 x 14   P. erecta x P. anglica = P. x suberecta Zimm.
          Potentilla x fallax Moretti ex Zimm.

13 x 15   P. erecta x P. reptans = P. x italica Lehm.
          Potentilla x nemoralis Nestler, nom. illegit.

14   P. anglica Laich.
     Potentilla procumbens Sibth., nom. illegit.

14 x 15   P. anglica x P. reptans = P. x mixta Nolte ex Reichb.

15   P. reptans L.

16   P. sterilis (L.) Garcke
Fragaria sterilis L.

10   SIBBALDIA L.

   1   S. procumbens L.

11   FRAGARIA L.

   1   F. vesca L.

   2   *F. muricata Miller
Fragaria moschata auct., non Duchesne; *F. vesca* L. race *?*
moschata Duchesne, nom. inval.

   3   *F. ananassa (Weston) Lois., Vilm., Nois & J.J. Deville
Fragaria chiloensis (L.) Miller var. *ananassa* Weston
Fragaria vesca L. race *? ananassa* Duchesne, nom. inval.

12   *DUCHESNEA Smith

   1   *D. indica (Andrews) Focke
Fragaria indica Andrews

13   GEUM L.

   1   G. rivale L.
Geum rivale L. subsp. *islandicum* Á. Löve & D. Löve

   1 x 2   G. rivale x **G. urbanum = G. x intermedium** Ehrh.

   2   G. urbanum L.

   3   *G. macrophyllum Willd.

14 DRYAS L.

    1 D. octopetala L.
    Dryas babingtonii Porsild

15 AGRIMONIA L.

    1 A. eupatoria L.

1 x 2 A. eupatoria x **A. procera** = **A. x wirtgenii** Asch. & Graebner

    2 A. procera Wallr.
    Agrimonia odorata auct., non (L.) Miller; *A. repens* sensu Leslie, non L.

16 *AREMONIA Necker ex Nestler

    1 *A. agrimonoides (L.) DC.
    Agrimonia agrimonoides L.

17 SANGUISORBA L.
Poterium L.

    1 S. officinalis L.
    Poterium officinale (L.) A. Gray

    2 *S. canadensis L.
    Poterium canadense (L.) A. Gray

    3 S. minor Scop.
    Poterium sanguisorba L.

        a subsp. **minor**

        b *subsp. **muricata** (Gremli) Briq.
        Sanguisorba muricata Gremli
        Poterium muricatum Spach, nom. illegit.; *P. polygamum* Waldst. & Kit.; *Sanguisorba minor* Scop. subsp. *polygama* (Waldst. & Kit.) Holub

18 *ACAENA Mutis ex L.

    1 *A. novae-zelandiae Kirk
      Acaena anserinifolia auct., non (Forster & G. Forster) Druce; *A. sanguisorbae* auct., non Vahl

    2 *A. anserinifolia (Forster & G. Forster) Druce
      Ancistrum anserinaefolium Forster & G. Forster
      Acaena pusilla (Bitter) Allan; *A. sanguisorbae* Vahl, nom. illegit.

   2 x 4 *A. anserinifolia x **A. inermis**

    3 *A. ovalifolia Ruíz Lopez & Pavón

    4 *A. inermis J.D. Hook.
      Acaena microphylla J.D. Hook. var. *inermis* (J.D. Hook.) Kirk; *A. microphylla* auct., non J.D. Hook.

19 ALCHEMILLA L.

    1 A. alpina L.

    2 *A. conjuncta Bab.

    3 A. glaucescens Wallr.
      Alchemilla minor auct., non Hudson

    4 A. monticola Opiz
      Alchemilla crinita auct., non Buser; *A. pastoralis* Buser

    5 *A. tytthantha Juz.

    6 A. subcrenata Buser

    7 A. acutiloba Opiz
      Alchemilla pratensis auct., non Schmidt

    8 A. gracilis Opiz

    9 A. xanthochlora Rothm.

   10 A. filicaulis Buser

    a   subsp. **filicaulis**
        Alchemilla salmoniana Jaq.

    b   subsp. **vestita** (Buser) Bradshaw
        Alchemilla filicaulis Buser forma *vestita* Buser
        Alchemilla colorata auct., non Buser; *A. vestita* (Buser)
        Raunk.

11 **A. minima** Walters

12 **A. glomerulans** Buser

13 **A. wichurae** (Buser) Stéfansson
      Alchemilla connivens Buser var. *wichurae* Buser

14 **A. glabra** Neyg.

15 *****A. mollis** (Buser) Rothm.
      Alchemilla acutiloba Opiz var. *mollis* Buser

20 **APHANES** L.

    1 **A. arvensis** L.
       Alchemilla arvensis (L.) Scop.

    2 **A. inexspectata** Lippert
       Alchemilla microcarpa auct., non Boiss. & Reuter; *Aphanes*
       microcarpa auct., non (Boiss. & Reuter) Rothm.

21 **ROSA** L.

    1 *****R. multiflora** Thunb. ex Murray

1 x 18 R. multiflora x R. rubiginosa

    2 *****R. setigera** Michaux

    3 *****R. luciae** Franchet & Rochebr.
       Rosa wichuraiana Crépin

    4 **R. arvensis** Hudson

4 x 10   **R. arvensis x R. gallica* = **R. x alba** L.
Rosa x collina Jacq.

4 x 11   **R. arvensis x R. stylosa** = **R. x pseudorusticana** Crépin ex
Rogers
Rosa x bibracteoides Wolley-Dod

4 x 12   **R. arvensis x R. canina** = **R. x verticillacantha** Mérat
Rosa x deseglisei Boreau; *R. x kosinsciana* Besser; *R. x pouzinii*
Tratt., pro parte; *R. x wheldonii* Wolley-Dod

4 x 13   **R. arvensis x R. caesia**

4 x 14   **R. arvensis x R. obtusifolia** = **R. x rouyana** Duffort ex Rouy
Rosa x concinnoides auct., non Wolley-Dod

4 x 16   **R. arvensis x R. sherardii**

4 x 18   **R. arvensis x R. rubiginosa** = **R. x consanguinea** Gren.

4 x 19   **R. arvensis x R. micrantha** = **R. x inelegans** Wolley-Dod

5   **R. pimpinellifolia** L.
Rosa spinosissima L., pro parte

5 x 12   **R. pimpinellifolia x R. canina** = **R. x hibernica** Templeton

5 x 13   **R. pimpinellifolia x R. caesia** = **R. x margerisonii** (Wolley-
Dod) Wolley-Dod
Rosa spinosissima x dumetorum forma *margerisonii* Wolley-Dod
Rosa x glabra (Baker) Wolley-Dod, non Andrews; *R. x
setonensis* Wolley-Dod

5 x 15   **R. pimpinellifolia x R. tomentosa** = **R. x coronata** Crépin ex
Reuter
Rosa x involuta auct., non Smith; *R. x pilosa* (Lindley) Wolley-
Dod, non Opiz; *R. x wilsonii* Borrer, pro parte

5 x 16   **R. pimpinellifolia x R. sherardii** = **R. x involuta** Smith
Rosa x gracilis J. Woods; *R. x wilsonii* Borrer, pro parte

5 x 17   **R. pimpinellifolia x R. mollis** = **R. x sabinii** J. Woods

5 x 18 **R. pimpinellifolia** x **R. rubiginosa** = **R. x cantiana** (Wolley-Dod) Wolley-Dod
Rosa spinosissima x rubiginosa forma *cantiana* Wolley-Dod
Rosa x moorei Wolley-Dod

6 ***R. rugosa** Thunb. ex Murray

6 x 12 **R. rugosa** x **R. canina** = **R. x praegeri** Wolley-Dod

7 ***R. 'Hollandica'** hort.
Rosa kamtchatica auct., ? an Vent.; *R. nitida* auct., non Willd.; *R. rugosa* 'Hollandica' hort.

8 ***R. glauca** Pourret
Rosa rubrifolia Villars, nom. illegit.

9 ***R. virginiana** Herrm.

10 ***R. gallica** L.

11 **R. stylosa** Desv.
Rosa systyla Bast.

11 x 12 **R. stylosa** x **R. canina** = **R. x andegavensis** Bast.
Rosa x rufescens Wolley-Dod

11 x 14 **R. stylosa** x **R. obtusifolia**

11 x 18 **R. stylosa** x **R. rubiginosa**

11 x 20 **R. stylosa** x **R. agrestis**
Rosa x belnensis auct., non Ozan

12 **R. canina** L.
Rosa corymbifera Borkh.; *R. dumetorum* auct., non Thuill.; *R. lutetiana* Léman; *R. squarrosa* auct., non (Rau) Boreau

12 x 13 **R. canina** x **R. caesia** = **R. x dumalis** Bechst.
Rosa x subcollina (Christ) Dalla Torre & Sarnth.; *R. x subcanina* (Christ) Dalla Torre & Sarnth.

12 x 14 **R. canina** x **R. obtusifolia** = **R. x dumetorum** Thuill.
Rosa x concinnoides Wolley-Dod; *R. x corymbifera* auct., non Borkh.; *R. x subobtusifolia* Wolley-Dod

12 x 15 **R. canina** x **R. tomentosa = R. x scabriuscula** Smith
Rosa x aberrans Wolley-Dod; *R. x curvispina* Wolley-Dod; *R. x
woodsiana* (Groves & J.Groves) Ley

12 x 16 **R. canina** x **R. sherardii**

12 x 17 **R. canina** x **R. mollis = R. x molletorum** Heslop-Harrison

12 x 18 **R. canina** x **R. rubiginosa = R. x nitidula** Besser
Rosa x latebrosa Déségl.; *R. x latens* Wolley-Dod

12 x 19 **R. canina** x **R. micrantha = R. x toddiae** Wolley-Dod

12 x 20 **R. canina** x **R. agrestis = R. x belnensis** Ozan

13 **R. caesia** Smith

    a subsp. **caesia**
      Rosa coriifolia Fries; *R. dumalis* Bechst. subsp. *coriifolia*
      (Fries) A.Pedersen

    b subsp. **glauca** (Nyman) G. Graham & Primavesi
      Rosa glauca Pourret subsp. *glauca* Nyman
      Rosa afzeliana Fries; *R. dumalis* auct., non Bechst.; *R.
        glauca* Villars ex Lois. et Fries, non Pourret; *R.
        vosagiaca* N. Desp.

13 x 14 **R. caesia** x **R. obtusifolia**

13 x 15 **R. caesia** x **R. tomentosa = R. x rogersii** Wolley-Dod

13 x 16 **R. caesia** x **R. sherardii**

13 x 17 **R. caesia** x **R. mollis = R. x glaucoides** Wolley-Dod

13 x 18 **R. caesia** x **R. rubiginosa**
Rosa x obovata (Baker) Ley, non Raf.

13 x 19 **R. caesia** x **R. micrantha = R. x longicolla** Ravaud ex Rouy

14 **R. obtusifolia** Desv.

14 x 15 **R. obtusifolia** x **R. tomentosa**

14 x 18 **R. obtusifolia** x **R. rubiginosa** = **R. x tomentelliformis** Wolley-Dod

15 **R. tomentosa** Smith
Rosa scabriuscula auct., non Smith

15 x 16 **R. tomentosa** x **R. sherardii** = **R. x suberectiformis** Wolley-Dod

15 x 17 **R. tomentosa** x **R. mollis**

15 x 18 **R. tomentosa** x **R. rubiginosa** = **R. x avrayensis** Rouy
Rosa x burdonii auct., non Wolley-Dod

15 x 20 **R. tomentosa** x **R. agrestis**

16 **R. sherardii** Davies
Rosa tomentosa Smith subsp. *sherardii* (Davies) A. Pedersen

16 x 17 **R. sherardii** x **R. mollis** = **R. x shoolbredii** Wolley-Dod

16 x 18 **R. sherardii** x **R. rubiginosa** = **R. x suberecta** (J. Woods) Ley
Rosa villosa L. var. *suberecta* J. Woods
Rosa x burdonii Wolley-Dod

16 x 19 **R. sherardii** x **R. micrantha**

16 x 20 **R. sherardii** x **R. agrestis**

17 **R. mollis** Smith
Rosa ? pseudo-rubiginosa Lej.; *R. villosa* auct., non L.

17 x 18 **R. mollis** x **R. rubiginosa** = **R. x molliformis** Wolley-Dod

18 **R. rubiginosa** L.

18 x 19 **R. rubiginosa** x **R. micrantha** = **R. x bigeneris** Duffort ex Rouy
Rosa x dubia Wolley-Dod, non Wibel

19 **R. micrantha** Borrer ex Smith
Rosa elliptica auct., non Tausch

19 x 20 **R. micrantha** x **R. agrestis** = **R. x bishopii** Wolley-Dod

20   **R. agrestis** Savi
Rosa elliptica auct., non Tausch

22   PRUNUS L.

    1 ***P. persica** (L.) Batsch
    Amygdalus persica L.

    2 ***P. dulcis** (Miller) D. Webb
    Amygdalus dulcis Miller
    Prunus amygdalus Batsch.

    3 ***P. cerasifera** Ehrh.

    4 **P. spinosa** L.

4 x 5   **P. spinosa** x **P. domestica** = **P. x fruticans** Weihe

    5 ***P. domestica** L.

        a *subsp. **domestica**

        b *subsp. **insititia** (L.) Bonnier & Layens
           Prunus insititia L.

        c *subsp. **italica** (Borkh.) Gams ex Hegi
           Prunus italica Borkh.
           Prunus insititia L. convar. *italica* (Borkh.) Dostál

    6 **P. avium** (L.) L.
    Prunus cerasus L. var. *avium* L.

    7 ***P. cerasus** L.

    8 ***P. mahaleb** L.

    9 ***P. pensylvanica** L.f.

  10 ***P. incisa** Thunb. ex Murray

  11 **P. padus** L.

  12 ***P. serotina** Ehrh.

13 **P. lusitanica* L.

14 **P. laurocerasus* L.

23 *OEMLERIA Reichb.
Osmaronia E. Greene

    1 **O. cerasiformis* (Torrey & A. Gray ex Hook. & Arn.) Landon
    Nuttallia cerasiformis Torrey & A. Gray ex Hook. & Arn.
    Osmaronia cerasiformis (Torrey & A. Gray ex Hook. & Arn.) E.
    Greene

24 *CYDONIA Miller

    1 **C. oblonga* Miller
    Pyrus cydonia L.

25 *CHAENOMELES Lindley

    1 **C. speciosa* (Sweet) Nakai
    Cydonia speciosa Sweet
    Cydonia japonica auct., non (Thunb.) Lindley ex Spach

26 PYRUS L.

    1 P. cordata Desv.

    2 **P. pyraster* (L.) Burgsd.
    Pyrus communis L. var. *pyraster* L.

    3 **P. communis* L.
    Pyrus pyraster (L.) Burgsd. subsp. *achras* (Wallr.) Terpó

27 MALUS Miller

    1 M. sylvestris (L.) Miller
    Pyrus malus L. var. *sylvestris* L.

    2 **M. domestica* Borkh.
    Malus sylvestris (L.) Miller subsp. *mitis* (Wallr.) Mansf.

nie x atr *M. niedzwetskyana Dieck x M. atrosanguinea (Spaeth) C. Schneider = M. x purpurea (Barbier) Rehder
Malus floribunda Siebold ex Van Houtte 'Purpurea' Barbier

28   SORBUS L.

1   S. aucuparia L.

1 x 7   S. aucuparia x S. intermedia
Sorbus x pinnatifida auct., non Düll

1 x 9   S. aucuparia x S. aria = S. x thuringiaca (Ilse) Fritsch
Pyrus x thuringiaca Ilse
Sorbus x pinnatifida Düll; *S. x semipinnata* (Roth) Hedlund, pro parte, non Borbás

2   S. pseudofennica E. Warb.
Sorbus fennica auct., non L.

3   *S. hybrida L.

4   S. arranensis Hedlund

5   S. leyana Wilm.

6   S. minima (Ley) Hedlund
Pyrus minima Ley

7   *S. intermedia (Ehrh.) Pers.
Pyrus intermedia Ehrh.

8   S. anglica Hedlund

9   S. aria (L.) Crantz
Crataegus aria L.
Pyrus aria (L.) Ehrh.

9 x 16   S. aria x S. rupicola

9 x 24   S. aria x S. torminalis = S. x vagensis Wilm.
Sorbus x latifolia auct., non (Lam.) Pers.

10   S. leptophylla E. Warb.

11   **S. wilmottiana** E. Warb.

12   **S. eminens** E. Warb.

13   **S. hibernica** E. Warb.

14   **S. porrigentiformis** E. Warb.
Sorbus porrigens Hedlund, pro parte

14 x 24   **S. porrigentiformis x S. torminalis**

15   **S. lancastriensis** E. Warb.

16   **S. rupicola** (Syme) Hedlund
Pyrus aria (L.) Ehrh. subsp. *rupicola* Syme

16 x 24   **S. rupicola x S. torminalis**

17   **S. vexans** E. Warb.

18   ***S. decipiens** (Bechst.) Irmisch
Pyrus decipiens Bechst.
Crataegus hybrida Bechst., non L.; *Sorbus hybrida* auct., non L.

19   **S. subcuneata** Wilm.

20   **S. devoniensis** E. Warb.

21   ***S. croceocarpa** Sell

22   **S. bristoliensis** Wilm.

23   ***S. latifolia** (Lam.) Pers.
Crataegus latifolia Lam.

24   **S. torminalis** (L.) Crantz
Crataegus torminalis L.
Pyrus torminalis (L.) Ehrh.

29   *ARONIA Medikus

1   ***A. arbutifolia** (L.) Pers.
Mespilus arbutifolia L.
Pyrus arbutifolia (L.) L.f.

1 x 2 *A. arbutifolia x **A. melanocarpa** = **A. x prunifolia** (Marshall)
Rehder
Mespilus x prunifolia Marshall
Pyrus x floribunda Lindley

2 *A. melanocarpa (Michaux) Elliott
Mespilus arbutifolia L. var. *melanocarpa* Michaux
Pyrus melanocarpa (Michaux) Willd.

30 *AMELANCHIER Medikus

1 *A. lamarckii F.-G. Schroeder
Amelanchier canadensis (L.) Medikus subsp. *confusa* auct., non
(N. Hylander) Á. Löve & D. Löve; *A. canadensis* auct., non
(L.) Medikus; *A. confusa* sensu Dandy et auct., non N.
Hylander; *A. grandiflora* auct., non Rehder

31 *PHOTINIA Lindley
Stranvaesia Lindley

1 *P. davidiana (Decne.) Cardot
Stranvaesia davidiana Decne.

32 COTONEASTER Medikus

1 *C. multiflorus Bunge
Cotoneaster reflexus Carrière

2 *C. ellipticus (Lindley) Loudon
Eriobotrya elliptica Lindley
Cotoneaster lindleyi Steudel, nom. illegit.; *C. nummularius*
Lindley, non Fischer & C. Meyer

3 *C. hissaricus Pojark.
Cotoneaster racemiflorus auct., non (Desf.) K. Koch

4 *C. ignotus Klotz
Cotoneaster hissaricus auct., non Pojark.

5 *C. affinis Lindley

6 *C. obtusus Wallich ex Lindley
  Cotoneaster cooperi auct., non Marquand

7 *C. bacillaris Wallich ex Lindley
  Cotoneaster affinis Lindley var. *bacillaris* (Wallich ex Lindley) C.
  Schneider

8 *C. transens Klotz

9 *C. frigidus Wallich ex Lindley
  Cotoneaster affinis auct., non Lindley

9 x 10 *C. frigidus x C. salicifolius = C. x watereri Exell

10 *C. salicifolius Franchet

11 *C. dammeri C. Schneider
   Cotoneaster humifusa Praeger

11 x 18 *C. dammeri x C. conspicuus = C. x suecicus Klotz

12 *C. pannosus Franchet

13 *C. lacteus W. Smith

14 *C. buxifolius Wallich ex Lindley
   Cotoneaster affinis DC., pro parte, non Lindley

15 *C. congestus Baker
   Cotoneaster microphyllus sensu Yü, non Wallich ex Lindley

16 *C. integrifolius (Roxb.) Klotz
   Crataegus integrifolia Roxb.
   Cotoneaster microphyllus Lodd., non Wallich ex Lindley; *C.
   thymifolius* Wallich ex Lindley

17 *C. linearifolius (Klotz) Klotz
   Cotoneaster microphyllus Wallich ex Lindley forma *linearifolius*
   Klotz
   Cotoneaster thymifolius auct., non Wallich ex Lindley

18 *C. conspicuus Marquand

19 *C. cashmiriensis Klotz
   Cotoneaster cochleatus auct., non (Franchet) Klotz

20 *C. nitidus Jacques
   Cotoneaster distichus Lange

21 *C. horizontalis Decne.

22 *C. hjelmqvistii Flinck & Hylmö
   Cotoneaster horizontalis Decne. var. *robustus* Vuyk van Nes

23 *C. atropurpureus Flinck & Hylmö

24 *C. adpressus Bois
   Cotoneaster horizontalis Decne. var. *adpressus* (Bois) C.
   Schneider

25 *C. nanshan A. Vilm. ex Mottet
   Cotoneaster praecox auct., non (Bois & Berthault) A. Vilm. ex
   Bois & Berthault

26 *C. divaricatus Rehder & E. Wilson

27 *C. nitens Rehder & E. Wilson

28 *C. lucidus Schldl.

29 *C. villosulus (Rehder & E. Wilson) Flinck & Hylmö
   Cotoneaster acutifolius Turcz. var. *villosulus* Rehder & E. Wilson
   Cotoneaster acuminatus auct., non Lindley

30 *C. laetevirens (Rehder & E. Wilson) Klotz
   Cotoneaster acutifolius Turcz. var. *laetevirens* Rehder & E.
   Wilson

31 C. integerrimus Medikus

32 *C. mucronatus Franchet

33 *C. simonsii Baker

34 *C. bullatus Bois

35 *C. rehderi Pojark.
   Cotoneaster bullatus Bois var. *macrophyllus* Rehder & E. Wilson

36 *C. moupinensis Franchet
   Cotoneaster foveolatus auct., non Rehder & E. Wilson

37 *C. dielsianus E. Pritzel ex Diels

38 *C. splendens Flinck & Hylmö

39 *C. franchetii Bois
   Cotoneaster wardii hort., non W. Smith

40 *C. sternianus (Turrill) Boom
   Cotoneaster franchetii Bois var. *sternianus* Turrill
   Cotoneaster wardii hort., non W. Smith

41 *C. insculptus Diels

42 *C. amoenus E. Wilson

43 *C. zabelii C. Schneider

33 *PYRACANTHA M. Roemer

   1 *P. coccinea M. Roemer

   2 *P. rogersiana (A.B. Jackson) Coltman-Rogers
      Pyracantha crenulata M. Roemer var. *rogersiana* A.B. Jackson

34 *MESPILUS L.

   1 *M. germanica L.

4 x 35 *MESPILUS x CRATAEGUS = X CRATAEMESPILUS Camus

   1 x 8 *M. germanica x C. laevigata = X C. grandiflora (Smith)
      Camus
      Mespilus x grandiflora Smith
      X *Crataegomespilus grandiflora* (Smith) Bean

35 CRATAEGUS L.

   1 *C. submollis Sarg.
      Crataegus coccinea auct., non L.

   2 *C. coccinioides Ashe

3 *C. pedicellata Sarg.
Crataegus coccinea auct., non L.

4 *C. crus-galli L.

5 *C. persimilis Sarg.
Crataegus crus-galli L. 'Splendens' hort.; *C. prunifolia* Pers., non
(Marshall) Baumg.; *Mespilus prunifolia* Poiret, non Marshall

6 *C. succulenta Schrader

7   C. monogyna Jacq.

    a   subsp. nordica Franco

7 x 8   C. monogyna x C. laevigata = C. x macrocarpa Hegetschw.
Crataegus x apiifolia Reichb., non Medikus; *C. x media* auct., non
Bechst.

8   C. laevigata (Poiret) DC.
Mespilus laevigata Poiret
Crataegus laevigata (Poiret) DC. subsp. *palmstruchii* (Lindman)
Franco; *C. oxyacantha* L. subsp. *palmstruchii* (Lindman)
Hrabetová; *C. oxyacanthoides* Thuill.

9 *C. heterophylla Fluegge

10 *C. laciniata Ucria
Crataegus orientalis Pallas ex M. Bieb.

76 *MIMOSACEAE
Leguminosae subfam. *Mimosoideae*

1 *ACACIA Miller

    1   *A. melanoxylon R. Br.

77 FABACEAE

Papilionaceae; Leguminosae subfam. *Papilionoideae*

1 *ROBINIA L.

    1 *R. pseudoacacia L.

2 *GALEGA L.

    1 *G. officinalis L.

3 *COLUTEA L.

    1 *C. arborescens L.

  1 x ori *C. arborescens x C. orientalis Miller = C. x media Willd.
          Colutea x orientalis auct., non Miller nec Lam.

4 ASTRAGALUS L.

    1 *A. cicer L.

    2 A. danicus Retz.

    3 A. alpinus L.

    4 A. glycyphyllos L.

    5 *A. odoratus Lam.

5 OXYTROPIS DC.

    1 O. halleri Bunge ex Koch

    2 O. campestris (L.) DC.
      Astragalus campestris L.
      Oxytropis campestris (L.) DC. subsp. *scotica* Jalas

6 ONOBRYCHIS Miller

    1 O. viciifolia Scop.

7 ANTHYLLIS L.

1 A. vulneraria L.

a subsp. **vulneraria**
Anthyllis maritima auct., non Schweigger ex Hagen; *A. vulneraria* L. subsp. *iberica* auct., non (Becker) Jalas; *A. vulneraria* L. subsp. *linnaei* (Sagorski) Jalas; *A. vulneraria* L. var. *coccinea* L.

b *subsp. **polyphylla** (DC.) Nyman
Anthyllis vulneraria L. var. *polyphylla* DC.

c subsp. **corbierei** (Salmon & Travis) Cullen
Anthyllis maritima Schweigger ex Hagen var. *corbierei* Salmon & Travis
Anthyllis vulneraria L. var. *sericea* Bréb.

d subsp. **carpatica** (Pant.) Nyman
Anthyllis carpatica Pant.
Anthyllis vulneraria L. subsp. *pseudovulneraria* (Sagorski) J. Duvign.; *A. vulneraria* L. subsp. *vulgaris* (Koch) Corbière

e subsp. **lapponica** (N. Hylander) Jalas
Anthyllis vulneraria L. var. *lapponica* N. Hylander

8 LOTUS L.

1 L. glaber Miller
Lotus corniculatus L. subsp. *tenuis* (Waldst. & Kit.) Syme; *L. tenuis* Waldst. & Kit. ex Willd.

2 L. corniculatus L.

3 L. pedunculatus Cav.
Lotus uliginosus Schk.

4 L. subbiflorus Lagasca
Lotus angustissimus L. subsp. *suaveolens* (Pers.) O. Bolòs & Vigo; *L. hispidus* auct., non Desf. ex DC.; *L. parviflorus* auct., non Desf.; *L. suaveolens* Pers.

5 L. angustissimus L.

9 *TETRAGONOLOBUS Scop.

1 *T. maritimus (L.) Roth
Lotus maritimus L.

10 ORNITHOPUS L.

1 *O. compressus L.

2 *O. sativus Brot.

a *subsp. **roseus** (Dufour) Dostál
Ornithopus roseus Dufour

3 O. perpusillus L.

4 O. pinnatus (Miller) Druce
Scorpiurus pinnatus Miller

11 *CORONILLA L.

1 *C. valentina L.

a *subsp. **glauca** (L.) Battand.
Coronilla glauca L.

2 *C. scorpioides (L.) Koch
Ornithopus scorpioides L.

12 HIPPOCREPIS L.

1 *H. emerus (L.) Lassen
Coronilla emerus L.

2 H. comosa L.

13 *SECURIGERA DC.

1 *S. varia (L.) Lassen
Coronilla varia L.

14 VICIA L.

1 V. orobus DC.

2 V. cracca L.

3 *V. tenuifolia Roth

4 V. sylvatica L.

5 *V. villosa Roth
   Vicia dasycarpa auct., ? an Ten.; *V. varia* Host

6 V. hirsuta (L.) Gray
   Ervum hirsutum L.

7 V. parviflora Cav.
   Vicia gracilis Lois., non Sol. ex Lowe; *V. laxiflora* Brot., nom.
   illegit.; *V. tenuissima* auct., non (M. Bieb.) Schinz & Thell.

8 V. tetrasperma (L.) Schreber
   Ervum tetraspermum L.

9 V. sepium L.

10 *V. pannonica Crantz

11 V. sativa L.

   a subsp. **nigra** (L.) Ehrh.
      Vicia sativa L. var. *nigra* L.
      Vicia angustifolia L.

   b subsp. **segetalis** (Thuill.) Gaudin
      Vicia segetalis Thuill.

   c *subsp. **sativa**

12 V. lathyroides L.

13 V. lutea L.
   Vicia laevigata Smith

14 V. bithynica (L.) L.
   Lathyrus bithynicus L.

15   LATHYRUS L.

1   *L. niger** (L.) Bernh.
   Orobus niger L.

2   **L. japonicus** Willd.

   a   subsp. **maritimus** (L.) P. Ball
      Pisum maritimum L.
      Lathyrus maritimus (L.) Bigelow

3   **L. linifolius** (Reichard) Bässler
   Orobus linifolius Reichard
   Lathyrus montanus Bernh.; *L. tuberosus* auct., non L.; *Orobus
   tuberosus* L.

4   **L. pratensis** L.

5   **L. palustris** L.

6   *L. tuberosus** L.

7   *L. grandiflorus** Smith
   Lathyrus tingitanus auct., non L.

8   **L. sylvestris** L.

9   *L. latifolius** L.

10   *L. heterophyllus** L.

11   *L. hirsutus** L.

12   **L. nissolia** L.

13   **L. aphaca** L.

16   ONONIS L.

1   *O. natrix** L.

2   **O. reclinata** L.

3 O. spinosa L.
Ononis campestris Koch; *O. repens* L. subsp. *spinosa* (L.) Greuter

3 x 4 O. spinosa x **O. repens** = **O. x pseudohircina** Schur

4 O. repens L.

> a   subsp. **repens**
> *Ononis repens* L. subsp. *arvensis* (L.) Greuter

> b   subsp. **maritima** (Gren. & Godron) Asch. & Graebner
> *Ononis procurrens* Wallr. var. *maritima* Gren. & Godron

17 *MELILOTUS Miller

> **1 *M. altissimus** Thuill.

> **2 *M. albus** Medikus

> **3 *M. officinalis** (L.) Lam.
> *Trifolium officinale* L.
> *Melilotus arvensis* Wallr., nom. illegit.

> **4 *M. indicus** (L.) All.
> *Trifolium indicum* L.

18 MEDICAGO L.

> **1 M. lupulina** L.
> *Medicago lupulina* L. subsp. *willdenowiana* (Koch) Soják

> **2 M. sativa** L.

>> a   subsp. **falcata** (L.) Arcang.
>> *Medicago falcata* L.

>> b   subsp. **varia** (Martyn) Arcang.
>> *Medicago x varia* Martyn

>> c   *subsp. **sativa**

> **3 M. minima** (L.) L.
> *Medicago polymorpha* L. var. *minima* L.

4 **M. polymorpha** L.
   Medicago apiculata Willd.; *M. denticulata* Willd.; *M. hispida*
   Gaertner, nom. illegit.; *M. nigra* (L.) Krocker; *M. polymorpha*
   L. subsp. *polycarpa* (Willd.) Zarco, nom. inval.

5 **M. arabica** (L.) Hudson
   Medicago polymorpha L. var. *arabica* L.

19 **TRIFOLIUM** L.
   Amoria C. Presl; *Calycomorphum* C. Presl; *Chrysaspis* Desv.; *Falcatula*
   Brot.; *Galearia* C. Presl; *Paramesus* C. Presl

1 **T. ornithopodioides** L.
   Trigonella ornithopodioides (L.) DC.

2 **T. repens** L.

3 **T. occidentale** Coombe
   Amoria occidentalis (Coombe) Soják; *Trifolium ? prostratum*
   Biasol.; *T. repens* L. subsp. *? prostratum* (Biasol.) Nyman; *T.*
   repens L. subsp. *occidentale* (Coombe) Laínz

4 *****T. hybridum** L.

   a *subsp. **hybridum**

   b *subsp. **elegans** (Savi) Asch. & Graebner
      Trifolium elegans Savi
      Amoria hybrida C. Presl subsp. *elegans* (Savi) Soják

5 **T. glomeratum** L.
   Amoria glomerata (L.) Soják

6 **T. suffocatum** L.
   Amoria suffocata (L.) Soják

7 **T. strictum** L.
   Paramesus strictus (L.) C. Presl

8 **T. fragiferum** L.
   Galearia fragifera (L.) C. Presl

   a subsp. **fragiferum**

    b   subsp. **bonannii** (C. Presl) Soják
       Trifolium bonannii C. Presl

9 ***T. resupinatum** L.
    Galearia resupinata (L.) C. Presl

10 ***T. aureum** Pollich

11 **T. campestre** Schreber

12 **T. dubium** Sibth.
    Trifolium filiforme auct., non L.

13 **T. micranthum** Viv.
    Chrysaspis micrantha (Vivant) Hendrych; *Trifolium filiforme* L.

14 **T. pratense** L.

15 **T. medium** L.

16 **T. ochroleucon** Hudson

17 ***T. pannonicum** Jacq.

18 ***T. stellatum** L.

19 **T. incarnatum** L.

    a *subsp. **incarnatum**

    b   subsp. **molinerii** (Balbis ex Hornem.) Syme
       Trifolium molinerii Balbis ex Hornem.

20 **T. striatum** L.

21 **T. bocconei** Savi

22 **T. scabrum** L.

23 **T. arvense** L.

24 **T. squamosum** L.

25 **T. subterraneum** L.
    Calycomorphum subterraneum (L.) C. Presl

20 *THERMOPSIS R. Br.

    1 *T. montana Nutt. ex Torrey & A. Gray

21 LUPINUS L.

    1 *L. arboreus Sims

    1 x 2 *L. arboreus x L. polyphyllus = L. x regalis Bergmans
        Lupinus x polyphyllus auct., non Lindley

  1 x 2 x 3 L. arboreus x L. polyphyllus x L. nootkatensis

    2 *L. polyphyllus Lindley

    2 x 3 L. polyphyllus x L. nootkatensis = L. x pseudopolyphyllus
        C.P. Smith

    3 *L. nootkatensis Donn ex Sims

22 *LABURNUM Fabr.

    1 *L. anagyroides Medikus

    1 x 2 *L. anagyroides x L. alpinum = L. x watereri (Wettst.) Dippel
        Cytisus x watereri Wettst.

    2 *L. alpinum (Miller) Bercht. & J.S. Presl
        Cytisus alpinus Miller

23 CYTISUS Desf.
Lembotropis Griseb.; *Sarothamnus* Wimmer

    1 *C. nigricans L.
        Lembotropis nigricans (L.) Griseb.

    2 *C. multiflorus (L'Hér. ex Aiton) Sweet
        Spartium multiflorum L'Hér. ex Aiton

    3 *C. striatus (Hill) Rothm.
        Genista striata Hill

4   **C. scoparius** (L.) Link
Spartium scoparium L.
Sarothamnus scoparius (L.) Koch

    a   subsp. **scoparius**

    b   subsp. **maritimus** (Rouy) Heyw.
       Genista scoparia (L.) Lam. var. *maritima* Rouy
       Sarothamnus scoparius (L.) Koch subsp. *maritimus* (Rouy)
         Ulbr.; *S. scoparius* (L.) Koch subsp. *prostratus* (C.
         Bailey) Tutin

24 ***SPARTIUM** L.

    1 ***S. junceum** L.

25 **GENISTA** L.
Teline Medikus

    1 ***G. monspessulana** (L.) L. Johnson
      Cytisus monspessulanus L.
      Teline monspessulana (L.) K. Koch

    2 **G. tinctoria** L.

       a   subsp. **tinctoria**

       b   subsp. **littoralis** (Corbière) Rothm.
          Genista tinctoria L. var. *littoralis* Corbière

    3 **G. pilosa** L.

    4 **G. anglica** L.

    5 ***G. hispanica** L.

       a   *subsp. **occidentalis** Rouy

    6 ***G. aetnensis** (Raf. ex Biv.) DC.
      Spartium aetnense Raf. ex Biv.

26   ULEX L.

    1   **U. europaeus** L.

    1 x **2**   **U. europaeus** x **U. gallii**

    2   **U. gallii** Planchon

    3   **U. minor** Roth

78 ELAEAGNACEAE

1   HIPPOPHAE L.

    1   **H. rhamnoides** L.

2 *ELAEAGNUS L.

    1   ***E. umbellata** Thunb.
        Elaeagnus angustifolia auct., non L.

79 HALORAGACEAE

1 *HALORAGIS Forster & G. Forster

    1   ***H. micrantha** (Thunb.) R. Br. ex Siebold & Zucc.
        Gonocarpus micranthus Thunb.

2   MYRIOPHYLLUM L.

    1   **M. verticillatum** L.

    2   ***M. aquaticum** (Vell. Conc.) Verdc.
        Enydria aquatica Vell. Conc.
        Myriophyllum brasiliense Cambess.

    3   **M. spicatum** L.

    4   **M. alterniflorum** DC.

80 *GUNNERACEAE

1 *GUNNERA L.

> **1 *G. tinctoria** (Molina) Mirbel
> *Panke tinctoria* Molina
> *Gunnera chilensis* Lam.

81 LYTHRACEAE

1 LYTHRUM L.
Peplis L.

> **1 L. salicaria** L.

> **2 L. hyssopifolia** L.

> **3 L. portula** (L.) D. Webb
> *Peplis portula* L.

>> **a** subsp. **portula**

>> **b** subsp. **longidentata** (Gay) Sell
>> *Peplis portula* L. var. *longidentata* Gay

82 THYMELAEACEAE

1 DAPHNE L.

> **1 D. mezereum** L.

> **1 x 2 D. mezereum** x **D. laureola** = **D. x houtteana** Lindley &
> Paxton

> **2 D. laureola** L.

83 *MYRTACEAE

1 *LEPTOSPERMUM Forster & G. Forster

    1 *L. scoparium Forster & G. Forster

    2 *L. lanigerum (Aiton) Smith
      Philadelphus laniger Aiton

2 *EUCALYPTUS L'Hér.

    1 *E. pulchella Desf.

3 *AMOMYRTUS (Burret) Legrand & Kausel
  Myrtus sect. *Amomyrtus* Burret

    1 *A. luma (Molina) Legrand & Kausel
      Myrtus luma Molina

84 ONAGRACEAE

1 EPILOBIUM L.

    1 E. hirsutum L.

  1 x 2 E. hirsutum x E. parviflorum = E. x subhirsutum Gennari

  1 x 3 E. hirsutum x E. montanum = E. x erroneum Hausskn.

  1 x 5 E. hirsutum x E. tetragonum = E. x brevipilum Hausskn.

  1 x 7 E. hirsutum x E. roseum = E. x goerzii Rubner

  1 x 8 E. hirsutum x E. ciliatum = E. x novae-civitatis Smejkal

  1 x 9 E. hirsutum x E. palustre = E. x waterfallii E. Marshall

    2 E. parviflorum Schreber

  2 x 3 E. parviflorum x E. montanum = E. x limosum Schur

2 x 3 x 6   E. parviflorum x E. montanum x E. obscurum

2 x 3 x 7   E. parviflorum x E. montanum x E. roseum

2 x 4   E. parviflorum x E. lanceolatum = E. x aschersonianum
Hausskn.

2 x 5   E. parviflorum x E. tetragonum = E. x palatinum F. Schultz
Epilobium x weissenburgense F. Schultz

2 x 5 x 6   E. parviflorum x E. tetragonum x E. obscurum

2 x 6   E. parviflorum x E. obscurum = E. x dacicum Borbás

2 x 7   E. parviflorum x E. roseum = E. x persicinum Reichb.

2 x 8   E. parviflorum x E. ciliatum

2 x 9   E. parviflorum x E. palustre = E. x rivulare Wahlenb.

3   E. montanum L.

3 x 4   E. montanum x E. lanceolatum = E. x neogradense Borbás

3 x 5   E. montanum x E. tetragonum = E. x haussknechtianum
Borbás
Epilobium x beckhausii Hausskn.

3 x 6   E. montanum x E. obscurum = E. x aggregatum Celak.

3 x 7   E. montanum x E. roseum = E. x mutabile Boiss. & Reuter

3 x 8   E. montanum x E. ciliatum

3 x 11   E. montanum x E. alsinifolium = E. x grenieri Rouy & Camus

3 x 12   E. montanum x E. brunnescens

4   E. lanceolatum Sebast. & Mauri

4 x 5   E. lanceolatum x E. tetragonum = E. x fallacinum Hausskn.
Epilobium x ambigens Hausskn.

4 x 6   E. lanceolatum x E. obscurum = E. x lamotteanum Hausskn.

4 x 7   E. lanceolatum x E. roseum = E. x abortivum Hausskn.

4 x 8   E. lanceolatum x E. ciliatum

5   E. tetragonum L.
Epilobium adnatum Griseb.; *E. lamyi* F. Schultz; *E. tetragonum* L.
subsp. *lamyi* (F. Schultz) Nyman

5 x 6   E. tetragonum x E. obscurum = E. x semiobscurum Borbás
Epilobium x thuringiacum Hausskn.

5 x 7   E. tetragonum x E. roseum = E. x borbasianum Hausskn.

5 x 8   E. tetragonum x E. ciliatum

5 x 9   E. tetragonum x E. palustre = E. x laschianum Hausskn.

6   E. obscurum Schreber

6 x 7   E. obscurum x E. roseum = E. x brachiatum Celak.

6 x 8   E. obscurum x E. ciliatum

6 x 9   E. obscurum x E. palustre = E. x schmidtianum Rostkov

6 x 10   E. obscurum x E. anagallidifolium = E. x marshallianum
Hausskn.

6 x 11   E. obscurum x E. alsinifolium = E. x rivulicola Hausskn.

7   E. roseum Schreber

7 x 8   E. roseum x E. ciliatum

7 x 9   E. roseum x E. palustre = E. x purpureum Fries

8   *E. ciliatum Raf.
Epilobium adenocaulon Hausskn.

8 x 9   E. ciliatum x E. palustre

9   E. palustre L.

9 x 10   E. palustre x E. anagallidifolium

9 x 11 E. palustre x E. alsinifolium = E. x haynaldianum Hausskn.

10 E. anagallidifolium Lam.
Epilobium alpinum L.

10 x 11 E. anagallidifolium x E. alsinifolium = E. x boissieri Hausskn.

11 E. alsinifolium Villars

12 *E. brunnescens (Cockayne) Raven & Engelhorn
Epilobium pedunculare Cunn. var. *brunnescens* Cockayne
Epilobium nerteroides auct., non Cunn.

13 *E. pedunculare Cunn.
Epilobium linnaeoides J.D. Hook.

14 *E. komarovianum A. Léveillé
Epilobium inornatum Melville

2 CHAMERION (Raf.) Raf.
Epilobium subgen. *Chamerion* Raf.; *Chamaenerion* Séguier, nom. illegit.

1 C. angustifolium (L.) Holub
Epilobium angustifolium L.
Chamaenerion angustifolium (L.) Scop., nom. illegit.

3 LUDWIGIA L.

1 L. palustris (L.) Elliott
Isnardia palustris L.

4 OENOTHERA L.

1 *O. glazioviana Micheli ex C. Martius
Oenothera erythrosepala Borbás; *O. grandiflora* L'Hér. subsp.
erythrosepala (Borbás) Á. Löve & D. Löve

1 x 2 O. glazioviana x O. fallax

1 x 3 O. glazioviana x O. biennis

1 x 4   **O. glazioviana** x **O. cambrica** = **O. x britannica** Rostánski

2   **O. fallax** Renner

2 x 3   **O. fallax** x **O. biennis**

2 x 4   **O. fallax** x **O. cambrica**

3   *__**O. biennis**__ L.

3 x 4   **O. biennis** x **O. cambrica**

4   **O. cambrica** Rostánski
Oenothera ammophila auct., non Focke; *O. novae-scotiae* auct., non Gates; *O. parviflora* auct., non L.

5   *__**O. stricta**__ Ledeb. ex Link
Oenothera odorata auct., non Jacq.

5 ***FUCHSIA** L.

1   *__**F. magellanica**__ Lam.

cor x glo ***F. cordifolia** Benth. x **F. globosa** hort. = **F. 'Corallina'** hort.

6   **CIRCAEA** L.

1   **C. lutetiana** L.

1 x 2   **C. lutetiana** x **C. alpina** = **C. x intermedia** Ehrh.

2   **C. alpina** L.

85 CORNACEAE

1   **CORNUS** L.
Chamaepericlymenum Hill; *Swida* Opiz; *Thelycrania* (Dumort.) Fourr.

1   **C. sanguinea** L.
Swida sanguinea (L.) Opiz; *Thelycrania sanguinea* (L.) Fourr.

2 *C. sericea L.
  Cornus stolonifera Michaux; *Swida sericea* (L.) Holub; *Thelycrania sericea* (L.) Dandy; *T. stolonifera* (Michaux) Pojark.

3 *C. alba L.
  Thelycrania alba (L.) Pojark.

4 *C. mas L.

5 C. suecica L.
  Chamaepericlymenum suecicum (L.) Asch. & Graebner

2 *AUCUBA Thunb.

  1 *A. japonica Thunb.

3 *GRISELINIA G. Forster

  1 *G. littoralis (Raoul) Raoul
    Pukateria littoralis Raoul

86 SANTALACEAE

1 THESIUM L.

  1 T. humifusum DC.

87 VISCACEAE

1 VISCUM L.

  1 V. album L.

88 CELASTRACEAE

1   EUONYMUS L.

1   E. europaeus L.

2   *E. latifolius (L.) Miller
    Euonymus europaeus L. var. *latifolius* L.

3   *E. japonicus L.f.

89 AQUIFOLIACEAE

1   ILEX L.

1   I. aquifolium L.

1 x per   *I. aquifolium x I. perado Aiton = I. x altaclerensis (hort. ex
    Loudon) Dallimore
    Ilex aquifolium L. var. *altaclerensis* hort. ex Loudon

90 BUXACEAE

1   BUXUS L.

1   B. sempervirens L.

91 EUPHORBIACEAE

1   MERCURIALIS L.

1   M. perennis L.

2   *M. annua L.

2   EUPHORBIA L.

1   E. peplis L.

2 *E. maculata L.

3 *E. corallioides L.

4 E. hyberna L.

5 *E. dulcis L.

6 E. platyphyllos L.

7 *E. serrulata Thuill.
Euphorbia stricta L., nom. illegit.

8 E. helioscopia L.

9 E. lathyris L.

10 E. exigua L.

11 E. peplus L.

12 E. portlandica L.
Euphorbia segetalis L. subsp. portlandica (L.) Litard.; E. segetalis L. var. portlandica (L.) Coutinho

12 x 13 E. portlandica x E. paralias

13 E. paralias L.

14 *E. esula L.

14 x 15 *E. esula x E. cyparissias = E. x pseudoesula Schur

14 x wal *E. esula x E. waldsteinii (Soják) R.-Smith = E. x pseudovirgata (Schur) Soó
Euphorbia virgata Waldst. & Kit. var. pseudovirgata Schur
Euphorbia x podperae Croizat; E. x uralensis auct., non Fischer & Link; E. x virgata auct., non Waldst. & Kit.

15 E. cyparissias L.

16 E. amygdaloides L.

a subsp. amygdaloides

b *subsp. **robbiae** (Turrill) Stace
Euphorbia robbiae Turrill
Euphorbia amygdaloides L. var. *robbiae* (Turrill) R.-Smith

17 *E. characias L.

a *subsp. **characias**

b *subsp. **wulfenii** (Hoppe ex Koch) R.-Smith
Euphorbia wulfenii Hoppe ex Koch

92 RHAMNACEAE

1 RHAMNUS L.

1 R. cathartica L.

2 *R. alaternus L.

2 FRANGULA Miller

1 F. alnus Miller
Rhamnus frangula L.

93 *VITACEAE

1 *VITIS L.

1 *V. vinifera L.

2 *PARTHENOCISSUS Planchon

1 *P. quinquefolia (L.) Planchon
Hedera quinquefolia L.

2 *P. inserta (A. Kerner) Fritsch
Ampelopsis inserta A. Kerner
Parthenocissus quinquefolia auct., non (L.) Planchon

3 ***P. tricuspidata** (Siebold & Zucc.) Planchon
  Ampelopsis tricuspidata Siebold & Zucc.

94 LINACEAE

1 **LINUM** L.

  1 **L. bienne** Miller

  2 *****L. usitatissimum** L.

  3 **L. perenne** L.

    a subsp. **anglicum** (Miller) Ockendon
      Linum anglicum Miller

  4 **L. catharticum** L.

2 **RADIOLA** Hill

  1 **R. linoides** Roth

95 POLYGALACEAE

1 **POLYGALA** L.

  1 **P. vulgaris** L.

    a subsp. **vulgaris**

    b subsp. **collina** (Reichb.) Borbás
      Polygala oxyptera Reichb. var. *collina* Reichb.

  1 x 3 **P. vulgaris** x **P. calcarea**

  1 x 4 **P. vulgaris** x **P. amarella** = **P. x skrivanekii** Podp.

  2 **P. serpyllifolia** Hose

  3 **P. calcarea** F. Schultz

4 P. amarella Crantz
Polygala amara sensu D. Don et auct., non L.; *P. austriaca*
Crantz

96 *STAPHYLEACEAE

1 *STAPHYLEA L.

1 *S. pinnata L.

97 *SAPINDACEAE

1 *KOELREUTERIA Laxm.

1 *K. paniculata Laxm.

98 *HIPPOCASTANACEAE

1 *AESCULUS L.

1 *A. hippocastanum L.

2 *A. carnea Zeyher

99 ACERACEAE

1 ACER L.

1 *A. platanoides L.

2 *A. cappadocicum Gled.
Acer pictum auct., non Thunb.

3 A. campestre L.

4 *A. pseudoplatanus L.

5 *A. saccharinum L.

6 *A. negundo L.

100 *ANACARDIACEAE

1 *RHUS L.

> 1 *R. hirta (L.) Sudw.
> *Datisca hirta* L.
> *Rhus typhina* L.

101 *SIMAROUBACEAE

1 *AILANTHUS Desf.

> 1 *A. altissima (Miller) Swingle
> *Toxicodendron altissimum* Miller

102 OXALIDACEAE

1 OXALIS L.

> 1 *O. valdiviensis Barnéoud

> 2 *O. rosea Jacq.

> 3 *O. corniculata L.
> *Oxalis stricta* sensu Robinson et auct., non L.

> 4 *O. exilis Cunn.
> *Oxalis corniculata* L. var. *microphylla* J.D. Hook.; *O. repens* sensu
> R.M. Burton, non Thunb.

> 5 *O. dillenii Jacq.
> *Oxalis corniculata* auct., non L.; *O. stricta* auct., non L.

6 *O. stricta L.
  Oxalis dillenii auct., non Jacq.; *O. europaea* Jordan; *O. fontana*
  Bunge

7 *O. megalorhiza Jacq.
  Oxalis carnosa auct., non Molina

8 *O. articulata Savigny
  Oxalis floribunda auct., non Lehm.

9 O. acetosella L.

10 *O. debilis Kunth
  Oxalis corymbosa DC.

11 *O. latifolia Kunth
  Oxalis vespertilionis Zucc.

12 *O. tetraphylla Cav.
  Oxalis deppei Lodd. ex Sweet

13 *O. pes-caprae L.

14 *O. incarnata L.

103 GERANIACEAE

1 GERANIUM L.

  1 *G. endressii Gay

  1 x 2 *G. endressii x G. versicolor = G. x oxonianum Yeo

  2 *G. versicolor L.

  3 *G. nodosum L.

  4 G. rotundifolium L.

  5 G. sylvaticum L.

  6 *G. psilostemon Ledeb.

7   G. pratense L.

8   *G. himalayense Klotzsch
    Geranium grandiflorum auct., non L.; *G. pratense* auct., non L.

9   G. sanguineum L.

10   G. columbinum L.

11   G. dissectum L.

12   *G. submolle Steudel
    Geranium core-core auct., non Steudel; *G. microphyllum* auct.,
    non J.D. Hook.

13   *G. ibericum Cav.

13 x pla   *G. ibericum x G. platypetalum Fischer & C. Meyer = **G. x
    magnificum** N. Hylander
    Geranium x ibericum auct., non Cav.; *G. x platypetalum* auct.,
    non Fischer & C. Meyer

14   G. pyrenaicum Burman f.

15   G. pusillum L.

16   G. molle L.

17   *G. macrorrhizum L.

18   G. lucidum L.

19   G. robertianum L.
    Geranium robertianum L. subsp. *celticum* Ostenf.; *G. robertianum*
    L. subsp. *maritimum* (Bab.) H.G. Baker

19 x 20   G. robertianum x G. purpureum

20   G. purpureum Villars
    Geranium purpureum Villars subsp. *forsteri* (Wilm.) H.G. Baker;
    G. robertianum L. subsp. *purpureum* (Villars) Nyman

21   *G. rubescens Yeo

22   *G. maderense Yeo

23 *G. phaeum L.

23 x ref *G. phaeum x G. reflexum L. = G. x monacense Harz
Geranium reflexum auct., non L.

2   ERODIUM L'Hér.

1   E. maritimum (L.) L'Hér.
Geranium maritimum L.

2   E. moschatum (L.) L'Hér.
Geranium cicutarium L. var. *moschatum* L.

3   E. cicutarium (L.) L'Hér.
Geranium cicutarium L.
Erodium ballii Jordan; *E. cicutarium* (L.) L'Hér. subsp. *arvale*
Andreas; *E. cicutarium* (L.) L'Hér. subsp. *bipinnatum* auct.,
non (Cav.) Tourlet; *E. cicutarium* (L.) L'Hér. subsp. *dunense*
Andreas; *E. pimpinellifolium* (Curtis ex With.) Sibth.; *E.
triviale* Jordan

3 x 4   E. cicutarium x E. lebelii = E. x anaristatum Andreas

4   E. lebelii Jordan
Erodium cicutarium (L.) L'Hér. subsp. *bipinnatum* auct., non
(Cav.) Tourlet; *E. glutinosum* Dumort.; *E. neglectum* Baker &
Salmon

3   *PELARGONIUM L'Hér. ex Aiton

1   *P. tomentosum Jacq.

104 *TROPAEOLACEAE

1   *TROPAEOLUM L.

1   *T. speciosum Poeppig & Endl.

105 BALSAMINACEAE

1 IMPATIENS L.

    1 I. noli-tangere L.

    2 *I. capensis Meerb.

    3 *I. parviflora DC.

    4 *I. glandulifera Royle
      Impatiens roylei Walp., nom. illegit.

106 ARALIACEAE

1 HEDERA L.

    1 *H. colchica (K. Koch) K. Koch
      Hedera helix L. var. *colchica* K. Koch

    2 H. helix L.

      a subsp. **helix**

      b subsp. **hibernica** (Kirchner) D. McClint.
        Hedera helix L. var. *hibernica* Kirchner
        Hedera hibernica (Kirchner) Bean

2 *ARALIA L.

    1 *A. chinensis L.

    2 *A. elata (Miq.) Seemann
      Dimorphanthus elatus Miq.

    3 *A. racemosa L.

107 APIACEAE
Hydrocotylaceae; Umbelliferae

1 **HYDROCOTYLE** L.

    1 **H. vulgaris** L.

    2 ***H. moschata** G. Forster
      Hydrocotyle microphylla Cunn.; *H. sibthorpioides* Colenso, non
      Lam.

    3 ***H. novae-zelandiae** DC.
      Hydrocotyle microphylla auct., non Cunn.

2 **SANICULA** L.

    1 **S. europaea** L.

3 ***ASTRANTIA** L.

    1 ***A. major** L.

4 **ERYNGIUM** L.

    1 ***E. giganteum** M. Bieb.

    2 ***E. planum** L.

    3 **E. maritimum** L.

    4 **E. campestre** L.

5 **CHAEROPHYLLUM** L.

    1 ***C. hirsutum** L.

    2 ***C. aureum** L.

    3 **C. temulum** L.
      Chaerophyllum temulentum L.

6   ANTHRISCUS Pers.

> **1   A. sylvestris** (L.) Hoffm.
> *Chaerophyllum sylvestre* L.

> **2   A. caucalis** M. Bieb.
> *Anthriscus neglecta* Boiss. & Reuter ex Lange; *A. scandicina* (G. Weber) Mansf., nom. illegit.; *A. vulgaris* Pers., non Bernh.

7   SCANDIX L.

> **1   S. pecten-veneris** L.

8   *MYRRHIS Miller

> **1   *M. odorata** (L.) Scop.
> *Scandix odorata* L.

9   *CORIANDRUM L.

> **1   *C. sativum** L.

10   *SMYRNIUM L.

> **1   *S. olusatrum** L.

> **2   *S. perfoliatum** L.

11   BUNIUM L.

> **1   B. bulbocastanum** L.
> *Carum bulbocastanum* (L.) Koch

12   CONOPODIUM Koch

> **1   C. majus** (Gouan) Loret
> *Bunium majus* Gouan

13 PIMPINELLA L.

1 **P. major** (L.) Hudson
Pimpinella saxifraga L. var. *major* L.

2 **P. saxifraga** L.

14 *AEGOPODIUM L.

1 ***A. podagraria** L.

15 SIUM L.

1 **S. latifolium** L.

16 BERULA Besser ex Koch

1 **B. erecta** (Hudson) Cov.
Sium erectum Hudson
Siella erecta (Hudson) Pin., nom. illegit.

17 CRITHMUM L.

1 **C. maritimum** L.

18 SESELI L.

1 **S. libanotis** (L.) Koch
Athamanta libanotis L.

19 OENANTHE L.

1 **O. fistulosa** L.

2 **O. silaifolia** M. Bieb.

3 **O. pimpinelloides** L.

4 **O. lachenalii** C. Gmelin

5   **O. crocata** L.

6   **O. fluviatilis** (Bab.) Coleman
Oenanthe phellandrium Lam., nom. illegit. var. *fluviatilis* Bab.

7   **O. aquatica** (L.) Poiret

20   **AETHUSA** L.

1   **A. cynapium** L.

a   subsp. **cynapium**

b   *subsp. **agrestis** (Wallr.) Dostál
Aethusa cynapium L. var. *agrestis* Wallr.

21   *****FOENICULUM** Miller

1   *****F. vulgare** Miller

22   **SILAUM** Miller

1   **S. silaus** (L.) Schinz & Thell.
Peucedanum silaus L.

23   **MEUM** Miller

1   **M. athamanticum** Jacq.

24   **PHYSOSPERMUM** Cusson ex A.L. Juss.
Danaa All.

1   **P. cornubiense** (L.) DC.
Ligusticum cornubiense L.
Danaa cornubiensis (L.) Burnat

25   **CONIUM** L.

1   **C. maculatum** L.

26   BUPLEURUM L.

1   *B. fruticosum L.

2   B. falcatum L.

3   B. tenuissimum L.

4   B. baldense Turra
    Bupleurum opacum (Cesati) Lange

5   *B. subovatum Link ex Sprengel
    Bupleurum lancifolium auct., non Hornem.

27   TRINIA Hoffm.

1   T. glauca (L.) Dumort.
    Pimpinella glauca L.

28   APIUM L.

1   A. graveolens L.
    Apium graveolens L. subsp. *dulce* (Miller) Lemke & Rothm.

2   A. nodiflorum (L.) Lagasca
    Sium nodiflorum L.

2 x 3   A. nodiflorum x A. repens

2 x 4   A. nodiflorum x A. inundatum = A. x moorei (Syme) Druce
        Helosciadium inundatum (L.) Koch var. *moorei* Syme

3   A. repens (Jacq.) Lagasca
    Sium repens Jacq.

4   A. inundatum (L.) Reichb.f.
    Sison inundatum L.

29   PETROSELINUM Hill

1   *P. crispum (Miller) Nyman ex A.W. Hill
    Apium crispum Miller

2 **P. segetum** (L.) Koch
Sison segetum L.
Carum segetum (L.) Benth. ex J.D. Hook.

30 **SISON** L.

1 **S. amomum** L.

31 **CICUTA** L.

1 **C. virosa** L.

32 ***AMMI** L.

1 ***A. majus** L.

33 ***FALCARIA** Fabr.

1 ***F. vulgaris** Bernh.

34 **CARUM** L.

1 ***C. carvi** L.

2 **C. verticillatum** (L.) Koch
Sison verticillatum L.

35 **SELINUM** L.

1 **S. carvifolia** (L.) L.
Seseli carvifolia L.

36 **LIGUSTICUM** L.

1 **L. scoticum** L.

37 ANGELICA L.

    1 A. sylvestris L.

    2 *A. archangelica L.

38 *LEVISTICUM Hill

    1 *L. officinale Koch

39 PEUCEDANUM L.

    1 P. officinale L.

    2 P. palustre (L.) Moench
      Selinum palustre L.

    3 *P. ostruthium (L.) Koch
      Imperatoria ostruthium L.

40 PASTINACA L.

    1 P. sativa L.
      Pastinaca sativa L. subsp. *sylvestris* (Miller) Rouy & Camus; *P. sylvestris* Miller

41 HERACLEUM L.

    1 H. sphondylium L.

      a subsp. **sphondylium**

      b subsp. **sibiricum** (L.) Simonkai
        Heracleum sibiricum L.

  1 x 2 H. sphondylium x **H. mantegazzianum**

    2 *H. mantegazzianum Sommier & Levier

42 *TORDYLIUM L.

    1 *T. maximum L.

43 TORILIS Adans.

    1 T. japonica (Houtt.) DC.
    Caucalis japonica Houtt.
    Torilis anthriscus (L.) C. Gmelin, non Gaertner

    2 T. arvensis (Hudson) Link
    Caucalis arvensis Hudson

    3 T. nodosa (L.) Gaertner
    Tordylium nodosum L.

44 DAUCUS L.

    1 D. carota L.

      a subsp. **carota**

      b *subsp. **sativus** (Hoffm.) Arcang.
      Daucus carota L. var. *sativa* Hoffm.

      c subsp. **gummifer** (Syme) J.D. Hook.
      Daucus carota L. var. *gummifer* Syme
      Daucus gingidium auct., non L.; *D. gummifer* Lam., non
      All.

108 GENTIANACEAE

1 CICENDIA Adans.

    1 C. filiformis (L.) Delarbre
    Gentiana filiformis L.

2 EXACULUM Caruel

    1 E. pusillum (Lam.) Caruel

Gentiana pusillum Lam.

3 CENTAURIUM Hill
Erythraea Borkh., nom. illegit.

    1 C. scilloides (L.f.) Samp.
        Gentiana scilloides L.f.
        Centaurium portense (Brot.) Butcher

    2 C. erythraea Rafn
        Centaurium capitatum (Willd. ex Cham.) Borbás; *C. latifolium*
        (Smith) Druce; *C. turneri* (Wheldon & Salmon) Butcher; *C.*
        umbellatum auct., non Gilib.

  2 x 3 C. erythraea x **C. littorale** = **C. x intermedium** (Wheldon)
        Druce
        Erythraea littoralis (D. Turner) Fries var. *intermedium* Wheldon

  2 x 4 C. erythraea x **C. pulchellum**

    3 C. littorale (Turner ex Smith) Gilmour
        Chironia littoralis Turner ex Smith
        Centaurium minus Moench

    4 C. pulchellum (Sw.) Druce
        Gentiana pulchella Sw.

    5 C. tenuiflorum (Hoffsgg. & Link) Fritsch
        Erythraea tenuiflora Hoffsgg. & Link

4 BLACKSTONIA Hudson

    1 B. perfoliata (L.) Hudson
        Gentiana perfoliata L.

5 GENTIANELLA Moench

    1 G. ciliata (L.) Borkh.
        Gentiana ciliata L.

    2 G. campestris (L.) Boerner
        Gentiana campestris L.

Gentianella baltica sensu E. Warb. et auct., non (Murb.)
Boerner; *G. campestris* (L.) Boerner subsp. *baltica* auct.

3 **G. germanica** (Willd.) Boerner
Gentiana germanica Willd.

3 x 4 **G. germanica** x **G. amarella** = **G. x pamplinii** (Druce) E.
Warb.
Gentiana x pamplinii Druce

4 **G. amarella** (L.) Boerner
Gentiana amarella L.

    a subsp. **amarella**

    b subsp. **hibernica** N. Pritch.

    c subsp. **septentrionalis** (Druce) N. Pritch.
      Gentiana amarella L. var. *septentrionalis* Druce
      Gentiana septentrionalis (Druce) Druce; *Gentianella
        amarella* (L.) Boerner subsp. *druceana* N. Pritch.; *G.
        septentrionalis* (Druce) E. Warb.

4 x 5 **G. amarella** x **G. anglica**

4 x 6 **G. amarella** x **G. uliginosa**

5 **G. anglica** (Pugsley) E. Warb.
Gentiana anglica Pugsley

    a subsp. **anglica**

    b subsp. **cornubiensis** N. Pritch.

6 **G. uliginosa** (Willd.) Boerner
Gentiana uliginosa Willd.
Gentianella amarella (L.) Boerner subsp. *uliginosa* (Willd.)
Tzvelev

6 GENTIANA L.

1 *G. asclepiadea L.

2 **G. pneumonanthe** L.

3 *G. clusii Perrier & Song.
Gentiana acaulis sensu Lousley, non L.

4 G. verna L.

5 G. nivalis L.

109 *APOCYNACEAE

1 *VINCA L.

1 *V. minor L.

2 *V. difformis Pourret
Vinca major auct., non L.

3 *V. major L.
Vinca herbacea auct., non Waldst. & Kit.; *V. major* L. subsp.
hirsuta sensu McClint. et auct., non (Boiss.) Stearn

110 SOLANACEAE

1 *NICANDRA Adans.

1 *N. physalodes (L.) Gaertner
Atropa physalodes L.

2 *LYCIUM L.

1 *L. barbarum L.
Lycium halimifolium Miller

2 *L. chinense Miller
Lycium barbarum auct., non L.

3 ATROPA L.

1 A. belladonna L.

4 HYOSCYAMUS L.

    1 H. niger L.

5 *SALPICHROA Miers

    1 *S. origanifolia (Lam.) Thell.
    Physalis origanifolia Lam.

6 *PHYSALIS L.

    1 *P. alkekengi L.
    Physalis franchetii Masters

7 *LYCOPERSICON Miller

    1 *L. esculentum Miller
    Solanum lycopersicum L.

8 SOLANUM L.

    1 S. nigrum L.

        a subsp. **nigrum**

        b *subsp. **schultesii** (Opiz) Wessely
        Solanum schultesii Opiz

    1 x 3   **S. nigrum** x **S. physalifolium** = **S. x procurrens** Leslie

    2 *S. chenopodioides Lam.
    Solanum gracile Moric. ex Dunal, non Sendtner; *S. sublobatum*
    Willd. ex Roemer & Schultes

    3 *S. physalifolium Rusby
    Solanum nigrum auct., non L.; *S. nitidibaccatum* Bitter; *S.*
    sarachoides auct., non Sendtner

4 *S. sarachoides Sendtner
  Solanum chenopodioides auct., non Lam.; *S. nigrum* auct., non L.;
    S. nitidibaccatum auct., non Bitter; *S. physalifolium* auct., non
    Rusby

5 *S. triflorum Nutt.

6 S. dulcamara L.

7 *S. tuberosum L.

8 *S. laciniatum Aiton
  Solanum aviculare auct., non G. Forster

9 *DATURA L.

1 *D. stramonium L.
  Datura tatula L.

111 CONVOLVULACEAE

1 *DICHONDRA Forster & G. Forster

1 *D. micrantha Urban
  Dichondra repens sensu J. Russell et Dandy, non Forster & G.
    Forster

2 CONVOLVULUS L.

1 C. arvensis L.

3 CALYSTEGIA R. Br.

1 C. soldanella (L.) R. Br.
  Convolvulus soldanella L.

2 C. sepium (L.) R. Br.
  Convolvulus sepium L.

a   subsp. **sepium**
Calystegia sepium (L.) R. Br. subsp. *baltica* Rothm.

b   subsp. **roseata** Brummitt

2 x 3   **C. sepium** x **C. pulchra** = **C. x scanica** Brummitt

2 x 4   **C. sepium** x **C. silvatica** = **C. x lucana** (Ten.) Don
Convolvulus x lucanus Ten.

  3 *C. pulchra** Brummitt & Heyw.
Calystegia dahurica sensu Walters & D. Webb, non (Herbert)
Don; *C. sepium* (L.) R. Br. subsp. *dahurica* sensu Tutin, non
(Herbert) D. Webb & Walters, nom. inval.; *C. sepium* (L.) R.
Br. subsp. *pulchra* (Brummitt & Heyw.) Tutin, nom. inval.;
C. silvatica (Kit.) Griseb. subsp. *pulchra* (Brummitt & Heyw.)
Rothm., nom. inval.; *C. silvatica* (Kit.) Griseb. var. *pulchra*
(Brummitt & Heyw.) Scholz, nom. inval.; *C. sylvestris*
(Waldst. & Kit. ex Willd.) Roemer & Schultes var. *pulchra*
(Brummitt & Heyw.) Scholz, nom. inval.; *Convolvulus*
dahuricus sensu Walters & D. Webb, non Herbert; *C. dubius*
J. Gilbert

3 x 4   **C. pulchra** x **C. silvatica** = **C. x howittiorum** Brummitt

  4 *C. silvatica** (Kit.) Griseb.
Convolvulus silvaticus Kit.
Calystegia sepium (L.) R. Br. subsp. *silvatica* (Kit.) Battand.; *C.*
sylvestris (Waldst. & Kit. ex Willd.) Roemer & Schultes

112 CUSCUTACEAE

1   **CUSCUTA** L.

  1 *C. campestris** Yuncker

  2   **C. europaea** L.

  3   **C. epithymum** (L.) L.
Cuscuta europaea L. var. *epithymum* L.

113 MENYANTHACEAE

1 **MENYANTHES** L.

    1   **M. trifoliata** L.

2 **NYMPHOIDES** Séguier
   Limnanthemum S. Gmelin

    1   **N. peltata** Kuntze
      Limnanthemum peltatum S. Gmelin, nom. illegit.

114 POLEMONIACEAE

1 **POLEMONIUM** L.

    1   **P. caeruleum** L.

115 *HYDROPHYLLACEAE

1 ***PHACELIA** A.L. Juss.

    1 ***P. tanacetifolia** Benth.

116 BORAGINACEAE

1 **LITHOSPERMUM** L.
  Buglossoides Moench

    1   **L. purpureocaeruleum** L.
      Buglossoides purpureocaerulea (L.) I.M. Johnston

    2   **L. officinale** L.

    3   **L. arvense** L.
      Buglossoides arvensis (L.) I.M. Johnston

2   ECHIUM L.

1   E. vulgare L.

2   E. plantagineum L.
Echium lycopsis auct., non L.

3   *E. rosulatum Lange
Echium humile auct., non Desf.

4   *E. pininana Webb & Berth.

3   PULMONARIA L.

1   *P. officinalis L.

2   P. obscura Dumort.
Pulmonaria officinalis L. subsp. *obscura* (Dumort.) Murb.

3   *P. rubra Schott

4   *P. 'Mawson's Blue' hort. ex E. Bowles
Pulmonaria longifolia auct., non (Bast.) Boreau

5   P. longifolia (Bast.) Boreau
Pulmonaria angustifolia L. var. *longifolia* Bast.
Pulmonaria azurea auct., non Besser

4   SYMPHYTUM L.

1   S. officinale L.

1 x 2   *S. officinale x **S. asperum = S. x uplandicum** Nyman
Symphytum x peregrinum auct., non Ledeb.

1 x 2 x 3   S. officinale x **S. asperum** x **S. tuberosum**

1 x 2 x 4   *S. officinale x **S. asperum** x **S. grandiflorum = S. 'Hidcote Blue'** hort. ex G. Thomas
Symphytum x tauricum auct., non Willd.

2   *S. asperum Lepechin

3   S. tuberosum L.

4   *S. grandiflorum DC.
    Symphytum ibericum Steven

5   *S. tauricum Willd.
    Symphytum orientale Pallas, non L.

6   *S. orientale L.

7   *S. caucasicum M. Bieb.

8   *S. bulbosum C. Schimper

5 *BRUNNERA Steven

1   *B. macrophylla (Adams) I.M. Johnston
    Myosotis macrophylla Adams
    Anchusa myosotidiflora Lehm.; *Brunnera myosotidiflora* (Lehm.)
    Steven

6   ANCHUSA L.
    Lycopsis L.

    1   *A. ochroleuca M. Bieb.

    1 x 2   A. ochroleuca x A. officinalis = A. x baumgartenii (Nyman)
            Gusul.
            Anchusa officinalis L. subsp. *baumgartenii* Nyman

    2   *A. officinalis L.

    3   *A. azurea Miller

    4   A. arvensis (L.) M. Bieb.
        Lycopsis arvensis L.

7 *CYNOGLOTTIS (Gusul.) Vural & Kit Tan
  Anchusa subgen. *Cynoglottis* Gusul.

    1   *C. barrelieri (All.) Vural & Kit Tan
        Buglossum barrelieri All.

Anchusa barrelieri (All.) Vitman

8 *PENTAGLOTTIS Tausch

1 *P. sempervirens (L.) Tausch ex L. Bailey
Anchusa sempervirens L.

9 *BORAGO L.

1 *B. officinalis L.

2 *B. pygmaea (DC.) Chater & Greuter
Campanula pygmaea DC.
Borago laxiflora (DC.) Fischer, non Poiret

10 *TRACHYSTEMON D. Don

1 *T. orientalis (L.) Don
Borago orientalis L.

11 MERTENSIA Roth

1 M. maritima (L.) Gray
Pulmonaria maritima L.

12 *AMSINCKIA Lehm.

1 *A. lycopsoides (Lehm.) Lehm.
Lithospermum lycopsoides Lehm.

2 *A. micrantha Suksd.
Amsinckia calycina auct., non (Moris) Chater; *A. intermedia*
auct., non Fischer & C. Meyer; *A. menziesii* auct., non
(Lehm.) Nelson & McBride

13 *PLAGIOBOTHRYS Fischer & C. Meyer

1 *P. scouleri (Hook. & Arn.) I.M. Johnston
Myosotis scouleri Hook. & Arn.

14 *ASPERUGO L.

   1 *A. procumbens L.

15 MYOSOTIS L.

   1 M. scorpioides L.

 1 x 4 M. scorpioides x **M. laxa** = **M. x suzae** Domin

   2 M. secunda A. Murray
     Myosotis repens Don ex Borrer, non Moench

   3 M. stolonifera (DC.) Gay ex Leresche & Levier
     Myosotis caespitosa Schultz var. *stolonifera* DC.
     Myosotis brevifolia Salmon; *M. secunda* A. Murray subsp.
       stolonifera (DC.) Laínz

   4 M. laxa Lehm.

     a   subsp. **caespitosa** (Schultz) N. Hylander ex Nordh.
        Myosotis caespitosa Schultz

   5 M. sicula Guss.

   6 M. alpestris F.W. Schmidt

   7 M. sylvatica Hoffm.

   8 M. arvensis (L.) Hill
     Myosotis scorpioides L. var. *arvensis* L.
     Myosotis arvensis (L.) Hill subsp. *umbrata* (Mert. & Koch) O.
       Schwarz

   9 M. ramosissima Rochel
     Myosotis collina auct., non Ehrh. ex Hoffm.; *M. hispida* Schltr.;
      M. ramosissima Rochel subsp. *globularis* (Samp.) Grau

  10 M. discolor Pers.
     Myosotis collina Ehrh. ex Hoffm.; *M. discolor* Pers. subsp. *dubia*
      (Arrond.) Blaise; *M. versicolor* (Pers.) Smith

16 *OMPHALODES Miller

    1 *O. verna Moench

17 CYNOGLOSSUM L.

    1 C. officinale L.

    2 C. germanicum Jacq.
    Cynoglossum germanicum Jacq. subsp. *pellucidum* (Lapeyr.)
    Sutory; *C. montanum* auct., non L. nec Lam.

117 VERBENACEAE

1 VERBENA L.

    1 V. officinalis L.

118 LAMIACEAE
Labiatae

1 STACHYS L.
Betonica L.

    1 S. officinalis (L.) Trev. St. Léon
    Betonica officinalis L.

    2 *S. byzantina K. Koch
    Stachys lanata Jacq., non Crantz

    3 S. germanica L.

    4 S. alpina L.

    5 S. sylvatica L.

  5 x 6 S. sylvatica x **S. palustris** = **S. x ambigua** Smith

    6 S. palustris L.

7 *S. recta L.

8 S. arvensis (L.) L.
Glechoma arvensis L.

2 BALLOTA L.

1 B. nigra L.

a subsp. foetida (Vis.) Hayek
Ballota nigra L. var. *foetida* Vis.
Ballota ruderalis auct., non Sw.

3 *LEONURUS L.

1 *L. cardiaca L.

4 LAMIASTRUM Heister ex Fabr.
Galeobdolon Adans.

1 L. galeobdolon (L.) Ehrend. & Polatschek
Galeopsis galeobdolon L.
Galeobdolon luteum Hudson; *Lamium galeobdolon* (L.) L.

a subsp. galeobdolon

b subsp. montanum (Pers.) Ehrend. & Polatschek
Pollichia montanum Pers.
Galeobdolon luteum Hudson subsp. *montanum* (Pers.)
Dvoráková; *Lamium galeobdolon* (L.) L. subsp.
montanum (Pers.) Hayek; *L. montanum* (Pers.) Á.
Löve & D. Löve

c *subsp. argentatum (Smejkal) Stace
Galeobdolon argentatum Smejkal
Lamium galeobdolon (L.) L. forma *argentatum* (Smejkal)
Mennema; *L. galeobdolon* (L.) L. subsp. *argentatum*
(Smejkal) J. Duvign.

5 LAMIUM L.

1 **L. album** L.

2 ***L. maculatum** (L.) L.
Lamium album L. var. *maculatum* L.

3 **L. purpureum** L.

4 **L. hybridum** Villars

5 **L. confertum** Fries
Lamium molucellifolium sensu Fries, non (Schum.) Fries

6 **L. amplexicaule** L.

6 GALEOPSIS L.

1 **G. segetum** Necker
Galeopsis dubia Leers

2 **G. angustifolia** Ehrh. ex Hoffm.

3 **G. speciosa** Miller

4 **G. tetrahit** L.

4 x 5 **G. tetrahit** x **G. bifida** = **G. x ludwigii** Hausskn.

5 **G. bifida** Boenn.

7 *PHLOMIS L.

1 ***P. russeliana** (Sims) Benth.
Phlomis lunariifolia Sibth. & Smith var. *russeliana* Sims

2 ***P. fruticosa** L.

8 MELITTIS L.

1 **M. melissophyllum** L.

9   MARRUBIUM L.

    1   M. vulgare L.

10   SCUTELLARIA L.

    1 *S. altissima L.
       Scutellaria columnae auct., non All.

    2   S. galericulata L.

  2 x 4   S. galericulata x S. minor = S. x hybrida Strail
       Scutellaria x nicholsonii Taubert

    3 *S. hastifolia L.

    4   S. minor Hudson

11   TEUCRIUM L.

    1   T. scorodonia L.

    2 *T. chamaedrys L.

    3   T. scordium L.

    4   T. botrys L.

12   AJUGA L.

    1   A. reptans L.

  1 x 2   A. reptans x A. pyramidalis = A. x pseudopyramidalis Schur
       Ajuga hampeana Braun & Vatke

    2   A. pyramidalis L.

    3   A. chamaepitys (L.) Schreber
       Teucrium chamaepitys L.

13 NEPETA L.

    1 N. cataria L.

rac x **nep** *N. racemosa** Lam. x **N. nepetella** L. = **N. x faassenii** Bergmans
    ex Stearn
    Nepeta x mussinii auct., non Sprengel ex Henkel

14 GLECHOMA L.

    1 G. hederacea L.
    Nepeta hederacea (L.) Trev. St. Léon

15 PRUNELLA L.

    1 P. vulgaris L.

    1 x 2 P. vulgaris x **P. laciniata** = **P. x intermedia** Link
    Prunella x hybrida Knaf

    2 *P. laciniata (L.) L.
    Prunella vulgaris L. var. *laciniata* L.

16 *MELISSA L.

    1 *M. officinalis L.

17 *SATUREJA L.

    1 *S. montana L.

18 CLINOPODIUM L.
Acinos Miller; *Calamintha* Miller

    1 C. menthifolium (Host) Stace
    Calamintha menthifolia Host
    Calamintha sylvatica Bromf.

    2 C. ascendens (Jordan) Samp.
    Calamintha ascendens Jordan

Calamintha sylvatica Bromf. subsp. *ascendens* (Jordan) P. Ball

3 **C. calamintha** (L.) Stace
Melissa calamintha L.
Calamintha nepeta (L.) Savi subsp. *glandulosa* (Req.) P. Ball

4 **C. vulgare** L.
Calamintha vulgaris Hal., non Clairv.

5 **C. acinos** (L.) Kuntze
Thymus acinos L.
Acinos arvensis (Lam.) Dandy; *Calamintha acinos* (L.) Clairv.

19 ***HYSSOPUS** L.

1 ***H. officinalis** L.

20 **ORIGANUM** L.

1 **O. vulgare** L.

21 **THYMUS** L.

1 ***T. vulgaris** L.

2 **T. pulegioides** L.

3 **T. polytrichus** A. Kerner ex Borbás

a subsp. **britannicus** (Ronn.) Kerguélen
Thymus britannicus Ronn.
Thymus drucei Ronn.; *T. praecox* Opiz subsp. *arcticus* (E. Durand) Jalas; *T. praecox* Opiz subsp. *britannicus* (Ronn.) Holub; *T. praecox* Opiz subsp. *polytrichus* (A. Kerner ex Borbás) Jalas

4 **T. serpyllum** L.

22 **LYCOPUS** L.

1 **L. europaeus** L.

23 MENTHA L.

1 M. arvensis L.
Mentha gentilis L.

1 x **2 M. arvensis** x **M. aquatica** = **M. x verticillata** L.

1 x **2** x **3** **M. arvensis* x **M. aquatica** x **M. spicata** = **M. x smithiana** R.A. Graham

1 x **3** **M. arvensis* x **M. spicata** = **M. x gracilis** Sole
Mentha x cardiaca (Gray) Baker; *M. x gentilis* auct., non L.

1 x **4** **M. arvensis* x **M. suaveolens** = **M. x carinthiaca** Host
Mentha x muelleriana F. Schultz; *M. x wohlwerthiana* F. Schultz

2 M. aquatica L.

2 x **3** **M. aquatica* x **M. spicata** = **M. x piperita** L.
Mentha x citrata Ehrh.; *M. x dumetorum* auct., non Schultes

2 x **4 M. aquatica** x **M. suaveolens** = **M. x suavis** Guss.
Mentha x maximilianea F. Schultz

3 **M. spicata* L.
Mentha longifolia auct., non (L.) Hudson; *M. scotica* R.A. Graham

3 x **4** **M. spicata* x **M. suaveolens** = **M. x villosa** Hudson
Mentha x alopecuroides Hull; *M. x cordifolia* auct., ? an Opiz; *M. x niliaca* auct., non Juss. ex Jacq.; *M. x rotundifolia* (L.) Hudson subsp. *alopecuroides* (Hull) R. Malagarr.; *M. x scotica* auct., non R.A. Graham; *M. x villosa* Hudson nm. *alopecuroides* (Hull) Harley

3 x **lon** **M. spicata* x **M. longifolia** (L.) Hudson = **M. x villosonervata** Opiz
Mentha x villosa auct., non Hudson

4 M. suaveolens Ehrh.
Mentha rotundifolia Robson et auct., non (L.) Hudson

4 x **lon** **M. suaveolens* x **M. longifolia** (L.) Hudson = **M. x rotundifolia** (L.) Hudson
Mentha spicata L. var. *rotundifolia* L.

Mentha x niliaca Juss. ex Jacq.

5   M. pulegium L.

6   *M. requienii Benth.

24 *ROSMARINUS L.

1   *R. officinalis L.

25 SALVIA L.

1   *S. sclarea L.

2   *S. glutinosa L.

3   S. pratensis L.

4   S. verbenaca L.

5   *S. viridis L.

6   *S. verticillata L.

119 HIPPURIDACEAE

1   HIPPURIS L.

1   H. vulgaris L.

120 CALLITRICHACEAE

1   CALLITRICHE L.

1   C. hermaphroditica L.
Callitriche autumnalis sensu Hudson, non L.

2   C. truncata Guss.

a subsp. **occidentalis** (Rouy) Braun-Blanquet
Callitriche truncata Guss. race *occidentalis* Rouy

3 **C. stagnalis** Scop.

4 **C. platycarpa** Kuetz.

5 **C. obtusangula** Le Gall

6 **C. brutia** Petagna
Callitriche intermedia Hoffm. subsp. *pedunculata* (DC.)
Clapham; *C. pedunculata* DC.

7 **C. hamulata** Kuetz. ex Koch
Callitriche intermedia Hoffm. subsp. *hamulata* (Kuetz. ex Koch)
Clapham

121 PLANTAGINACEAE

1 **PLANTAGO** L.

1 **P. coronopus** L.
Plantago sabrinae (E.G. Baker & Cardew) Druce

2 **P. maritima** L.

3 **P. major** L.

a subsp. **major**

b subsp. **intermedia** (Gilib.) Lange
Plantago intermedia Gilib.

4 **P. media** L.

5 **P. lanceolata** L.

6 *****P. arenaria** Waldst. & Kit.
Plantago psyllium sensu L.(1759) et auct., non L.(1753); *P. scabra*
Moench, nom. illegit.

2 LITTORELLA P. Bergius

> **1 L. uniflora** (L.) Asch.
> *Plantago uniflora* L.

122 *BUDDLEJACEAE

1 *BUDDLEJA L.

> **1 *B. alternifolia** Maxim.
>
> **2 *B. davidii** Franchet
>
> **3 *B. globosa** Hope

123 OLEACEAE

1 *FORSYTHIA Vahl

sus x **vir *F. suspensa** (Thunb.) Vahl x **F. viridissima** Lindley = **F. x intermedia** hort. ex Zabel
Forsythia x suspensa auct., non (Thunb.) Vahl

2 FRAXINUS L.

> **1 F. excelsior** L.

3 *SYRINGA L.

> **1 *S. vulgaris** L.

4 LIGUSTRUM L.

> **1 L. vulgare** L.
>
> **2 *L. ovalifolium** Hassk.

124 SCROPHULARIACEAE

1   VERBASCUM L.

    1 *V. blattaria L.

  1 x 9 V. blattaria x V. nigrum = V. x intermedium Rupr. ex Bercht. & Pfund

    2 V. virgatum Stokes

  2 x 7 *V. virgatum x V. thapsus = V. x lemaitrei Boreau

    3 *V. pyramidatum M. Bieb.

  3 x 7 V. pyramidatum x V. thapsus

  3 x 9 V. pyramidatum x V. nigrum

    4 *V. bombyciferum Boiss.

    5 *V. phlomoides L.

  5 x 7 V. phlomoides x V. thapsus = V. x kerneri Fritsch

    6 *V. densiflorum Bertol.
       Verbascum thapsiforme Schrader

    7 V. thapsus L.

  7 x 9 V. thapsus x V. nigrum = V. x semialbum Chaub.
       Verbascum x collinum Schrader, non Salisb.

  7 x 10 V. thapsus x V. speciosum = V. x duernsteinense Teyber

  7 x 11 V. thapsus x V. pulverulentum = V. x godronii Boreau
       Verbascum x lamottei Franchet

  7 x 12 V. thapsus x V. lychnitis = V. x thapsi L.

    8 *V. chaixii Villars

    9 V. nigrum L.

9 x 11   V. nigrum x V. pulverulentum = V. x mixtum Ramond ex
DC.
Verbascum x wirtgenii Franchet

9 x 12   V. nigrum x V. lychnitis = V. x incanum Gaudin
Verbascum x schiedeanum Koch

10   *V. speciosum Schrader

11   V. pulverulentum Villars

11 x 12   *V. pulverulentum x V. lychnitis = V. x regelianum Wirtgen

12   V. lychnitis L.

2   **SCROPHULARIA** L.

1   S. nodosa L.

2   S. auriculata L.
Scrophularia aquatica auct., non L.

3   S. umbrosa Dumort.

4   S. scorodonia L.

5   *S. vernalis L.

3   *PHYGELIUS E. Meyer ex Benth.

1   *P. capensis E. Meyer ex Benth.

4   *MIMULUS L.

1   *M. moschatus Douglas ex Lindley

2   *M. guttatus DC.
Mimulus luteus auct., non L.

2 x 3   *M. guttatus x M. luteus = M. x robertsii Silverside
Mimulus x luteus auct., non L.

2 x 3 x cup *M. guttatus x M. luteus x M. cupreus Dombrain

2 x cup *M. guttatus x M. cupreus Dombrain = **M. x burnetii** S. Arn.
Mimulus x cupreus auct., non Dombrain

3 *M. luteus L.
Mimulus smithii auct., non Lindley, vix Paxton; *M. variegatus* Lodd., nom. nud.

3 x cup *M. luteus x M. cupreus Dombrain = **M. x maculosus** T. Moore

5 LIMOSELLA L.

1 L. aquatica L.

1 x 2 L. aquatica x **L. australis**

2 L. australis R. Br.
Limosella subulata Ives

6 *CALCEOLARIA L.

1 *C. chelidonioides Kunth

7 *ANTIRRHINUM L.

1 *A. majus L.

8 CHAENORHINUM (DC. ex Duby) Reichb.
Linaria sect. *Chaenorhinum* DC. ex Duby

1 *C. origanifolium (L.) Kostel.
Antirrhinum origanifolium L.

2 C. minus (L.) Lange
Antirrhinum minus L.

9 MISOPATES Raf.

1 M. orontium (L.) Raf.

Antirrhinum orontium L.

10 *ASARINA Miller

    1 *A. procumbens Miller
      Antirrhinum asarina L.

11 *CYMBALARIA Hill

    1 *C. muralis P. Gaertner, Meyer & Scherb.
      Linaria cymbalaria (L.) Miller

        a *subsp. muralis

        b *subsp. visianii (Kümm. ex Jáv.) D. Webb
          Cymbalaria muralis P. Gaertner, Meyer & Scherb. forma
          visianii Kümm. ex Jáv.

    2 *C. pallida (Ten.) Wettst.
      Antirrhinum pallidum Ten.

    3 *C. hepaticifolia (Poiret) Wettst.
      Antirrhinum hepaticifolium Poiret

12 KICKXIA Dumort.

    1 K. elatine (L.) Dumort.
      Antirrhinum elatine L.
      Linaria elatine (L.) Miller

    2 K. spuria (L.) Dumort.
      Antirrhinum spurium L.
      Linaria spuria (L.) Miller

13 LINARIA Miller

    1 L. vulgaris Miller

    1 x 4 L. vulgaris x L. repens = L. x sepium Allman

2 *L. dalmatica (L.) Miller
Antirrhinum dalmaticum L.
Linaria genistifolia (L.) Miller subsp. *dalmatica* (L.) Maire &
Petitm.

3 *L. purpurea (L.) Miller
Antirrhinum purpureum L.

3 x 4 **L. purpurea** x **L. repens** = **L. x dominii** Druce

4 **L. repens** (L.) Miller
Antirrhinum repens L.

4 x 5 **L. repens** x **L. supina** = **L. x cornubiensis** Druce

5 *L. supina (L.) Chaz.
Antirrhinum supinum L.

6 *L. arenaria DC.

7 **L. pelisseriana** (L.) Miller
Antirrhinum pelisserianum L.

14   DIGITALIS L.

1   D. purpurea L.

2 *D. lutea L.

15 *ERINUS L.

1 *E. alpinus L.

16   VERONICA L.

1   V. serpyllifolia L.

a   subsp. **serpyllifolia**

b   subsp. **humifusa** (Dickson) Syme
Veronica humifusa Dickson

2 *V. reptans D.H. Kent
   Veronica repens Clarion ex DC., non Gilib.

3 V. alpina L.

4 V. fruticans Jacq.

5 *V. austriaca L.

   a *subsp. teucrium (L.) D. Webb
      Veronica teucrium L.

6 V. officinalis L.

7 V. chamaedrys L.

8 V. montana L.

9 V. scutellata L.

10 V. beccabunga L.

11 V. anagallis-aquatica L.

11 x 12 V. anagallis-aquatica x V. catenata = V. x lackschewitzii J.
   Keller

12 V. catenata Pennell
   Veronica aquatica Bernh., non Gray

13 *V. acinifolia L.

14 *V. praecox All.

15 V. triphyllos L.

16 V. arvensis L.

17 V. verna L.

18 *V. peregrina L.

19 V. agrestis L.

20 V. polita Fries

21 *V. persica Poiret

22 *V. crista-galli Steven

23 *V. filiformis Smith

24 V. hederifolia L.

    a subsp. hederifolia

    b subsp. lucorum (Klett & H. Richter) Hartl
        Veronica hederifolia L. var. *lucorum* Klett & H. Richter
        Veronica sublobata M. Fischer

25 *V. longifolia L.

25 x 26 *V. longifolia x V. spicata

26 V. spicata L.

    a subsp. spicata

    b subsp. hybrida (L.) Gaudin
        Veronica hybrida L.

17 *HEBE Comm. ex A.L. Juss.

    1 *H. salicifolia (G. Forster) Pennell
        Veronica salicifolia G. Forster

1 x ell *H. salicifolia x H. elliptica (G. Forster) Pennell = H. x lewisii
        (J. Armstr.) Wall
        Veronica x lewisii J. Armstr.

    2 *H. brachysiphon Summerh.
        Veronica traversii Masters, non J.D. Hook.

    3 *H. dieffenbachii (Benth.) Cockayne & Allan
        Veronica dieffenbachii Benth.

    4 *H. barkeri (Cockayne) Wall
        Veronica barkeri Cockayne

ell x **spec** *H. elliptica** (G. Forster) Pennell x **H. speciosa** (R. Cunn. ex Cunn.) Cockayne & Allan = **H. x franciscana** (Eastw.) Souster

Veronica x franciscana Eastw.

Hebe x speciosa auct., non (R. Cunn. ex Cunn.) Cockayne & Allan

18 SIBTHORPIA L.

    1 S. europaea L.

19 MELAMPYRUM L.

    1 M. cristatum L.

    2 M. arvense L.

    3 M. pratense L.

        a subsp. **pratense**

        b subsp. **commutatum** (Tausch ex A. Kerner) C. Britton
        Melampyrum commutatum Tausch ex A. Kerner

    4 M. sylvaticum L.

20 EUPHRASIA L.

    1 E. rostkoviana Hayne
    Euphrasia officinalis L. subsp. *rostkoviana* (Hayne) F. Towns.

        a subsp. **rostkoviana**
        Euphrasia hirtella auct., non Jordan & Reuter

        b subsp. **montana** (Jordan) Wettst.
        Euphrasia montana Jordan
        Euphrasia officinalis L. subsp. *montana* (Jordan) Berher;
          E. officinalis L. subsp. *monticola* Silverside

    1 x 3 E. rostkoviana x **E. anglica**

    1 x 9 E. rostkoviana x **E. confusa**

1 x 18   E. rostkoviana x E. micrantha

1 x 19   E. rostkoviana x E. scottica

2   **E. rivularis** Pugsley

3   **E. anglica** Pugsley
Euphrasia hirtella auct., non Jordan & Reuter; *E. officinalis* L.
subsp. *anglica* (Pugsley) Silverside

3 x 5   E. anglica x E. arctica

3 x 7   E. anglica x E. nemorosa = E. x glanduligera Wettst.

3 x 9   E. anglica x E. confusa

3 x 18   E. anglica x E. micrantha

4   **E. vigursii** Davey

4 x 6   E. vigursii x E. tetraquetra

5   **E. arctica** Lange ex Rostrup

    a   subsp. **arctica**
       Euphrasia borealis auct., non (F. Towns.) Wettst.

    b   subsp. **borealis** (F. Towns.) Yeo
       Euphrasia rostkoviana Hayne forma *borealis* F. Towns.
       Euphrasia borealis (F. Towns.) Wettst.

5 x 6   E. arctica x E. tetraquetra = E. x pratiuscula F. Towns.

5 x 7   E. arctica x E. nemorosa

5 x 9   E. arctica x E. confusa

5 x 12   E. arctica x E. foulaensis

5 x 15   E. arctica x E. marshallii

5 x 18   E. arctica x E. micrantha

5 x 19   E. arctica x E. scottica

5 x 20   E. arctica x E. heslop-harrisonii

5 x 21   E. arctica x E. salisburgensis

6   E. tetraquetra (Bréb.) Arrond.
Euphrasia officinalis L. var. *tetraquetra* Bréb.
Euphrasia occidentalis Wettst.

6 x 7   E. tetraquetra x E. nemorosa

6 x 8   E. tetraquetra x E. pseudokerneri

6 x 9   E. tetraquetra x E. confusa

6 x 10   E. tetraquetra x E. stricta

6 x 14   E. tetraquetra x E. ostenfeldii

6 x 18   E. tetraquetra x E. micrantha

7   E. nemorosa (Pers.) Wallr.
Euphrasia officinalis L. var. *nemorosa* Pers.
Euphrasia curta (Fries) Wettst.

7 x 8   E. nemorosa x E. pseudokerneri

7 x 9   E. nemorosa x E. confusa

7 x 10   E. nemorosa x E. stricta = E. x haussknechtii Wettst.

7 x 12   E. nemorosa x E. foulaensis

7 x 14   E. nemorosa x E. ostenfeldii

7 x 15   E. nemorosa x E. marshallii

7 x 18   E. nemorosa x E. micrantha

7 x 19   E. nemorosa x E. scottica

8   E. pseudokerneri Pugsley

8 x 9   E. pseudokerneri x E. confusa

9   E. confusa Pugsley

9 x 11   E. confusa x E. frigida

9 x 14   E. confusa x E. ostenfeldii

9 x 17   E. confusa x E. campbelliae

9 x 18   E. confusa x E. micrantha

9 x 19   E. confusa x E. scottica

9 x 20   E. confusa x E. heslop-harrisonii

10   *E. stricta D. Wolff ex J. Lehm.
Euphrasia brevipila Burnat & Gremli ex Gremli; *E. stricta* D.
Wolff ex J. Lehm. var. *brevipila* (Burnat & Gremli ex Gremli)
Hartl

11   E. frigida Pugsley

11 x 12   E. frigida x E. foulaensis

11 x 17   E. frigida x E. campbelliae

11 x 18   E. frigida x E. micrantha

11 x 19   E. frigida x E. scottica

12   E. foulaensis F. Towns. ex Wettst.

12 x 14   E. foulaensis x E. ostenfeldii

12 x 15   E. foulaensis x E. marshallii

12 x 16   E. foulaensis x E. rotundifolia

12 x 18   E. foulaensis x E. micrantha

12 x 19   E. foulaensis x E. scottica

13   E. cambrica Pugsley

14   E. ostenfeldii (Pugsley) Yeo
Euphrasia curta (Fries) Wettst. var. *ostenfeldii* Pugsley
Euphrasia curta auct., non (Fries) Wettst.; *E. eurycarpa* Pugsley

14 x 18   **E. ostenfeldii** x **E. micrantha**
Euphrasia ? x areschougii Wettst.

14 x 19   **E. ostenfeldii** x **E. scottica**

15   **E. marshallii** Pugsley

15 x 16   **E. marshallii** x **E. rotundifolia**

15 x 17   **E. marshallii** x **E. campbelliae**

15 x 18   **E. marshallii** x **E. micrantha**

16   **E. rotundifolia** Pugsley
Euphrasia frigida Pugsley subsp. *rotundifolia* (Pugsley) Á. Löve

16 x 17   **E. rotundifolia** x **E. campbelliae**

17   **E. campbelliae** Pugsley

17 x 19   **E. campbelliae** x **E. scottica**

18   **E. micrantha** Reichb.
Euphrasia ? rhumica Pugsley; *E. gracilis* (Fries) Drejer

18 x 19   **E. micrantha** x **E. scottica** = **E. x electa** F. Towns.

18 x 20   **E. micrantha** x **E. salisburgensis**

19   **E. scottica** Wettst.

20   **E. heslop-harrisonii** Pugsley

21   **E. salisburgensis** Funck

21   ODONTITES Ludwig

1   *****O. jaubertianus** (Boreau) D. Dietr. ex Walp.
Euphrasia jaubertiana Boreau
Odontites luteus sensu Bowen, non (L.) Clairv.

2   **O. vernus** (Bellardi) Dumort.
Euphrasia verna Bellardi

a   subsp. **vernus**

b   subsp. **serotinus** (Syme) Corbière
Bartsia odontites (L.) Hudson var. *serotina* Syme
Odontites ruber Gilib., nom. illegit.; *O. vernus* (Bellardi)
Dumort. subsp. *pumilus* (Nordst.) A. Pedersen; *O.
vulgaris* Moench subsp. *pumilus* (Nordst.) Soó

c   subsp. **litoralis** (Fries) Nyman
Euphrasia litoralis Fries
Odontites vernus (Bellardi) Dumort. subsp. *pumilus*
auct., non (Nordst.) A. Pedersen; *O. vulgaris* Moench
subsp. *pumilus* auct., non (Nordst.) Soó

22   BARTSIA L.

1   **B. alpina** L.

23   PARENTUCELLIA Viv.

1   **P. viscosa** (L.) Caruel
Bartsia viscosa L.

24   RHINANTHUS L.

1   **R. angustifolius** C. Gmelin
Rhinanthus aestivalis (Zinger) Schischkin & Serg.; *R.
angustifolius* C. Gmelin subsp. *apterus* (Fries) N. Hylander;
R. major Ehrh., non L.; *R. polyclados* (Chabert) Clapham,
nom. inval.; *R. serotinus* (Schoenheit) Oborny

2   **R. minor** L.

a   subsp. **minor**

b   subsp. **stenophyllus** (Schur) O. Schwarz
Rhinanthus minor L. var. *stenophyllus* Schur
Rhinanthus stenophyllus (Schur) Druce

c   subsp. **monticola** (Stern.) O. Schwarz
Alectorolophus monticola Stern.
Rhinanthus spadiceus Wilm.

d subsp. **calcareus** (Wilm.) E. Warb.
Rhinanthus calcareus Wilm.

e subsp. **lintonii** (Wilm.) Sell
Rhinanthus lintonii Wilm.
Rhinanthus gardineri Druce; *R. lochabrensis* Wilm.

f subsp. **borealis** (Stern.) Sell
Alectorolophus borealis Stern.
Rhinanthus minor L. var. *drummond-hayi* (F.B. White) Á.
Löve; *R. perrieri* auct., non Chabert

25 PEDICULARIS L.

1 **P. palustris** L.

2 **P. sylvatica** L.

a subsp. **sylvatica**

b subsp. **hibernica** D. Webb

125 OROBANCHACEAE

1 LATHRAEA L.

1 **L. squamaria** L.

2 ***L. clandestina** L.

2 OROBANCHE L.

1 **O. purpurea** Jacq.

2 **O. rapum-genistae** Thuill.

3 **O. caryophyllacea** Smith
Orobanche vulgaris Poiret

4 **O. elatior** Sutton

5   **O. alba** Stephan ex Willd.

6   **O. reticulata** Wallr.

7   *****O. crenata** Forsskål

8   **O. hederae** Duby

9   **O. artemisiae-campestris** Vaucher ex Gaudin
    Orobanche loricata Reichb.; *O. picridis* F. Schultz

10 **O. minor** Smith
    Orobanche amethystea auct., non Thuill.; *O. apiculata* Wallr.; *O. maritima* Pugsley

126 *GESNERIACEAE

1 *****RAMONDA** Rich.

   1 *****R. myconi** (L.) Reichb.
      Verbascum myconi L.

127 *ACANTHACEAE

1 *****ACANTHUS** L.

   1 *****A. mollis** L.

   2 *****A. spinosus** L.

128 LENTIBULARIACEAE

1 **PINGUICULA** L.

   1 **P. lusitanica** L.

   2 †**P. alpina** L.

   3 **P. vulgaris** L.

3 x 4   **P. vulgaris** x **P. grandiflora** = **P. x scullyi** Druce

4   **P. grandiflora** Lam.

2   UTRICULARIA L.

1   **U. vulgaris** L.

2   **U. australis** R. Br.
Utricularia major auct., non Schmid; *U. neglecta* Lehm.; *U. vulgaris* auct., non L.

3   **U. intermedia** Hayne
Utricularia ochroleuca auct., non R. Hartman

4   **U. stygia** Thor

5   **U. ochroleuca** R. Hartman
Utricularia intermedia Hayne forma *ochroleuca* (R. Hartman) Komiya; *U. intermedia* auct., non Hayne

6   **U. minor** L.
Utricularia bremii auct., non Heer

129 CAMPANULACEAE
Lobeliaceae

1   CAMPANULA L.

1   **C. patula** L.

2   ***C. rapunculus** L.

3   ***C. lactiflora** M. Bieb.

4   ***C. persicifolia** L.

5   ***C. medium** L.

6   ***C. alliariifolia** Willd.

7   **C. glomerata** L.

8 *C. pyramidalis L.

9 *C. portenschlagiana Schultes

10 *C. poscharskyana Degen

11 C. latifolia L.

12 C. trachelium L.

13 *C. rapunculoides L.

14 *C. rhomboidalis L.

15 C. rotundifolia L.
    Campanula giesekiana auct., non Vest

2 **LEGOUSIA** Durande
  Specularia Heister ex A. DC.

    1 **L. hybrida** (L.) Delarbre
      Campanula hybrida L.
      Specularia hybrida (L.) A. DC.

3 **WAHLENBERGIA** Schrader ex Roth

    1 **W. hederacea** (L.) Reichb.
      Campanula hederacea L.

4 *TRACHELIUM L.

    1 *T. caeruleum L.

5 **PHYTEUMA** L.

    1 **P. spicatum** L.

    2 **P. orbiculare** L.
      Phyteuma tenerum R. Schulz subsp. *anglicum* R. Schulz

    3 *P. scheuchzeri All.

6 JASIONE L.

    1   **J. montana** L.

7 LOBELIA L.

    1   **L. urens** L.

    2   ***L. erinus** L.

    3   **L. dortmanna** L.

8 *PRATIA Gaudich.

    1   ***P. angulata** (G. Forster) J.D. Hook.
          Lobelia angulata G. Forster

9 *DOWNINGIA Torrey

    1   ***D. elegans** (Douglas ex Lindley) Torrey
          Clintonia elegans Douglas ex Lindley

130 RUBIACEAE

1 *COPROSMA Forster & G. Forster

    1   ***C. repens** A. Rich.
          Coprosma baueri auct., non Endl.

2 *NERTERA Banks & Sol. ex Gaertner

    1   ***N. granadensis** (Mutis ex L.f.) Druce
          Gomozia granadensis Mutis ex L.f.
          Nertera depressa Banks & Sol. ex Gaertner

3 SHERARDIA L.

    1 S. arvensis L.
       Sherardia arvensis L. subsp. *maritima* (Griseb.) Soják

4 *PHUOPSIS (Griseb.) J.D. Hook.
    Asperula sect. *Phuopsis* Griseb.

    1 *P. stylosa (Trin.) Benth. & J.D. Hook. ex B.D. Jackson
       Crucianella stylosa Trin.

5 ASPERULA L.

    1 A. cynanchica L.

       a subsp. **cynanchica**

       b subsp. **occidentalis** (Rouy) Stace
         Asperula occidentalis Rouy

    2 *A. taurina L.

6 GALIUM L.

    1 G. boreale L.

    2 G. odoratum (L.) Scop.
       Asperula odorata L.

    3 G. uliginosum L.

    4 G. constrictum Chaub.
       Galium debile Desv., non Hoffsgg. & Link

    5 G. palustre L.

       a subsp. **palustre**
         Galium palustre L. subsp. *tetraploideum* Clapham; *G. witheringii* Smith

       b subsp. **elongatum** (C. Presl.) Arcang.
         Galium elongatum C. Presl

6 **G. verum** L.
   Galium verum L. subsp. *maritimum* (DC.) Adema

6 x 7 **G. verum** x **G. mollugo = G. x pomeranicum** Retz.

7 **G. mollugo** L.

   a subsp. **mollugo**

   b subsp. **erectum** Syme
      Galium album Miller; *G. erectum* Hudson(1778), non
         Hudson(1762); *G. mollugo* L. subsp. *album* (Miller)
         Clapham, nom. inval.

8 **G. pumilum** Murray
   Galium fleurotii auct., ? an Jordan; *G. timeroyi* Jordan subsp.
      fleurotii auct., ? an (Jordan) J. Duvign.

9 **G. sterneri** Ehrend.
   Galium pumilum Murray subsp. *septentrionale* Sterner ex N.
      Hylander

9 x 10 **G. sterneri** x **G. saxatile**

10 **G. saxatile** L.
    Galium rupicola Bertol.

11 **G. aparine** L.

12 **G. spurium** L.
    Galium vaillantii DC.

13 **G. tricornutum** Dandy

14 **G. parisiense** L.

7 **CRUCIATA** Miller

   1 **C. laevipes** Opiz
      Cruciata chersonensis auct., non (Willd.) Ehrend.; *Galium
         cruciata* (L.) Scop.

8   **RUBIA** L.

   1   R. peregrina L.

131 **CAPRIFOLIACEAE**

1   **SAMBUCUS** L.

   1 *S. racemosa L.
     Sambucus pubens Michaux; *S. racemosa* L. subsp. *pubens*
     (Michaux) Hultén; *S. racemosa* L. subsp. *sieboldiana*
     (Michaux) H. Hara; *S. sieboldiana* (Michaux) Graebner

   2   S. nigra L.

   3 *S. canadensis L.

   4   S. ebulus L.

2   **VIBURNUM** L.

   1   V. opulus L.

   2   V. lantana L.

  2 x 4 *V. lantana x V. rhytidophyllum = V. x rhytidophylloides
     Valcken.

   3 *V. tinus L.

   4 *V. rhytidophyllum Hemsley ex Forbes & Hemsley

3 ***SYMPHORICARPOS** Duhamel

   1 *S. albus (L.) S.F. Blake
     Vaccinium album L.
     Symphoricarpos racemosus Michaux; *S. rivularis* Suksd.

orb x mic *S. orbiculatus Moench x S. microphyllus Kunth = S. x
     chenaultii Rehder

4   LINNAEA L.

    1   L. borealis L.

5   *LEYCESTERIA Wallich

    1   *L. formosa Wallich
      Leycesteria crocothyrsos auct., non Airy Shaw

6   LONICERA L.

    1   *L. pileata Oliver

    2   *L. nitida E. Wilson

    3   *L. involucrata (Richardson) Banks ex Sprengel
      Xylosteon involucrata Richardson
      Lonicera ledebourii Eschsch.

    4   L. xylosteum L.

    5   *L. henryi Hemsley

    6   *L. japonica Thunb. ex Murray

    7   L. periclymenum L.

    8   *L. caprifolium L.

8 x etr   *L. caprifolium x **L. etrusca** Santi = **L. x italica** Schmidt ex
      Tausch
      Lonicera americana auct., non (Miller) K. Koch

132   ADOXACEAE

1   ADOXA L.

    1   A. moschatellina L.

133 VALERIANACEAE

1 VALERIANELLA Miller

    1 V. locusta (L.) Laterr.
    Valeriana locusta L.
    Valerianella locusta (L.) Laterr. subsp. *dunensis* (D. Allen) Sell

    2 V. carinata Lois.

    3 V. rimosa Bast.

    4 V. dentata (L.) Pollich
    Valeriana locusta L. var. *dentata* L.

    5 *V. eriocarpa Desv.

2 VALERIANA L.

    1 V. officinalis L.
    Valeriana officinalis L. subsp. *collina* Nyman; *V. officinalis* L.
    subsp. *sambucifolia* (J.C. Mikan ex Pohl) Hayw.; *V.*
    sambucifolia J.C. Mikan ex Pohl

    2 *V. pyrenaica L.

    3 V. dioica L.

3 *CENTRANTHUS Necker ex Lam. & DC.

    1 *C. ruber (L.) DC.
    Valeriana rubra L.

    2 *C. calcitrapae (L.) Dufr.
    Valeriana calcitrapae L.

134 DIPSACACEAE

1 DIPSACUS L.

1 D. fullonum L.
Dipsacus fullonum L. subsp. *sylvestris* (Hudson) P. Fourn.; *D. sylvestris* Hudson

2 *D. sativus (L.) Honck.
Dipsacus fullonum L. var. *sativus* L.
Dipsacus fullonum L. subsp. *fullonum* sensu Clapham

3 D. pilosus L.

4 *D. strigosus Willd.

2 *CEPHALARIA Schrader ex Roemer & Schultes

1 *C. gigantea (Ledeb.) Bobrov
Scabiosa gigantea Ledeb.
Cephalaria elata (Hornem.) Schrader ex Roemer & Schultes

3 KNAUTIA L.

1 K. arvensis (L.) Coulter
Scabiosa arvensis L.

4 SUCCISA Haller

1 S. pratensis Moench
Scabiosa succisa L.

5 SCABIOSA L.
Sixalix Raf.

1 S. columbaria L.

2 *S. atropurpurea L.
Sixalix atropurpurea (L.) Greuter & Burdet

135 ASTERACEAE
Compositae

1 *ECHINOPS L.

   1 *E. sphaerocephalus L.

   2 *E. exaltatus Schrader
     Echinops commutatus Juratzká; *E. sphaerocephalus* auct., non L.

   3 *E. bannaticus Rochel ex Schrader
     Echinops ritro auct., non L.

2 CARLINA L.

   1 C. vulgaris L.

3 ARCTIUM L.

   1 A. lappa L.
     Arctium lappa L. subsp. *majus* Arènes

  1 x 2 A. lappa x A. minus = A. x nothum (Ruhmer) J. Weiss
     Lappa x notha Ruhmer
     Arctium x debrayi Senay

   2 A. minus (Hill) Bernh.
     Lappa minor Hill

      a subsp. **pubens** (Bab.) Arènes
         Arctium pubens Bab.
         Arctium vulgare A. Evans, pro parte

      b subsp. **nemorosum** (Lej.) Syme
         Arctium nemorosum Lej.
         Arctium vulgare A. Evans, pro parte

      c subsp. **minus**

4 SAUSSUREA DC.

   1 S. alpina (L.) DC.

Serratula alpina L.

5 CARDUUS L.

1 C. tenuiflorus Curtis
Carduus pycnocephalus L. var. *tenuiflorus* (Curtis) Ball

2 *C. pycnocephalus L.
Carduus tenuiflorus auct., non Curtis

3 C. crispus L.

    a subsp. **multiflorus** (Gaudin) Franco
       Carduus multiflorus Gaudin
       Carduus acanthoides auct., non L.; *C. crispus* L. subsp.
         occidentalis Chassagne & Arènes

3 x 4 C. crispus x **C. nutans = C. x dubius** Balbis
Carduus x orthocephalus auct., non Wallr., nec Curtis; *C. x*
    polyacanthus Schleicher, non Lam.

4 C. nutans L.

6 CIRSIUM Miller

1 C. eriophorum (L.) Scop.
Carduus eriophorus L.
Cirsium eriophorum (L.) Scop. subsp. *britannicum* Petrak

1 x 2 C. eriophorum x **C. vulgare = C. x grandiflorum** Kittel
Cirsium x gerhardtii Schultz-Bip.

2 C. vulgare (Savi) Ten.
Carduus vulgaris Savi
Cirsium lanceolatum (L.) Scop., non Hill

2 x 8 C. vulgare x **C. acaule = C. x sabaudum** Loehr

2 x 9 C. vulgare x **C. palustre = C. x subspinuligerum** Peterm.

3 C. dissectum (L.) Hill
Carduus dissectus L.

3 x 8   **C. dissectum** x **C. acaule** = **C. x woodwardii** (H. Watson)
         Nyman
         Carduus x woodwardii H. Watson

3 x 9   **C. dissectum** x **C. palustre** = **C. x forsteri** (Smith) Loudon
         Cnicus x forsteri Smith

    4   **C. tuberosum** (L.) All.
         Carduus tuberosus L.

4 x 8   **C. tuberosum** x **C. acaule** = **C. x medium** All.
         Cirsium x zizianum Koch

4 x 9   **C. tuberosum** x **C. palustre** = **C. x semidecurrens** H. Richter

    5   *****C. erisithales** (Jacq.) Scop.
         Carduus erisithales Jacq.

    6   **C. heterophyllum** (L.) Hill
         Carduus heterophyllus L.
         Carduus helenioides auct., non L.; *Cirsium helenioides* auct., non
         (L.) Hill

6 x 9   **C. heterophyllum** x **C. palustre** = **C. x wankelii** Reichardt

    7   *****C. oleraceum** (L.) Scop.
         Cnicus oleraceus L.

    8   **C. acaule** (L.) Scop.
         Carduus acaulos L.

8 x 9   **C. acaule** x **C. palustre** = **C. x kirschlegeri** Schultz-Bip.

8 x 10   **C. acaule** x **C. arvense** = **C. x boulayi** Camus

    9   **C. palustre** (L.) Scop.
         Carduus palustris L.

9 x 10   **C. palustre** x **C. arvense** = **C. x celakovskianum** Knaf

   10   **C. arvense** (L.) Scop.
         Serratula arvensis L.

7 ONOPORDUM L.

    1 O. acanthium L.

8 *SILYBUM Adans.

    1 *S. marianum (L.) Gaertner
    Carduus marianus L.

9 SERRATULA L.

    1 S. tinctoria L.

10 *ACROPTILON Cass.

    1 *A. repens (L.) DC.
    Centaurea repens L.

11 CENTAUREA L.

    1 C. scabiosa L.

    2 *C. montana L.

    3 *C. cyanus L.

  3 x jac C. nigra x **C. jacea** L. = **C. x moncktonii** C. Britton
    Centaurea x drucei C. Britton; *C. x jacea* auct., non L.; *C. x*
    surrejana C. Britton

    4 *C. calcitrapa L.

    5 *C. aspera L.

    6 *C. solstitialis L.

    7 C. nigra L.
    Centaurea debeauxii Gren. & Godron subsp. *nemoralis* (Jordan)
    Dostál; *C. nemoralis* Jordan; *C. nigra* L. subsp. *nemoralis*
    (Jordan) Gremli

12 CICHORIUM L.

   1 C. intybus L.

13 †ARNOSERIS Gaertner

   1 †A. minima (L.) Schweigger & Koerte
     Hyoseris minima L.

14 LAPSANA L.

   1 L. communis L.

     a subsp. **communis**

     b *subsp. **intermedia** (M. Bieb.) Hayek
       Lapsana intermedia M. Bieb.

15 HYPOCHAERIS L.

   1 H. radicata L.

  1 x 2 H. radicata x H. glabra = H. x intermedia H. Richter

   2 H. glabra L.

   3 H. maculata L.

16 LEONTODON L.

   1 L. autumnalis L.

     a subsp. **autumnalis**

     b subsp. **pratensis** (Hornem.) Gremli
       Apargia pratensis Hornem.
       Leontodon autumnalis L. var. *pratensis* (Hornem.) Koch;
        L. pratensis (Hornem.) Reichb.

   2 L. hispidus L.

2 x 3　**L. hispidus** x **L. saxatilis**

3　**L. saxatilis** Lam.
Hyoseris taraxacoides Villars; *Leontodon leysseri* (Wallr.) G. Beck;
L. taraxacoides (Villars) Mérat

17　**PICRIS** L.

1　**P. echioides** L.

2　**P. hieracioides** L.
Picris spinulosa sensu C.E. Britton, non Bertol. ex Guss.

18　**SCORZONERA** L.

1　**S. humilis** L.

19　**TRAGOPOGON** L.

1　**T. pratensis** L.

a　*subsp. **pratensis**

b　subsp. **minor** (Miller) Wahlenb.
Tragopogon minor Miller

1 x 2　**T. pratensis** x **T. porrifolius** = **T. x mirabilis** Rouy

2　*T. porrifolius** L.

20　***AETHEORHIZA** Cass.

1　***A. bulbosa** (L.) Cass.
Leontodon bulbosus L.

21　**SONCHUS** L.

1　**S. palustris** L.

2   **S. arvensis** L.
Sonchus arvensis L. subsp. *uliginosus* auct., non (M. Bieb.) Nyman

3   **S. oleraceus** L.

3 x 4   **S. oleraceus** x **S. asper**

4   **S. asper** (L.) Hill
Sonchus oleraceus L. var. *asper* L.
Sonchus asper (L.) Hill subsp. *glaucescens* (Jordan) J. Ball

22   **LACTUCA** L.
Mulgedium Cass.

   1   **L. serriola** L.
    Lactuca scariola L.

   2   **L. virosa** L.

   3   **L. saligna** L.

   4   *****L. tatarica** (L.) C. Meyer
    Sonchus tataricus L.

23   **CICERBITA** Wallr.
Mulgedium auct., non Cass.

   1   **C. alpina** (L.) Wallr.
    Sonchus alpinus L.
    Mulgedium alpinum (L.) Less.

   2   *****C. macrophylla** (Willd.) Wallr.
    Sonchus macrophyllus Willd.
    Mulgedium macrophyllum (Willd.) DC.

      a *subsp. **uralensis** (Rouy) Sell
       Mulgedium uralense Rouy

   3   *****C. plumieri** (L.) Kirschl.
    Sonchus plumieri L.
    Mulgedium plumieri (L.) DC.

4 *C. bourgaei (Boiss.) Beauverd
Mulgedium bourgaei Boiss.

24 MYCELIS Cass.

1 M. muralis (L.) Dumort.
Prenanthes muralis L.
Lactuca muralis (L.) Gaertner

25 TARAXACUM Wigg.

sect. Erythrosperma (Lindb.f.) Dahlst.
Erythrospermum Lindb.f.

1 T. acutum A. Richards

2 T. arenastrum A. Richards

3 T. argutum Dahlst.

4 T. brachyglossum (Dahlst.) Dahlst.
Taraxacum erythrospermum Andrz. ex Besser subsp.
brachyglossum Dahlst.
Taraxacum hispanicum sensu A. Richards, non Lindb.f.; *T.*
vachelliae Dahlst.

5 T. cenabense Sahlin

6 T. commixtum Hagl.
Taraxacum commutatum Dahlst.

7 T. degelii Hagl.

8 T. disseminatum Hagl.

9 T. dunense Soest

10 T. falcatum Brenner
Taraxacum canulum auct., non Hagl. ex Markl.

11 T. fulviforme Dahlst.
Taraxacum simile sensu A. Richards, non Raunk.

12 **T. fulvum** Raunk.

13 **T. glauciniforme** Dahlst.

14 **T. inopinatum** C. Haworth

15 **T. lacistophyllum** (Dahlst.) Raunk.
Taraxacum erythrospermum Andrz. ex Besser subsp.
lacistophyllum Dahlst.

16 **T. oxoniense** Dahlst.
Taraxacum helvicarpum Dahlst.

17 **T. placidum** A. Richards

18 **T. proximiforme** Soest ex Lambinon & Soest

19 **T. proximum** (Dahlst.) Dahlst.
Taraxacum erythrospermum Andrz. ex Besser subsp. *proximum*
Dahlst.

20 **T. pseudoproximum** Soest

21 **T. retzii** Soest

22 **T. rubicundum** (Dahlst.) Dahlst.
Taraxacum erythrospermum Andrz. ex Besser subsp. *rubicundum*
Dahlst.

23 **T. scanicum** Dahlst.

24 **T. scoticum** A. Richards

25 **T. silesiacum** Dahlst. ex Hagl.

26 **T. tanylepis** Dahlst.

27 **T. tortilobum** Florström

28 **T. wallonicum** Soest

sect. **Obliqua** Dahlst.

29 **T. obliquum** (Fries) Dahlst.
Leontodon obliquum Fries

30   **T. platyglossum** Raunk.

sect. **Palustria** (Dahlst.) Dahlst.
Taraxacum group *Palustria* Dahlst.

31   **T. anglicum** Dahlst.

32   **T. palustre** (Lyons) Symons
      Leontodon palustre Lyons
      Taraxacum ? pollichii Soest; *T. limnanthes* Hagl. subsp.
      limnanthoides Soest

33   **T. sarniense** A. Richards
      Taraxacum austrinum sensu A. Richards et auct., non Hagl.

34   **T. webbii** A. Richards

sect. **Spectabilia** (Dahlst.) Dahlst.
Taraxacum group *Spectabilia* Dahlst.

35   **T. faeroense** (Dahlst.) Dahlst.
      Taraxacum spectabile Dahlst. var. *faeroense* Dahlst.
      Taraxacum cimbricum Wiinst.; *T. eximium* auct., non Dahlst.; *T.
      spectabile* sensu A. Richards, non Dahlst.; *T. reclinatum*
      sensu A. Richards et auct., non M. Christiansen

36   **T. serpenticola** A. Richards

sect. **Naevosa** M. Christiansen

37   **T. cornubiense** A. Richards

38   **T. drucei** Dahlst.
      Taraxacum lainzii sensu A. Richards, non Soest

39   **T. euryphyllum** (Dahlst.) M. Christiansen
      Taraxacum maculigerum Lindb.f. subsp. *euryphyllum* Dahlst.

40   **T. maculosum** A. Richards
      Taraxacum maculigerum sensu A. Richards, non Lindb.f.

41   **T. naevosiforme** Dahlst.
      Taraxacum hamatifrons Dahlst.; *T. plicatum* Dahlst.; *T.
      acidodontum* Dahlst.

42   **T. naevosum** Dahlst.
     Taraxacum subsimile Dahlst.

43   **T. pseudolarssonii** A. Richards
     Taraxacum edmondsonii A. Richards

44   **T. richardsianum** C. Haworth

45   **T. stictophyllum** Dahlst.
     Taraxacum calophyllum Dahlst.; *T. laetifrons* Dahlst.

46   **T. subnaevosum** A. Richards

sect. **Taraxacum**

47   **T. ceratolobum** Dahlst.
     Taraxacum acidotum M. Christiansen; *T. croceum* sensu A.
     Richards, non Dahlst.

48   **T. clovense** A. Richards

49   **T. craspedotum** Dahlst.

50   **T. cymbifolium** Lindb.f. ex Dahlst.
     Taraxacum acromaurum Dahlst.

51   **T. pycnostictum** M. Christiansen

52   **T. xiphoideum** Hagl.
     Taraxacum hypochaeris sensu A. Richards, non Dahlst.

sect. **Celtica** A. Richards

53   **T. beeftinkii** Hagend., Soest & Zevenb.

54   **T. berthae** C. Haworth

55   **T. bracteatum** Dahlst.

56   **T. britannicum** Dahlst.
     Taraxacum hibernicum Hagl.

57   **T. caledonicum** A. Richards

58   **T. cambricum** A. Richards

59   **T. celticum** A. Richards

60   **T. duplidentifrons** Dahlst.
Taraxacum raunkiaeri Wiinst.

61   **T. excellens** Dahlst.

62   **T. fulgidum** Hagl.

63   **T. fulvicarpum** Dahlst.
Taraxacum hamatifrons Dahlst.; *T. unguilobiforme* Dahlst.

64   **T. gelertii** Raunk.
Taraxacum adamii sensu A. Richards, non Claire

65   **T. haematicum** Hagl.
Taraxacum haematopus Dahlst., non Lindb.f.

66   **T. hesperium** C. Haworth

67   **T. hygrophilum** Soest

68   **T. inane** A. Richards
Taraxacum ardlense A. Richards

69   **T. lancastriense** A. Richards

70   **T. landmarkii** Dahlst.

71   **T. luteum** C. Haworth & A. Richards

72   **T. nordstedtii** Dahlst.
Taraxacum cambriense A. Richards

73   **T. oellgaardii** C. Haworth

74   **T. olgae** A. Richards

75   **T. orcadense** Dahlst.
Taraxacum perlaciniatum Dahlst.; *T. tanylepioides* Dahlst.

76   **T. ostenfeldii** Raunk.
Taraxacum duplidens Lindb.f.; *T. parvuliceps* sensu A. Richards, non Lindb.f.; *T. biforme* sensu A. Richards et auct., non Dahlst.

77   **T. palustrisquameum** A. Richards

78   **T. porteri** C. Haworth

79   **T. pseudonordstedtii** A. Richards

80   **T. subbracteatum** A. Richards
Taraxacum crispifolium sensu A. Richards, non Lindb.f.

81   **T. tamesense** A. Richards

82   **T. texelense** Hagend., Soest & Zevenb.

83   **T. unguilobum** Dahlst.
Taraxacum chloroleucophyllum Dahlst.; *T. johnstonii* Dahlst.; *T. serratilobum* Dahlst.; *T. unguilobiforme* Dahlst.

sect. **Hamata** Oellgaard

84   **T. atactum** Sahlin & Soest

85   **T. boekmanii** Borgv.

86   **T. fusciflorum** Oellgaard

87   **T. hamatiforme** Dahlst.
Cotoneaster humifusa Praeger

88   **T. hamatulum** Hagend., Soest & Zevenb.

89   **T. hamatum** Raunk.

90   **T. hamiferum** Dahlst.
Taraxacum atrovirens auct., non Dahlst.

91   **T. kernianum** Hagend., Soest & Zevenb.

92   **T. lamprophyllum** M. Christiansen

93   **T. lancidens** Hagend., Soest & Zevenb.

94   **T. marklundii** Palmgren

95   **T. polyhamatum** Oellgaard

96   **T. prionum** Hagend., Soest & Zevenb.

97   **T. pruinatum** M. Christiansen

98   **T. pseudohamatum** Dahlst.

99   **T. quadrans** Oellgaard

100 **T. spiculatum** M. Christiansen
     Taraxacum subditivum auct., non Hagend., Soest & Zevenb.

101 **T. subhamatum** M. Christiansen

sect. **Ruderalia** Kirschner, Oellgaard & Stepanek

102 **T. aberrans** Hagend., Soest & Zevenb.

103 **T. acroglossum** Dahlst.
     Taraxacum praeradians Dahlst.

104 **T. acutifidum** M. Christiansen

105 **T. acutifrons** Markl.

106 **T. aequilobum** Dahlst.

107 **T. aequisectum** M. Christiansen

108 **T. alatum** Lindb.f.
     Taraxacum semiprivum Dahlst.

109 **T. altissimum** Lindb.f.

110 **T. amplum** Markl.

111 **T. ancistrolobum** Dahlst.

112 **T. angulare** Hagend., Soest & Zevenb.

113 **T. angustisquameum** Dahlst. ex Lindb.f.

114 **T. atonolobum** Hagend., Soest & Zevenb.

115 **T. aurosulum** Lindb.f.

116 **T. caloschistum** Dahlst.

117 **T. cherwellense** A. Richards
Taraxacum stenoglossum Dahlst., non Brenner

118 **T. chloroticum** Dahlst.

119 **T. chrysophaenum** Rail.

120 **T. cophocentrum** Dahlst.

121 **T. cordatum** Palmgren

122 **T. corynodes** Hagl.

123 **T. croceiflorum** Dahlst.

124 **T. curtifrons** Oellgaard

125 **T. cyanolepis** Dahlst.

126 **T. dahlstedtii** Lindb.f.

127 **T. densilobum** Dahlst.
Taraxacum pericrispum M. Christiansen

128 **T. diastematicum** Markl.

129 **T. dilaceratum** M. Christiansen

130 **T. dilatatum** Lindb.f.

131 **T. ekmanii** Dahlst.
Taraxacum connexum Dahlst.

132 **T. exacutum** Markl.
Taraxacum spilophyllum sensu A. Richards, pro parte, non
Dahlst.

133 **T. expallidiforme** Dahlst.
Taraxacum oncolobum Dahlst.

134 **T. exsertiforme** Hagend., Soest & Zevenb.

135 **T. exsertum** Hagend., Soest & Zevenb.

136   **T. fagerstroemii** Såltin

137   **T. fasciatum** Dahlst.
Taraxacum sublatissimum Dahlst.

138   **T. hemicyclum** Hagl.

139   **T. hexhamense** A. Richards

140   **T. horridifrons** Rail.

141   **T. huelphersianum** Dahlst.

142   **T. incisum** Oellgaard

143   **T. insigne** Ekman ex M. Christiansen & Wiinst.
Taraxacum ordinatum Hagend., Soest & Zevenb.

144   **T. interveniens** Hagl.

145   **T. intumescens** Hagl.

146   **T. lacerifolium** Hagl.
Taraxacum lacinulatum Markl.

147   **T. laciniosifrons** Dahlst.

148   **T. laciniosum** Dahlst.
Taraxacum naeviferum Dahlst.

149   **T. laeticolor** Dahlst.

150   **T. laticordatum** Markl.
Taraxacum uncosum Hagl.

151   **T. latisectum** Lindb.f.

152   **T. latissimum** Palmgren

153   **T. leptaleum** M. Christiansen

154   **T. leptodon** Markl.

155   **T. leucopodum** Hagl.

156 **T. linguatum** Dahlst. ex M. Christiansen & Wiinst.

157 **T. lingulatum** Markl.
Taraxacum aequatum Dahlst.; *T. subpallescens* Dahlst.

158 **T. longisquameum** Lindb.f.
Taraxacum adsimile Dahlst.; *T. latispina* Dahlst.; *T. mucronatum*
sensu A. Richards et auct., non Lindb.f.

159 **T. lucidum** Dahlst.

160 **T. lunare** M. Christiansen

161 **T. macranthoides** Hagl.

162 **T. macrolobum** Dahlst.
Taraxacum lacerabile Dahlst.

163 **T. maculatum** Jordan

164 **T. margettsii** C. Haworth

165 **T. melanthoides** Dahlst.

166 **T. mimulum** Dahlst.

167 **T. mirum** Oellgaard

168 **T. multicolorans** Hagend., Soest & Zevenb.

169 **T. necessarium** Oellgaard

170 **T. nitidum** Hagend., Soest & Zevenb.

171 **T. obliquilobum** Dahlst.
Taraxacum similatum Dahlst.

172 **T. oblongatum** Dahlst.
Taraxacum perhamatum Dahlst.

173 **T. obtusifrons** Markl.

174 **T. obtusilobum** Dahlst.

175 **T. ochrochlorum** Hagl.

176   **T. pachylobum** Dahlst.

177   **T. pachymerum** Hagl.

178   **T. pallescens** Dahlst.

179   **T. pallidipes** Markl. ex Hagl.

180   **T. pannucium** Dahlst.

181   **T. pannulatiforme** Dahlst.

182   **T. pannulatum** Dahlst.
      Taraxacum tarachodum Hagend., Soest & Zevenb.

183   **T. pectinatiforme** Lindb.f.

184   **T. piceatum** Dahlst.

185   **T. planum** Raunk.

186   **T. polyodon** Dahlst.
      Taraxacum ardisodon Dahlst.; *T. naeviferum* Dahlst.

187   **T. porrigens** Markl. ex Puol.

188   **T. procerisquameum** Oellgaard
      Taraxacum procerum sensu A. Richards et auct., non Hagl.

189   **T. pseudoretroflexum** M. Christiansen

190   **T. pulchrifolium** Markl.

191   **T. recurvum** Dahlst.

192   **T. remanentilobum** Soest

193   **T. retroflexum** Lindb.f.

194   **T. rhamphodes** Dahlst.

195   **T. sagittipotens** Dahlst. & R. Ohlsen ex Hagl.

196   **T. scotiniforme** Dahlst. ex Hagl.
      Taraxacum obscuratum Hagl.

197 **T. sellandii** Dahlst.

198 **T. semiglobosum** Lindb.f.

199 **T. sinuatum** Dahlst.

200 **T. speciosum** Raunk.

201 **T. stenacrum** Dahlst.

202 **T. stereodes** E. Ekman ex T. Lange

203 **T. subcyanolepis** M. Christiansen

204 **T. subexpallidum** Dahlst.
Taraxacum sublaciniosum sensu A. Richards et auct., non Dahlst.

205 **T. subhuelphersianum** M. Christiansen

206 **T. sublacerifolium** Hagend., Soest & Zevenb.

207 **T. sublaeticolor** Dahlst.

208 **T. sublongisquameum** M. Christiansen

209 **T. subpraticola** Hagl.

210 **T. subundulatum** Dahlst.
Taraxacum amphiodon Dahlst. ex Hagl.; *T. hemipolyodon* Dahlst.; *T. similatum* Dahlst.

211 **T. subxanthostigma** Oellgaard

212 **T. tanyphyllum** Dahlst.

213 **T. tenebricans** (Dahlst.) Dahlst.
Taraxacum officinale Wigg. subsp. *tenebricans* Dahlst.

214 **T. trilobatum** Palmgren

215 **T. tumentilobum** Markl. ex Hagl.

216 **T. undulatiflorum** M. Christiansen

217 **T. undulatum** Lindb.f. & Markl.

218 **T. valens** Markl.

219 **T. vastisectum** Markl. ex Puol.

220 **T. xanthostigma** Lindb.f.

26 **CREPIS** L.

    1 **C. paludosa** (L.) Moench
       Hieracium paludosum L.

    2 **C. mollis** (Jacq.) Asch.
       Hieracium molle Jacq.

    3 **C. biennis** L.

    4 **C. capillaris** (L.) Wallr.
       Lapsana capillaris L.

    5 *****C. vesicaria** L.

        a *subsp. **taraxacifolia** (Thuill.) Thell. ex Schinz & Keller
           Crepis taraxacifolia Thuill.
           Crepis polymorpha Pourret; *C. vesicaria* L. subsp.
              haenseleri (Boiss. ex DC.) Sell

    6 **C. foetida** L.
       Barkhausia foetida (L.) Schmidt

    7 *****C. praemorsa** (L.) F. Walther
       Hieracium praemorsum L.

27 **PILOSELLA** Hill
Hieracium subgen. *Pilosella* (Hill) Gray

    1 **P. peleteriana** (Mérat) F. Schultz & Schultz-Bip.
       Hieracium peleterianum Mérat

        a subsp. **peleteriana**

b   subsp. **subpeleteriana** (Naeg. & Peter) Sell
     Hieracium subpeleterianum Naeg. & Peter

c   subsp. **tenuiscapa** (Pugsley) Sell & C. West
     Hieracium peleterianum Mérat var. *tenuiscapum* Pugsley
     Hieracium peleterianum Mérat subsp. *tenuiscapum*
     (Pugsley) Sell

1 x 2   **P. peleteriana** x **P. officinarum** = **P. x longisquama** (Peter)
     Holub
     Hieracium x longisquamum Peter
     Pilosella x pachylodes (Naeg. & Peter) Soják, nom. illegit.

2   **P. officinarum** F. Schultz & Schultz-Bip.
     Hieracium pilosella L.; *H. pilosella* L. subsp. *euronotum* Naeg. &
     Peter; *H. pilosella* L. subsp. *melanops* Peter; *H. pilosella* L.
     subsp. *micradenium* Naeg. & Peter; *H. pilosella* L. subsp.
     tricholepium Naeg. & Peter; *H. pilosella* L. subsp. *trichosoma*
     Peter; *Pilosella euronota* (Naeg. & Peter) Dostál; *P. melanops*
     (Peter) Dostál; *P. officinarum* F. Schultz & Schultz-Bip.
     subsp. *concinnata* (F. Hanb.) Sell & C. West; *P. officinarum* F.
     Schultz & Schultz-Bip. subsp. *euronota* (Naeg. & Peter) Sell
     & C. West; *P. officinarum* F. Schultz & Schultz-Bip. subsp.
     melanops (Peter) Sell & C. West; *P. officinarum* F. Schultz &
     Schultz-Bip. subsp. *micradenia* (Naeg. & Peter) Sell & C.
     West; *P. officinarum* F. Schultz & Schultz-Bip. subsp.
     nigrescens (Fries) Sell & C. West; *P. officinarum* F. Schultz &
     Schultz-Bip. subsp. *tricholepia* (Naeg. & Peter) Sell & C.
     West; *P. officinarum* F. Schultz & Schultz-Bip. subsp.
     trichoscapa (Naeg. & Peter) Sell & C. West; *P. officinarum* F.
     Schultz & Schultz-Bip. subsp. *trichosoma* (Peter) Sell & C.
     West; *P. trichocarpa* (Naeg. & Peter) Dostál; *P. tricholepia*
     (Naeg. & Peter) Dostál

2 x 6   ***P. officinarum** x **P. aurantiaca** = **P. x stoloniflora** (Waldst. &
     Kit.) F. Schultz & Schultz-Bip.
     Hieracium x stoloniflorum Waldst. & Kit.

3   **P. flagellaris** (Willd.) Sell & C. West
     Hieracium flagellare Willd.

a   *subsp. **flagellaris**
     Hieracium stoloniflorum auct., non Waldst. & Kit.

b   subsp. **bicapitata** Sell & C. West
Hieracium flagellare Willd. subsp. *bicapitata* (Sell & C. West) Sell

4 ***P. praealta** (Villars ex Gochnat) F. Schultz & Schultz-Bip.
Hieracium praealtum Villars ex Gochnat

a *subsp. **praealta**

b *subsp. **thaumasia** (Peter) Sell
Hieracium magyaricum Naeg. & Peter subsp. *thaumasium* Peter
Hieracium praealtum Villars ex Gochnat subsp.
thaumasium (Peter) Sell; *H. spraguei* Pugsley; *Pilosella praealta* (Villars ex Gochnat) F. Schultz & Schultz-Bip. subsp. *arvorum* (Naeg. & Peter) Sell & C. West; *P. praealta* (Villars ex Gochnat) F. Schultz & Schultz-Bip. subsp. *spraguei* (Pugsley) Sell & C. West; *P. thaumasia* (Peter) Dostál

5 ***P. caespitosa** (Dumort.) Sell & C. West
Hieracium caespitosum Dumort.

a *subsp. **colliniformis** (Peter) Sell & C. West
Hieracium collinum Gochnat subsp. *colliniforme* Peter

6 ***P. aurantiaca** (L.) F. Schultz & Schultz-Bip.
Hieracium aurantiacum L.

a *subsp. **aurantiaca**

b *subsp. **carpathicola** (Naeg. & Peter) Soják
Hieracium aurantiacum L. subsp. *carpathicola* Naeg. & Peter
Hieracium brunneocroceum Pugsley; *Pilosella aurantiaca* (L.) F. Schultz & Schultz-Bip. subsp. *brunneocrocea* (Pugsley) Sell & C. West

28   **HIERACIUM** L.

sect. **Sabauda** F. Williams

1   **H. sabaudum** L.

Hieracium argutifolium Pugsley; *H. bladonii* Pugsley; *H. eminentiforme* Pugsley; *H. obliquum* Jordan; *H. perpropinquum* (Zahn) Druce

2 H. virgultorum Jordan

3 H. rigens Jordan

4 H. salticola (Sudre) Sell & C. West
Hieracium virgultorum Jordan var. *salticolum* Sudre
Hieracium sublactucaceum auct., non (Zahn) Druce & Zahn

5 H. vagum Jordan
Hieracium croceostylum Pugsley; *H. subquercetorum* Pugsley

sect. **Umbellata** F. Williams

6 H. umbellatum L.

   a subsp. **umbellatum**

   b subsp. **bichlorophyllum** (Druce & Zahn) Sell & C. West
      Hieracium laevigatum Willd. subsp. *bichlorophyllum* Druce & Zahn
      Hieracium bichlorophyllum (Druce & Zahn) Pugsley

sect. **Foliosa** Pugsley

7 H. maritimum (F. Hanb.) F. Hanb.
Hieracium crocatum Fries var. *maritimum* F. Hanb.
Hieracium obesifolium Pugsley

8 †H. pycnotrichum (W.R. Linton) Roffey
Hieracium corymbosum Pers. var. *pycnotrichum* W.R. Linton

9 H. bakerianum Pugsley
Hieracium crocatum auct., non Fries

10 H. subumbellatiforme (Zahn) Roffey
Hieracium aestivum Fries subsp. *subumbellatiforme* Zahn
Hieracium angustatum auct., non Lindeb.; *H. pseudamplidentatum* Pugsley

11 H. reticulatum Lindeb.

12 H. strictiforme (Zahn) Roffey
Hieracium inuloides Tausch subsp. *strictiforme* Zahn
Hieracium listerae Pugsley; *H. opsianthum* (Dahlst.) Roffey; *H. strictum* auct., non Ledeb.

13 H. drummondii Pugsley

14 H. subcrocatum (E.F. Linton) Roffey
Hieracium strictum Ledeb. var. *subcrocatum* E.F. Linton
Hieracium bartonii Pugsley; *H. corymbosum* sensu W.R. Linton
et auct., non Pers.; *H. neocorymbosum* Pugsley

15 H. latobrigorum (Zahn) Roffey
Hieracium inuloides Tausch subsp. *latobrigorum* Zahn
Hieracium auratum auct., non F. Hanb.

16 H. tavense (Ley ex W.R. Linton) Ley
Hieracium rigidum Hartman var. *tavense* Ley ex W.R. Linton

sect. **Tridentata** F. Williams

17 H. calcaricola (F. Hanb.) Roffey
Hieracium rigidum Hartman var. *calcaricola* F. Hanb.
Hieracium scabrescens auct., non (Johansson ex Dahlst.) W.
Martin & G.T. Fraser; *H. tridentatum* auct., non Fries

18 H. ornatilorum Sell & C. West

19 H. eboracense Pugsley
Hieracium tridentatum auct., non Fries

20 H. cambricogothicum Pugsley

21 H. trichocaulon (Dahlst.) Johansson
Hieracium rigidum Hartman subsp. *trichocaulon* Dahlst.
Hieracium acrifolium auct., non Dahlst.; *H. scabrescens* auct., non
(Johansson ex Dahlst.) W. Martin & G.T. Fraser; *H. tridentatum* auct., non Fries

22 H. acamptum Sell & C. West
Hieracium cantianum F. Hanb. var. *subrigidum* W.R. Linton ex
F. Hanb.

23 H. cantianum F. Hanb.

24 H. scabrisetum (Zahn) Roffey
Hieracium laevigatum Willd. subsp. *scabrisetum* Zahn
Hieracium ? amphiboloides (Zahn) Roffey; *H. ? rubefactum* (W.R.
Linton) Roffey; *H. backhouseanum* (Zahn) Roffey var.
radnoricum Pugsley; *H. cambricogothicum* Pugsley var.
glandulosum Pugsley; *H. fragilicaule* Pugsley; *H. obatrescens*
auct., non Dahlst.; *H. rhayaderense* Pugsley; *H. rigidum* auct.,
non Hartman nec Backh.; *H. boreophilum* (Zahn) Roffey; *H.
pseudacrifolium* Pugsley

25 H. stewartii (F. Hanb.) Roffey
Hieracium friesii Hartman var. *stewartii* F. Hanb.
Hieracium ardaricum Pugsley; *H. backhouseanum* auct., non
(Zahn) Roffey; *H. donegalense* Pugsley; *H. hartianum*
Pugsley; *H. longiciliatum* (F. Hanb.) Roffey

26 H. scullyi W.R. Linton

27 H. nidense (F. Hanb.) Roffey
Hieracium rigidum Hartman var. *nidense* F. Hanb.

28 H. subintegrifolium Pugsley

29 H. placerophylloides Pugsley
Hieracium grandescens auct., non Dahlst.; *H. palcerophyllum*
auct., non Dahlst.

30 H. substrigosum (Zahn) Roffey
Hieracium laevigatum Willd. subsp. *substrigosum* Zahn
Hieracium rigidum Hartman var. *strigosum* Ley

31 H. gothicoides Pugsley
Hieracium ? backhouseanum (Zahn) Roffey; *H. gothicum* auct.,
non Fries

32 H. uiginskyense Pugsley
Hieracium backhouseanum auct., non (Zahn) Roffey; *H. trinitatis*
Pugsley

33 H. lissolepium (Zahn) Roffey
Hieracium laevigatum Willd. subsp. *lissolepium* Zahn
Hieracium claviceps Pugsley; *H. calviceps* Pugsley

34 H. sparsifolium Lindeb.

Hieracium pseudoprotractum Pugsley, non Notø; *H.*
stictophyllum Dahlst. ex W.R. Linton

35 **H. hibernicum** F. Hanb.

36 **H. sparsifrons** Sell & C. West
Hieracium oligodon (E.F. Linton ex W.R. Linton) Pugsley, non
Naeg. & Peter

37 **H. linguans** (Zahn) Roffey
Hieracium laevigatum Willd. subsp. *linguans* Zahn
Hieracium sparsifolium Lindeb. var. *lingua* Ley ex W.R. Linton

sect. **Prenanthoidea** Koch

38 †**H. borreri** Syme
Hieracium denticulatum auct., non Smith

39 **H. prenanthoides** Villars
Hieracium lanceolatum auct., non Villars; *H. strictissimum* auct.,
non Peter; *H. subelatum* auct., non Almq. ex Dahlst.

sect. **Alpestria** F. Williams

40 **H. carpathicum** Besser
Hieracium perthense F. Williams

41 **H. dewarii** Syme

42 **H. mirandum** Sell & C. West

43 **H. vinicaule** Sell & C. West
Hieracium platylepium auct., non Dahlst. ex Druce; *H. vinaceum*
(Beeby) Pugsley

44 **H. northroense** Pugsley
Hieracium congestum (Beeby) Roffey, non Freyn

45 **H. subtruncatum** Beeby
Hieracium truncatum auct., non Lindeb.

46 **H. dilectum** Sell & C. West

47 **H. pugsleyi** Sell & C. West

48   **H. attenuatifolium** Sell & C. West

49   †**H. hethlandiae** (F. Hanb.) Pugsley
     Hieracium dovrense Fries var. *hethlandiae* F. Hanb.

50   **H. praethulense** Pugsley
     Hieracium auratum F. Hanb. var. *thulense* F. Hanb.; *H. thulense*
     auct., non Dahlst.

51   **H. dovrense** Fries

52   **H. australius** (Beeby) Pugsley
     Hieracium dovrense Fries var. *australius* Beeby

53   **H. difficile** Sell & C. West

54   **H. gratum** Sell & C. West
     Hieracium pulchelliforme (W.R. Linton) Pugsley, non Dahlst. ex
     Omang; *H. pulchellum* auct., non Lindeb.

55   **H. solum** Sell & C. West

56   **H. breve** Beeby

57   **H. zetlandicum** Beeby

sect. **Vulgata** F. Williams

58   **H. pollichiae** Schultz-Bip.
     Hieracium roffeyanum Pugsley

59   **H. caesionigrescens** Fries ex Stenstroem

60   **H. cravoniense** (F. Hanb.) Roffey
     Hieracium duriceps F. Hanb. var. *cravoniense* F. Hanb.

61   **H. triviale** Norrlin

62   **H. vulgatum** Fries
     Hieracium sejunctum (W.R. Linton) Roffey; *H. subravusculum*
     (W.R. Linton) Roffey

63   **H. rubiginosum** F. Hanb.
     Hieracium caesiopilosum Pugsley; *H. lintonii* Ley; *H. orarium*
     sensu Pugsley, pro parte, non Lindeb.

64 †H. subramosum Lönnr.

65 H. lepidulum Stenstroem

66 H. surrejanum F. Hanb.

67 H. subamplifolium (Zahn) Roffey
Hieracium vulgatum Fries subsp. *subamplifolium* Zahn

68 H. cheriense Jordan ex Boreau
Hieracium lachenalii C. Gmelin var. *pseudoporrigens* Pugsley; *H. porrigens* auct., non W.R. Linton; *H. tunbridgense* Pugsley

69 H. acuminatum Jordan
Hieracium chlorophyllum auct., non Jordan ex Boreau; *H. lachenalii* auct., non C. Gmelin; *H. strumosum* (Ley ex W.R. Linton) Ley

70 H. diaphanoides Lindeb.
Hieracium megapodium auct., non Dahlst.; *H. neopinnatifidum* auct., non Pugsley; *H. subglaucovirens* auct., non (Zahn) Roffey

71 H. subminutidens (Zahn) Pugsley
Hieracium caesium Fries var. *subminutidens* Zahn

72 H. diaphanum Fries
Hieracium anglorum (Ley) Pugsley; *H. barbareifolium* auct., non Lonnr. ex Dahlst.; *H. cacuminatum* auct., non (Ley) Ley; *H. daedalolepioides* (Zahn) Roffey; *H. diphanoides* auct., non Lindeb.; *H. irriguum* auct., non (Fries) Dahlst.; *H. ornatum* sensu Ley, non Dahlst.; *H. scanicum* sensu Ley, non Dahlst.; *H. scotophyllum* auct., non Vukot.; *H. scytophyllum* auct., non Omang

73 H. glanduliceps Sell & C. West

74 H. maculatum Smith

75 H. pulchrius (Ley) W.R. Linton
Hieracium sciaphilum Uechtr. var. *pulchrius* Ley

76 H. rectulum Ley

77 **H. submutabile** (Zahn) Pugsley
Hieracium vulgatum Fries var. *submutabile* Zahn
Hieracium mutabile (Ley) Ley, non F. Schultz; *H. reclinatum*
auct., non Almq. ex Dahlst.

78 **H. orcadense** W.R. Linton
Hieracium clivicola (F. Hanb.) Pugsley; *H. euprepes* F. Hanb.,
non Peter; *H. subalpestrifrons* Dahlst.; *H. subexpallescens*
Dahlst.; *H. orarium* sensu Pugsley, pro parte, non Lindeb.

79 **H. oxyodus** W.R. Linton

80 **H. maculoides** Sell & C. West

81 **H. fulvocaesium** Pugsley

82 **H. stenophyes** W.R. Linton

83 **H. caesiomurorum** Lindeb.

84 **H. rhomboides** (Stenstroem) Johansson
Hieracium gravastellum Dahlst. var. *rhomboides* Stenstroem

85 **H. dipteroides** Dahlst.

86 **H. radyrense** (Pugsley) Sell & C. West
Hieracium lachenalii C. Gmelin var. *radyrense* Pugsley
Hieracium paucifoliatum auct. non Jordan ex Boreau

87 **H. cuneifrons** (Ley ex W.R. Linton) Pugsley
Hieracium subulatidens auct., non Dahlst. var. *cuneifrons* Ley ex
W.R. Linton

88 **H. breadalbanense** F. Hanb.

89 **H. uisticola** Pugsley

90 **H. orithales** E.F. Linton
Hieracium lintonianum Druce

91 **H. oistophyllum** Pugsley
Hieracium philanthrax auct., non (Stenstroem) Johansson &
Samuelsson; *H. sagittatum* (Lindeb. ex Stenstroem) Dahlst.,
non Hoffsgg. & Link

92   **H. silvaticoides** Pugsley

93   **H. neocoracinum** Pugsley

94   **H. subhirtum** (F. Hanb.) Pugsley
Hieracium rivale F. Hanb. var. *subhirtum* F. Hanb.

95   **H. subtenue** (W.R. Linton) Roffey
Hieracium silvaticum Smith, non Gouan var. *subtenue* W.R.
Linton

96   **H. aggregatum** Backh.

97   **H. anguinum** (W.R. Linton) Roffey
Hieracium stenolepis Lindeb. var. *anguinum* W.R. Linton

98   **H. variifolium** Sell & C. West

99   **H. pauculidens** Sell & C. West

100 **H. mucronellum** Sell & C. West

101 **H. maculosum** Dahlst. ex Stenstroem

102 **H. auratiflorum** Pugsley

103 **H. crebridentiforme** Pugsley
Hieracium crebridens auct., non Dahlst.

104 **H. rivale** F. Hanb.
Hieracium morulum auct., non (Dahlst.) Roffey; *H. ciliatiflorum*
sensu Pugsley(1948), non Pugsley(1941)

105 **H. pachyphylloides** (Zahn) Roffey
Hieracium murorum L. subsp. *pachyphylloides* Zahn
Hieracium pachyphyllum (Purchas) F. Williams, non Brenner

106 **H. sanguineum** (Ley) W.R. Linton
Hieracium murorum L. var. *sanguineum* Ley

107 **H. pseudosarcophyllum** Pugsley
Hieracium sarcophyllum auct., non Stenstroem

108 **H. pseudostenstroemii** Pugsley
Hieracium stenstroemii auct., non (Dahlst.) Johansson

109   **H. cymbifolium** Purchas

110   **H. piligerum** (Pugsley) Sell & C. West
Hieracium variicolor Dahlst. ex Stenstroem var. *piligerum*
Pugsley
Hieracium variicolor sensu Pugsley, non Dahlst. ex Stenstroem

111   **H. pollinarioides** Pugsley

112   **H. pictorum** E.F. Linton
Hieracium crassiceps auct., non Dahlst.; *H. semicrassiceps*
Pugsley

113   ***H. gougetianum** Gren. & Godron
Hieracium murorum L. var. *maculosum* sensu Colgan

114   ***H. zygophorum** N. Hylander

115   ***H. scotostictum** N. Hylander
Hieracium praecox auct., non Schultz-Bip.

116   **H. duriceps** F. Hanb.
Hieracium killinense (Zahn) Roffey; *H. micracladium* (F.
Williams) Ley, non Dahlst.; *H. pulcherrimum* (F. Hanb.)
Roffey; *H. praetenerum* sensu Pugsley, pro parte, non Almq.
ex Dahlst.

117   **H. asteridiophyllum** Sell & C. West

118   **H. discophyllum** Sell & C. West

119   **H. subprasinifolium** Pugsley

120   **H. prolixum** Norrlin

121   **H. itunense** Pugsley

122   **H. pollinarium** F. Hanb.

123   **H. stenstroemii** (Dahlst.) Johansson
Hieracium serratifrons Almq. ex Dahlst. subsp. *stenstroemii*
Dahlst.
Hieracium crassiceps auct., non Dahlst.; *H. cuneifrons* (Ley ex
W.R. Linton) Pugsley var. *decipiens* Pugsley; *H. elatius* (Ley)
Druce, non Rehmann; *H. exotericum* Jordan ex Boreau var.

glevense Pugsley; *H. glevense* (Pugsley) Sell & C. West; *H. stenstroemii* (Dahlst.) Johansson var. *subcordatum* Pugsley; *H. subulatidens* auct., non Dahlst.; *H. torticeps* auct., non Ley

124 **H. candelabrae** W.R. Linton
Hieracium exotericum Jordan ex Boreau var. *candelabrae* (W.R. Linton) Pugsley

125 **H. uistense** (Pugsley) Sell & C. West
Hieracium clovense E.F. Linton var. *uistense* Pugsley

126 **H. pruinale** (Zahn) Sell & C. West
Hieracium murorum L. subsp. *pruinale* Zahn
Hieracium euprepes Peter var. *pruiniferum* W.R. Linton

127 **H. snowdoniense** Sell & C. West
Hieracium pulcherrimum sensu Pugsley et auct., non (F. Hanb.) Roffey

128 **H. camptopetalum** (F. Hanb.) Sell & C. West
Hieracium murorum L. var. *camptopetalum* F. Hanb.
Hieracium caliginosum sensu Pugsley, non (P. Hanb.) Roffey; *H. duriceps* F. Hanb. var. *camptopetalum* (F. Hanb.) Pugsley

129 **H. pellucidum** Laest.
Hieracium lucidulum (Ley) Roffey; *H. praetenerum* sensu Pugsley, pro parte, non Almq. ex Dahlst.

130 ***H. hjeltii** Norrlin ex T. Saelan, W. Nylander & T.S. Nylander

131 **H. integratum** Dahlst. ex Stenstroem
Hieracium silvaticum Smith, non Gouan subsp. *integratum* Dahlst. ex Stenstroem

132 ***H. oblongum** Jordan

133 **H. subcrassum** (Almq. ex Dahlst.) Johansson
Hieracium murorum L. subsp. *subcrassum* Almq. ex Dahlst.

134 ***H. patale** Norrlin

135 **H. cinderella** (Ley) Ley
Hieracium serratifrons Almq. ex Dahlst. var. *cinderella* Ley
Hieracium exotericum Jordan ex Boreau var. *cinderella* (Ley) Pugsley

136 **H. sublepistoides** (Zahn) Druce
Hieracium murorum L. subsp. *sublepistoides* Zahn
Hieracium exotericum Jordan ex Boreau var. *sublepistoides*
(Zahn) Pugsley

137 *****H. severiceps** Wiinst.

138 *****H. grandidens** Dahlst.
Hieracium exotericum Jordan ex Boreau forma *grandidens*
(Dahlst.) Pugsley

139 *****H. cardiophyllum** Jordan ex Sudre

140 **H. exotericum** Jordan ex Boreau

sect. **Oreadea** Zahn
Hieracium sect. *Suboreadea* Pugsley

141 **H. chloranthum** Pugsley
Hieracium pseudonosmoides auct., non W.R. Linton; *H.*
saxifragum Fries var. *pseudonosmoides* auct., non F. Hanb.

142 **H. orimeles** F. Hanb. ex W.R. Linton
Hieracium beebyanum Pugsley

143 **H. subrude** (Arv.-Touv.) Arv.-Touv.
Hieracium buglossoides Arv.-Touv. var. *subrude* Arv.-Touv.
Hieracium buglossoides auct., non Arv.-Touv.

144 **H. proximum** F. Hanb.
Hieracium erythraeum E.F. Linton ex Pugsley; *H. hanburyanum*
Zahn

145 **H. scoticum** F. Hanb.
Hieracium caledonicum F. Hanb. var. *pseudozetlandicum* Pugsley

146 **H. angustisquamum** (Pugsley) Pugsley
Hieracium holophyllum W.R. Linton var. *angustisquamum*
Pugsley

147 **H. caledonicum** F. Hanb.
Hieracium boswellii E.F. Linton; *H. farrense* F. Hanb.; *H.*
rubicundiforme (Zahn) Roffey; *H. rubicundum* F. Hanb.

148 **H. holophyllum** W.R. Linton

149 **H. leyanum** (Zahn) Roffey
Hieracium sagittatum Hoffsgg. & Link subsp. *leyanum* Zahn

150 **H. angustatiforme** Sell & C. West

151 **H. cacuminum** (Ley) Ley
Hieracium diaphanum Fries var. *cacuminum* Ley
Hieracium nitidum Backh. var. *siluriense* F. Hanb.

152 **H. angustatum** (Lindeb.) Lindeb.
Hieracium caesium Fries var. *angustatum* Lindeb.

153 **H. argenteum** Fries
Hieracium orimeles F. Hanb. ex W.R. Linton var. *argentatum*
(Fries) Pugsley; *H. pseudomicrodon* Dahlst.; *H. stenotum*
auct., non Dahlst.

154 **H. vagense** (F. Hanb.) Ley
Hieracium britannicum F. Hanb. var. *vagense* F. Hanb.

155 **H. cambricum** (Baker) F. Hanb.
Hieracium caesium Fries var. *cambricum* Baker

156 **H. sommerfeltii** Lindeb.
Hieracium basicrinum (Zahn) Roffey

157 **H. carneddorum** Pugsley
Hieracium sommerfeltii Lindeb. var. *splendens* F. Hanb.

158 **H. pseudoleyi** (Zahn) Roffey
Hieracium saxifragum Fries subsp. *pseudoleyi* Zahn
Hieracium decolorans auct., non Fries; *H. smithii* (Baker) Druce

159 **H. decolor** (W.R. Linton) Ley
Hieracium caesium Fries var. *decolor* W.R. Linton
Hieracium cordigerum Norrlin var. *asymmetricum* (Ley) Roffey;
H. expallidiforme auct., non (Dahlst.) Roffey; *H. subcyaneum*
(W.R. Linton) Pugsley; *H. tricolorans* (Zahn) Pugsley

160 **H. cyathis** (Ley) W.R. Linton
Hieracium hypochaeroides Gibson var. *cyathis* Ley

161 **H. leyi** F. Hanb.

162 **H. jovimontis** (Zahn) Roffey
Hieracium pallidum Biv. subsp. *jovimontis* Zahn

163 **H. nitidum** Backh.
Hieracium carenorum F. Hanb.

164 **H. cillense** Pugsley
Hieracium griseum auct., non Forman; *H. hypochaeroides* Gibson
var. *griseum* Ley ex W.R. Linton

165 **H. lasiophyllum** Koch

166 **H. brigantum** (F. Hanb.) Roffey
Hieracium lima F. Hanb. var. *brigantum* F. Hanb.

167 **H. schmidtii** Tausch
Hieracium lima F. Hanb.

168 **H. hypochaeroides** Gibson

169 **H. repandulare** Druce
Hieracium pseudorepandum Pugsley; *H. repandum* Ley, non
Schrank

170 **H. riddelsdellii** Pugsley
Hieracium ciliatum Willd. var. *venosum* Ley; *H. venosum* auct.,
non L.

171 **H. ebudicum** Pugsley

172 **H. eucallum** Sell & C. West
Hieracium praetermissum Sell & C. West, non Juksip

173 **H. saxorum** (F. Hanb.) Sell & C. West
Hieracium hypochaeroides Gibson var. *saxorum* F. Hanb.
Hieracium sommerfeltii Lindeb. var. *subtruncatum* Pugsley

174 **H. subplanifolium** Pugsley
Hieracium lasiophyllum Koch var. *planifolium* F. Hanb.; *H.*
planifolium auct., non Brenner

175 **H. basalticola** Pugsley
Hieracium britannicum auct., non F. Hanb.

176 **H. dicella** Sell & C. West
Hieracium britannicum F. Hanb. var. *glaucinum* Pugsley; *H. furcilliferum* Dahlst., non Omang

177 **H. sarcophylloides** Dahlst.
Hieracium dasypodum Dahlst.; *H. pycnodon* sensu Pugsley, non Dahlst.

178 **H. fratrum** Pugsley
Hieracium sordidum W.R. Linton ex E.F. Linton, non Gillies

179 **H. britannicum** F. Hanb.

180 **H. britanniciforme** Pugsley

181 **H. naviense** J.N. Mills

182 **H. subbritannicum** (Ley) Sell & C. West
Hieracium stenolepis Lindeb. var. *subbritannicum* Ley
Hieracium britannicum F. Hanb. var. *subbritannicum* (Ley) Pugsley

183 **H. stenolepiforme** (Pugsley) Sell & C. West
Hieracium britannicum F. Hanb. var. *stenolepiforme* Pugsley
Hieracium caesium auct., non Fries; *H. stenolepis* auct., non Lindeb.

184 **H. stenopholidium** (Dahlst.) Omang
Hieracium integrilaterum Dahlst. ex Johansson var. *stenopholidium* Dahlst.

185 **H. eustomon** (E.F. Linton) Roffey
Hieracium schmidtii Tausch var. *eustomen* E.F. Linton
Hieracium devoniense (F. Hanb.) Roffey

sect. **Amplexicaulia** Zahn

186 *H. speluncarum** Arv.-Touv.

187 *H. pulmonarioides** Villars

188 *H. amplexicaule** L.

sect. **Cerinthoidea** Koch

189 **H. scarpicum** Pugsley

190 **H. magniceps** Sell & C. West

191 **H. iricum** Fries

192 **H. anglicum** Fries
Hieracium cerinthoides auct., non L.; *H. iricum* auct., non Fries;
    H. patens Dahlst.; *H. subimpressum* Dahlst.

193 **H. hartii** (F. Hanb.) Sell & C. West
Hieracium cerinthiforme F. Hanb. var. *hartii* F. Hanb.

194 **H. langwellense** F. Hanb.

195 **H. ampliatum** (W.R. Linton) Ley
Hieracium sarcophyllum Stenstroem var. *ampliatum* W.R. Linton

196 **H. hebridense** Pugsley

197 **H. flocculosum** Backh.

198 **H. shoolbredii** E. Marshall
Hieracium anglicum Fries var. *longibracteatum* F. Hanb.

sect. **Subalpina** Pugsley

199 **H. pseudanglicoides** J. Raven, Sell & C. West

200 **H. pseudanglicum** Pugsley

201 **H. cumbriense** F. Hanb.

202 **H. petrocharis** (E.F. Linton) W.R. Linton
Hieracium caesium Fries var. *petrocharis* E.F. Linton

203 **H. dasythrix** (E.F. Linton) Pugsley
Hieracium pictorum E.F. Linton var. *dasythrix* E.F. Linton

204 **H. laetificum** Sell & C. West
Hieracium nigrisquamum Sell & C. West, non N. Hylander

205 **H. gracilifolium** (F. Hanb.) Pugsley
Hieracium nigrescens Willd. var. *gracilifolium* F. Hanb.

206 **H. chrysolorum** Sell & C. West

207 **H. clovense** E.F. Linton
Hieracium leucograptum auct., non Dahlst.

208 **H. melanochloricephalum** Pugsley

209 **H. vennicontium** Pugsley
Hieracium duplicatum auct., non Almq. ex Dahlst.; *H. euprepes*
Peter var. *glabratum* E.F. Linton; *H. glabratum* auct., non
Hoppe ex Willd.

210 **H. isabellae** E. Marshall

211 **H. callistophyllum** F. Hanb.

212 **H. hyparcticoides** Pugsley

213 **H. glandulidens** Sell & C. West

214 **H. longilobum** (Dahlst. ex Zahn) Roffey
Hieracium murorum L. subsp. *longilobum* Dahlst. ex Zahn

215 **H. centripetale** F. Hanb.

216 **H. anfractiforme** E. Marshall
Hieracium neomarshallianum (Zahn) Roffey; *H. subanfractum* E.
Marshall

217 **H. cuspidens** Sell & C. West
Hieracium dissimile (Lindeb.) Lindeb. ex Elfstr. var. *majus*
Pugsley

218 **H. dissimile** (Lindeb.) Lindeb. ex Elfstr.
Hieracium murorum L. var. *dissimile* Lindeb.

219 **H. hastiforme** Sell & C. West

220 **H. diversidens** Sell & C. West

221 **H. westii** Sell
Hieracium submurorum sensu Sell & C. West, non Lindeb.

222   **H. marshallii** E.F. Linton

223   **H. molybdochroum** Dahlst.

224   **H. senescens** Backh.

225   **H. sinuans** F. Hanb.
      Hieracium pulmonarium Smith

226   **H. cremnanthes** (F. Hanb.) Pugsley
      Hieracium marshallii E.F. Linton var. *cremnanthes* F. Hanb.

227   **H. eustales** E.F. Linton

228   **H. insulare** (F. Hanb.) F. Hanb.
      Hieracium caesium Fries var. *insulare* F. Hanb.

229   **H. lingulatum** Backh. ex Hook. & Arn.

sect. **Alpina** F. Williams

230   **H. hanburyi** Pugsley
      Hieracium atraticeps (Pugsley) Sell & C. West; *H. chrysanthum*
      Backh. ex Hook. & Arn., non Ledeb.; *H. hanburyi* Pugsley
      var. *atraticeps* Pugsley

231   **H. pseudocurvatum** (Zahn) Pugsley
      Hieracium nigrescens Willd. subsp. *pseudocurvatum* Zahn
      Hieracium curvatum sensu F. Hanb. et auct., non Elfstr.

232   **H. calenduliflorum** Backh.

233   **H. macrocarpum** Pugsley

234   **H. graniticola** W.R. Linton

235   **H. larigense** (Pugsley) Sell & C. West
      Hieracium globosiflorum Pugsley var. *larigense* Pugsley

236   **H. globosiflorum** Pugsley
      Hieracium globosum Backh., non Desf.

237   **H. grovesii** Pugsley

238   **H. backhousei** F. Hanb.

239   **H. memorabile** Sell & C. West
      Hieracium backhousei auct., non F. Hanb.

240   **H. marginatum** Sell & C. West
      Hieracium globosiflorum Pugsley var. *lancifolium* Pugsley

241   **H. eximium** Backh.

242   **H. notabile** Sell & C. West

243   **H. subgracilentipes** (Zahn) Roffey
      Hieracium nigrescens Willd. subsp. *subgracilentipes* Zahn
      Hieracium chrysanthum Ledeb. var. *gracilentiforme* F. Hanb.

244   **H. tenuifrons** Sell & C. West
      Hieracium alpinum L. var. *gracilentum* auct., non F. Williams; *H. gracilentum* Backh.

245   **H. pseudopetiolatum** (Zahn) Roffey
      Hieracium nigrescens Willd. subsp. *pseudopetiolatum* Zahn
      Hieracium petiolatum auct., non F. Hanb.

246   **H. insigne** Backh.

247   **H. alpinum** L.

248   **H. holosericeum** Backh.

29   ***GAZANIA** Gaertner

  1   ***G. rigens** (L.) Gaertner
      Othonna rigens L.
      Gazania splendens hort. ex E.G. & A. Henderson; *G. uniflora* (L.f.) Sims

30   **FILAGO** L.
Logfia Cass.

  1   **F. vulgaris** Lam.
      Filago germanica L., non Hudson; *Gnaphalium germanicum* L., nom. inval.

2   **F. lutescens** Jordan
      Filago apiculata G.E. Smith ex Bab.; *F. germanica* auct., non L.
      nec Hudson

3   **F. pyramidata** L.
      Filago spathulata auct., non C. Presl

4   **F. minima** (Smith) Pers.
      Gnaphalium minimum Smith
      Logfia minima (Smith) Dumort.

5   *__F. gallica__ L.
      Logfia gallica (L.) Cosson & Germ.

31   **ANTENNARIA** Gaertner

1   **A. dioica** (L.) Gaertner
      Gnaphalium dioicum L.
      Antennaria hibernica Braun-Blanquet

32   *__ANAPHALIS__ DC.

1   *__A. margaritacea__ (L.) Benth.
      Gnaphalium margaritaceum L.

33   **GNAPHALIUM** L.
      Filaginella Opiz; *Omalotheca* Cass.

1   **G. norvegicum** Gunnerus
      Omalotheca norvegica (Gunnerus) Schultz-Bip. & F. Schultz

2   **G. sylvaticum** L.
      Omalotheca sylvatica (L.) Schultz-Bip. & F. Schultz

3   **G. supinum** L.
      Omalotheca supina (L.) DC.

4   *__G. purpureum__ L.
      Gnaphalium pensylvanicum Willd., nom. illegit.

5   **G. uliginosum** L.
      Filaginella uliginosa (L.) Opiz

6 G. luteoalbum L.

7 *G. undulatum L.
   Gnaphalium polycephalum auct., non Michaux

34 *HELICHRYSUM Miller

1 *H. bellidioides (G. Forster) Willd.
   Xeranthemum bellidioides G. Forster

35 INULA L.

1 *I. helenium L.

2 I. salicina L.

3 I. conyzae (Griess.) Meikle
   Aster conyzae Griess.
   Inula conyza DC.

4 I. crithmoides L.

36 *DITTRICHIA Greuter

1 *D. viscosa (L.) Greuter
   Erigeron viscosus L.
   Inula viscosa (L.) Aiton

37 PULICARIA Gaertner

1 P. dysenterica (L.) Bernh.
   Inula dysenterica L.

2 P. vulgaris Gaertner

38 *TELEKIA Baumg.

1 *T. speciosa (Schreber) Baumg.
   Buphthalmum speciosum Schreber

39 *GRINDELIA Willd.

1 *G. stricta DC.
Grindelia rubricaulis auct., non DC.

40 SOLIDAGO L.
Euthamia Nutt.

1 S. virgaurea L.
Solidago angustifolia Miller

1 x **3 S. virgaurea** x **S. canadensis** = **S. x niederederi** Khek

2 *S. rugosa Miller
Solidago altissima Aiton, non L.

3 *S. canadensis L.
Solidago altissima L.

4 *S. gigantea Aiton

a *subsp. **serotina** (Kuntze) McNeill
Aster latissimifolius Kuntze var. *serotinus* Kuntze;
Solidago serotina Aiton, non Retz.

5 *S. graminifolia (L.) Salisb.
Chrysocoma graminifolia L.
Euthamia graminifolia (L.) Elliott; *Solidago lanceolata* L.

41 ASTER L.
Crinitaria Cass.

1 *A. schreberi Nees
Aster macrophyllus auct., non L.

2 *A. novae-angliae L.

3 *A. laevis L.

3 x **4 *A. laevis** x **A. novi-belgii** = **A. x versicolor** Willd.
Aster novi-belgii L. subsp. *laevigatus* auct., non (Lam.) Thell.; *A. x laevigatus* auct., non Lam.

4 *A. novi-belgii L.
Aster brumalis Nees; A. floribundus auct., ? an Willd.; A.
longifolius auct., non Lam.; A. novi-belgii L. subsp.
floribundus (Willd.) Thell.

4 x 5 *A. novi-belgii x A. lanceolatus = A. x salignus Willd.
Aster x lanceolatus auct., non Willd.; A. x longifolius sensu
Clapham et auct., non Lam.

5 *A. lanceolatus Willd.
Aster lamarckianus auct., non Nees; A. paniculatus auct., non
Lam.; A. tradescantii auct., non L.

6 A. tripolium L.

7 A. linosyris (L.) Bernh.
Chrysocoma linosyris L.
Crinitaria linosyris (L.) Less.

42 *CHRYSOCOMA L.

1 *C. coma-aurea L.

43 ERIGERON L.

1 *E. glaucus Ker Gawler

2 *E. philadelphicus L.

3 E. borealis (Vierh.) Simmons
Trimorpha borealis Vierh.
Erigeron alpinus sensu Dickson et auct., non L.; Trimorpha
alpina Gray

4 *E. karvinskianus DC.
Erigeron mucronatus DC.

5 *E. annuus (L.) Pers.
Aster annuus L.
Erigeron annuus (L.) Pers. subsp. strigosus (Mühlenb. ex Willd.)
Wagenitz; E. strigosus Mühlenb. ex Willd.

6 E. acer L.

43 x 44 **ERIGERON** x **CONYZA** = **X CONYZIGERON** Rauschert
X Conygeron Holub

    6 x 1 **E. acer** x **C. canadensis** = **X C. huelsenii** (Vatke) Rauschert
    Erigeron x huelsenii Vatke
    X Conygeron huelsenii (Vatke) Holub

44 ***CONYZA** Less.

    1 ***C. canadensis** (L.) Cronq.
    Erigeron canadensis L.

    2 ***C. sumatrensis** (Retz.) E. Walker
    Erigeron sumatrensis Retz.
    Conyza albida Willd. ex Sprengel; *C. ambigua* DC.; *C. bonariensis*
    auct., non (L.) Cronq.; *C. floribunda* Kunth; *Erigeron*
    bonariensis auct., non L.

45 ***OLEARIA** Moench

    1 ***O. paniculata** (Forster & G. Forster) Druce
    Shawia paniculata Forster & G. Forster

    2 ***O. macrodonta** Baker
    Olearia dentata (J.D. Hook.) J.D. Hook., non Moench

    3 ***O. traversii** (F. Muell.) J.D. Hook.
    Eurybia traversii F. Muell.

avi x mos ***O. avicenniifolia** (Raoul) J.D. Hook. x **O. moschata** J.D. Hook.
    = **O. x haastii** J.D. Hook.

46 ***BACCHARIS** L.

    1 ***B. halimifolia** L.

47 **BELLIS** L.

    1 **B. perennis** L.

48 TANACETUM L.

1 **T. parthenium** (L.) Schultz-Bip.
Matricaria parthenium L.
Chrysanthemum parthenium (L.) Bernh.

2 *****T. macrophyllum** (Waldst. & Kit.) Schultz-Bip.
Chrysanthemum macrophyllum Waldst. & Kit.

3 **T. vulgare** L.
Chrysanthemum vulgare (L.) Bernh., non (Lam.) Gaterau

49 SERIPHIDIUM (Besser ex Hook.) Fourr.
Artemisia sect. *Seriphidium* Besser ex Hook.

1 **S. maritimum** (L.) Polj.
Artemisia maritima L.
Artemisia gallica auct., non Willd.

50 ARTEMISIA L.

1 **A. vulgaris** L.

1 x 2 **A. vulgaris** x **A. verlotiorum**

2 *****A. verlotiorum** Lamotte

3 **A. absinthium** L.

4 *****A. stelleriana** Besser

5 **A. norvegica** Fries
Artemisia norvegica Fries subsp. *scotica* (Hultén) Á. Löve & D.
Löve

6 *****A. abrotanum** L.

7 *****A. biennis** Willd.

8 **A. campestris** L.

51 *SANTOLINA L.

    1 *S. chamaecyparissus L.

52 OTANTHUS Hoffsgg. & Link

    1 O. maritimus (L.) Hoffsgg. & Link
    Filago maritima L.

53 ACHILLEA L.

    1 A. ptarmica L.

    2 *A. ligustica All.

    3 A. millefolium L.

    4 *A. distans Waldst. & Kit. ex Willd.

        a *subsp. **tanacetifolia** Janchen
        Achillea tanacetifolia All., non Miller

54 CHAMAEMELUM Miller

    1 C. nobile (L.) All.
    Anthemis nobilis L.

55 ANTHEMIS L.

    1 *A. punctata Vahl

        a *subsp. **cupaniana** (Tod. ex Nyman) Ros. Fernandes
        Anthemis cupaniana Tod. ex Nyman

    2 A. arvensis L.

    3 A. cotula L.

    4 *A. tinctoria L.

5 x 60 **ANTHEMIS** x **TRIPLEUROSPERMUM** = **X TRIPLEUROTHEMIS**
Stace

3 x 2 **A. cotula** x **T. inodorum** = **X T. maleolens** (P. Fourn.) Stace
X *Anthemimatricaria maleolens* P. Fourn.
X *Anthemimatricaria celakovskyi* Geisenh. ex Domin, nom. inval.

56 **CHRYSANTHEMUM** L.

1 **C. segetum** L.

57 ***LEUCANTHEMELLA** Tzvelev

1 ***L. serotina** (L.) Tzvelev
Chrysanthemum serotinum L.
Chrysanthemum uliginosum (Waldst. & Kit. ex Willd.) Pers.

58 **LEUCANTHEMUM** Miller

1 **L. vulgare** Lam.
Chrysanthemum leucanthemum L.

lac x max ***L. lacustre** (Brot.) Samp. x **L. maximum** (Ramond) DC. = **L. x**
superbum (Bergmans ex J. Ingram) D.H. Kent
Chrysanthemum x superbum Bergmans ex J. Ingram
Chrysanthemum x maximum hort., non Ramond; *Leucanthemum x maximum* hort., non (Ramond) DC.

59 **MATRICARIA** L.
Chamomilla Gray

1 **M. recutita** L.
Chamomilla recutita (L.) Rauschert; *Matricaria chamomilla* L. var. *recutita* (L.) Grierson; *M. chamomilla* L., pro parte

2 ***M. discoidea** DC.
Chamomilla suaveolens (Pursh) Rydb.; *Matricaria matricarioides* (Less.) Porter, pro parte, nom. illegit.

60 TRIPLEUROSPERMUM Schultz-Bip.
Matricaria auct., non L.

   1 T. maritimum (L.) Koch
    Matricaria maritima L.
    Tripleurospermum maritimum (L.) Koch var. *salinum* (Wallr.)
    Kay

  1 x 2 T. maritimum x **T. inodorum**

   2 T. inodorum (L.) Schultz-Bip.
    Matricaria inodora L.
    Matricaria maritima L. subsp. *inodora* (L.) Soó; *Tripleurospermum*
     maritimum (L.) Koch subsp. *inodorum* (L.) N. Hylander ex
     Vaar.; *M. perforata* Mérat

61 *COTULA L.
Leptinella Cass.

   1 *C. coronopifolia L.

   2 *C. australis (Sieber ex Sprengel) J.D. Hook.
    Anacyclus australis Sieber ex Sprengel

   3 *C. dioica (J.D. Hook.) J.D. Hook.
    Leptinella dioica J.D. Hook.

   4 *C. squalida (J.D. Hook.) J.D. Hook.
    Leptinella squalida J.D. Hook.

62 SENECIO L.

   1 *S. cineraria DC.
    Senecio bicolor (Willd.) Tod.; *S. bicolor* (Willd.) Tod. subsp.
    cineraria (DC.) Chater

  1 x 10 S. cineraria x **S. jacobaea** = **S. x albescens** Burb. & Colgan

  1 x 12 S. cineraria x **S. erucifolius** = **S. x thuretii** Briq. & Cavill.
    Senecio x patersonianus R.M. Burton

   2 *S. grandiflorus P. Bergius

3 *S. inaequidens DC.
   Senecio lautus auct., non Sol. ex Willd.

4 *S. fluviatilis Wallr.
   Senecio sarracenicus sensu L.(1754) et auct., non L.(1753)

5 *S. ovatus (P. Gaertner, Meyer & Scherb.) Willd.
   Jacobaea ovata P. Gaertner, Meyer & Scherb.
   Senecio fuchsii C. Gmelin

6 *S. doria L.

7 S. paludosus L.

8 *S. doronicum (L.) L.
   Solidago doronicum L.

9 *S. smithii DC.

10 S. jacobaea L.
   Senecio jacobaea L. subsp. *dunensis* (Dumort.) Kadereit & Sell

10 x 11 S. jacobaea x S. aquaticus = S. x ostenfeldii Druce

11 S. aquaticus Hill
   Senecio erraticus sensu Drabble et auct., non Bertol.

12 S. erucifolius L.

13 *S. squalidus L.
   Senecio rupestris Waldst. & Kit.

13 x 15 S. squalidus x S. vulgaris = S. x baxteri Druce

13 x 18 S. squalidus x S. viscosus = S. x subnebrodensis Simonkai
   Senecio x londinensis Lousley

14 S. cambrensis Rosser

15 S. vulgaris L.
   Senecio vulgaris L. subsp. *denticulatus* (Mueller) Sell

15 x 16 S. vulgaris x S. vernalis = S. x helwingii Beger ex Hegi.

16 *****S. vernalis** Waldst. & Kit.
Senecio leucanthemifolius Poiret var. *vernalis* (Waldst. & Kit.)
J.C.M. Alexander

17 **S. sylvaticus** L.

17 x 18 **S. sylvaticus** x **S. viscosus** = **S. x viscidulus** Scheele

18 **S. viscosus** L.

63 *****PERICALLIS** D. Don

1 *****P. hybrida** R. Nordenstam
Cineraria hybrida Willd., non Bernh.; *Senecio cruentus* auct., non
Roth nec (L'Hér.) DC.; *S. hybridus* N. Hylander, nom. inval.

64 **TEPHROSERIS** (Reichb.) Reichb.
Cineraria taxon *Tephroseris* Reichb.

1 **T. integrifolia** (L.) Holub
Othonna integrifolia L.
Senecio integrifolius (L.) Clairv.

    a subsp. **integrifolia**
    Senecio campestris (Retz.) DC.

    b subsp. **maritima** (Syme) R. Nordenstam
    Senecio campestris (Retz.) DC. var. *maritimus* Syme
    Senecio integrifolius (L.) Clairv. subsp. *maritimus* (Syme)
      Chater; *S. integrifolius* (L.) Clairv. var. *maritimus*
      (Syme) Clapham, nom. inval.; *S. spathulifolius* auct.,
      non Griess.

2 †**T. palustris** (L.) Fourr.
Othonna palustris L.
Senecio palustris (L.) Hook., non Vell.

    a †subsp. **congestus** (R. Br.) Holub
    Cineraria congesta R. Br.
    Senecio congestus (R. Br.) DC.; *S. congestus* (R. Br.) DC.
      subsp. *palustris* (L.) Rauschert, nom. inval.; *S.*
      tubicaulis Mansf.

65 *DELAIREA Lemaire

    1 *D. odorata Lemaire
      Senecio mikanioides Otto ex Walp.

66 *BRACHYGLOTTIS Forster & G. Forster

    1 *B. monroi (J.D. Hook.) R. Nordenstam
      Senecio monroi J.D. Hook.

    2 *B. repanda Forster & G. Forster

com x lax ***B. compacta** (T. Kirk) R. Nordenstam x **B. laxifolia** (J. Buch.)
      R. Nordenstam = **B. 'Sunshine'** C. Jeffrey
      Brachyglottis x compacta hort., non (T. Kirk) R. Nordenstam; *B.*
      x greyii hort., non (J.D. Hook.) R. Nordenstam; *Senecio x*
      compactus hort., non T. Kirk; *S. x greyii* hort., non J.D. Hook.

67 *SINACALIA H. Robinson & Brettell

    1 *S. tangutica (Maxim.) R. Nordenstam
      Senecio tanguticus Maxim.

68 *LIGULARIA Cass.

    1 *L. dentata (A. Gray) H. Hara
      Erythrochaete dentata A. Gray
      Ligularia clivorum Maxim.

    2 *L. przewalskii (Maxim.) Diels
      Senecio przewalskii Maxim.

69 *DORONICUM L.

    1 *D. pardalianches L.

1 x 2 ***D. pardalianches** x **D. plantagineum** = **D. x willdenowii**
      Rouy

1 x 2 x 3 *D. pardalianches x **D. plantagineum** x **D. columnae = D. x excelsum** (N.E. Br.) Stace
Doronicum plantagineum L. var. *excelsum* N.E. Br.
Doronicum x draytonense hort.; *D. x hybridum* hort.

2 *D. plantagineum L.

3 *D. columnae Ten.
Doronicum cordatum Schultz-Bip., non Lam.

70 TUSSILAGO L.

1 T. farfara L.

71 PETASITES Miller

1 P. hybridus (L.) P. Gaertner, Meyer & Scherb.
Tussilago hybrida L.

2 *P. japonicus (Siebold & Zucc.) Maxim.
Nardosmia japonica Siebold & Zucc.
Petasites japonicus (Siebold & Zucc.) Maxim. subsp. *giganteus* Kitam.

3 *P. albus (L.) Gaertner
Tussilago alba L.

4 *P. fragrans (Villars) C. Presl
Tussilago fragans Villars
Petasites ? pyrenaicus (L.) G. Lopez

72 *HOMOGYNE Cass.

1 *H. alpina (L.) Cass.
Tussilago alpina L.

73 *CALENDULA L.

1 *C. officinalis L.

2 *C. arvensis L.

74 *AMBROSIA L.

1 *A. artemisiifolia L.
Ambrosia elatior L.

2 *A. psilostachya DC.
Ambrosia coronopifolia Torrey & A. Gray

75 *IVA L.

1 *I. xanthifolia Nutt.

76 *XANTHIUM L.

1 *X. strumarium L.

2 *X. spinosum L.

3 *X. ambrosioides Hook. & Arn.

77 *SIGESBECKIA L.

1 *S. serrata DC.
Sigesbeckia cordifolia auct., non Kunth; *S. jorullensis* auct., non
Kunth; *S. orientalis* auct., non L.

78 *RUDBECKIA L.

1 *R. hirta L.
Rudbeckia serotina Nutt., non Sweet

2 *R. laciniata L.

79 *HELIANTHUS L.

1 *H. annuus L.

1 x dec *H. annuus x H. decapetalus L. = H. x multiflorus L.

2 *H. tuberosus L.

2 x rig *H. tuberosus x H. rigidus (Cass.) Desf. = H. x laetiflorus Pers.
Helianthus x scaberrimus Elliott

80 *GALINSOGA Ruíz Lopez & Pavón

    1 *G. parviflora Cav.

    2 *G. quadriradiata Ruíz Lopez & Pavón
      Galinsoga ciliata (Raf.) S.F. Blake; *G. parviflora* auct., non Cav.

81 BIDENS L.

    1 B. cernua L.

    2 B. tripartita L.

    3 *B. connata Mühlenb. ex Willd.

    4 *B. frondosa L.

82 *COREOPSIS L.

    1 *C. grandiflora Hogg ex Sweet

83 *COSMOS Cav.

    1 *C. bipinnatus Cav.

84 *GAILLARDIA Foug.

ari x pul *G. aristata Pursh x G. pulchella Foug. = G. x grandiflora hort.
    ex Van Houtte

85 *HELENIUM L.

    1 *H. autumnale L.

86 **EUPATORIUM** L.

1   **E. cannabinum** L.

LILIIDAE

136 BUTOMACEAE

1 **BUTOMUS** L.

1   **B. umbellatus** L.

137 ALISMATACEAE

1 **SAGITTARIA** L.

1   **S. sagittifolia** L.

2   ***S. latifolia** Willd.

3   ***S. rigida** Pursh
     Sagittaria heterophylla Pursh, non Schreber

4   ***S. subulata** (L.) Buchenau
     Alisma subulata L.
     Sagittaria pusilla Nutt.

2 **BALDELLIA** Parl.

1   **B. ranunculoides** (L.) Parl.
     Alisma ranunculoides L.

3 **LURONIUM** Raf.

1   **L. natans** (L.) Raf.
     Alisma natans L.

4 ALISMA L.

1 A. plantago-aquatica L.

1 x 2 A. plantago-aquatica x A. lanceolatum = A. x rhicnocarpum
Schotsman

2 A. lanceolatum With.

3 A. gramineum Lej.
Alisma gramineum Lej. subsp. *wahlenbergii* O. Holmb.; *A.
wahlenbergii* (O. Holmb.) Juz.

5 DAMASONIUM Miller

1 D. alisma Miller
Alisma damasonium L.

138 HYDROCHARITACEAE

1 HYDROCHARIS L.

1 H. morsus-ranae L.

2 STRATIOTES L.

1 S. aloides L.

3 *EGERIA Planchon

1 *E. densa Planchon
Elodea densa (Planchon) Caspary

4 *ELODEA Michaux

1 *E. canadensis Michaux
Anacharis alsinastrum Bab.; *A. canadensis* (Michaux) Planchon

2 *E. nuttallii** (Planchon) H. St. John
Anacharis nuttallii Planchon
Hydrilla lithuanica Dandy, pro parte

3 *E. callitrichoides** (Rich.) Caspary
Anacharis callitrichoides Rich.
Elodea ernstiae H. St. John

5 *HYDRILLA** Rich.

1 *H. verticillata** (L.f.) Royle
Serpicula verticillata L.f.
Elodea nuttallii auct., non (Planchon) H. St. John; *Hydrilla lithuanica* Dandy, pro parte

6 *LAGAROSIPHON** Harvey

1 *L. major** (Ridley) Moss
Lagarosiphon muscoides Harvey var. *major* Ridley
Elodea crispa hort.

7 *VALLISNERIA** L.

1 *V. spiralis** L.

139 *APONOGETONACEAE

1 *APONOGETON** L.f.

1 *A. distachyos** L.f.

140 SCHEUCHZERIACEAE

1 SCHEUCHZERIA L.

1 S. palustris L.

141 JUNCAGINACEAE

1   **TRIGLOCHIN** L.

    1   **T. palustre** L.

    2   **T. maritimum** L.

142 POTAMOGETONACEAE

1   **POTAMOGETON** L.

    1   **P. natans** L.

  1 x 2   **P. natans** x **P. polygonifolius** = **P. x gessnacensis** G. Fischer

  1 x 5   **P. natans** x **P. lucens** = **P. x fluitans** Roth

  1 x 6   **P. natans** x **P. gramineus** = **P. x sparganiifolius** Laest. ex Fries

 1 x 15   **P. natans** x **P. berchtoldii** = **P. x variifolius** Thore

    2   **P. polygonifolius** Pourret

  2 x 6   **P. polygonifolius** x **P. gramineus** = **P. x lanceolatifolius** (Tisel.) Preston
Potamogeton gramineus L. forma *lanceolatifolius* Tisel.
Potamogeton x seemenii Asch. & Graebner

    3   **P. coloratus** Hornem.

  3 x 6   **P. coloratus** x **P. gramineus** = **P. x billupsii** Fryer

 3 x 15   **P. coloratus** x **P. berchtoldii** = **P. x lanceolatus** Smith

    4   **P. nodosus** Poiret

    5   **P. lucens** L.

  5 x 6   **P. lucens** x **P. gramineus** = **P. x zizii** Koch ex Roth

  5 x 7   **P. lucens** x **P. alpinus** = **P. x nerviger** Wolfg.

5 x 9   P. lucens x P. perfoliatus = P. x salicifolius Wolfg.

5 x 19   P. lucens x P. crispus = P. x cadburyae Dandy & G. Taylor

6   P. gramineus L.

6 x 7   P. gramineus x P. alpinus = P. x nericius Hagstr.

6 x 9   P. gramineus x P. perfoliatus = P. x nitens G. Weber

7   P. alpinus Balbis

7 x 8   P. alpinus x P. praelongus = P. x griffithii A. Bennett

7 x 9   P. alpinus x P. perfoliatus = P. x prussicus Hagstr.

7 x 19   P. alpinus x P. crispus = P. x olivaceus Baagøe ex G. Fischer
Potamogeton x venustus Baagøe ex A. Bennett

8   P. praelongus Wulfen
Potamogeton salicifolius auct., non Wolfg.

8 x 9   P. praelongus x P. perfoliatus = P. x cognatus Asch. &
Graebner

8 x 19   P. praelongus x P. crispus = P. x undulatus Wolfg.

9   P. perfoliatus L.

9 x 19   P. perfoliatus x P. crispus = P. x cooperi (Fryer) Fryer
Potamogeton x undulatus Wolfg. var. *cooperi* Fryer

10   P. epihydrus Raf.
Potamogeton pensylvanicus Willd. ex Cham. & Schltr.

11   P. friesii Rupr.

11 x 18   P. friesii x P. acutifolius = P. x pseudofriesii Dandy & G.
Taylor

11 x 19   P. friesii x P. crispus = P. x lintonii Fryer

12   P. rutilus Wolfg.

13   **P. pusillus** L.
Potamogeton friesii auct., non Rupr.; *P. panormitanus* Biv.; *P. trichoides* auct., non Cham. & Schltr.

13 x 16   **P. pusillus** x **P. trichoides** = **P. x grovesii** Dandy & G. Taylor
Potamogeton x trinervius sensu Dandy, non G. Fischer

14   **P. obtusifolius** Mert. & Koch

15   **P. berchtoldii** Fieber
Potamogeton friesii auct., non Rupr.; *P. pusillus* auct., non L.; *P. trinervius* auct., non G. Fischer

15 x 18   **P. berchtoldii** x **P. acutifolius** = **P. x sudermannicus** Hagstr.

16   **P. trichoides** Cham. & Schldl.

16 x 19   **P. trichoides** x **P. crispus** = **P. x bennettii** Fryer

17   **P. compressus** L.

18   **P. acutifolius** Link

19   **P. crispus** L.

20   **P. filiformis** Pers.

20 x 21   **P. filiformis** x **P. pectinatus** = **P. x suecicus** K. Richter

21   **P. pectinatus** L.

2   **GROENLANDIA** Gay

1   **G. densa** (L.) Fourr.
Potamogeton densus L.

143 RUPPIACEAE

1   RUPPIA L.

1   **R. maritima** L.

2 **R. cirrhosa** (Petagna) Grande
   Buccaferrea cirrhosa Petagna
   Ruppia maritima auct., non L.; *R. spiralis* L. ex Dumort.

144 NAJADACEAE

1 **NAJAS** L.

1 **N. flexilis** (Willd.) Rostkov & W. Schmidt
   Caulinia flexilis Willd.

2 **N. marina** L.

   a subsp. **intermedia** (Wolfg. ex Gorki) Casper
      Najas intermedia Wolfg. ex Gorki
      Najas major auct., non All.

145 ZANNICHELLIACEAE

1 **ZANNICHELLIA** L.

1 **Z. palustris** L.
   Zannichellia gibberosa Reichb.; *Z. pedunculata* Reichb.

146 ZOSTERACEAE

1 **ZOSTERA** L.

1 **Z. marina** L.

2 **Z. angustifolia** (Hornem.) Reichb.
   Zostera marina L. var. *angustifolia* Hornem.
   Zostera hornemanniana Tutin; *Z. marina* L. subsp. *hornemanniana*
   (Tutin) Rothm., nom. nud.

3 **Z. noltii** Hornem.
   Zostera nana sensu Bab., non Roth

147 ARACEAE

1 *ACORUS L.

    1 *A. calamus L.

    2 *A. gramineus Aiton

2 *LYSICHITON Schott

    1 *L. americanus Hultén & H. St. John

    2 *L. camtschatcensis (L.) Schott
    Dracontium camtschatcense L.

3 *CALLA L.

    1 *C. palustris L.

4 *ZANTEDESCHIA Sprengel

    1 *Z. aethiopica (L.) Sprengel
    Calla aethiopica L.

5 ARUM L.

    1 A. maculatum L.

    1 x 2 A. maculatum x **A. italicum**

    2 A. italicum Miller

        a subsp. **neglectum** (F. Towns.) Prime
        Arum italicum Miller var. *neglectum* F. Towns.
        Arum neglectum (F. Towns.) Ridley

        b *subsp. **italicum**

6 *DRACUNCULUS Miller

    1 *D. vulgaris Schott

7 *ARISARUM Miller

    1 *A. proboscideum (L.) Savi
       Arum proboscideum L.

148 LEMNACEAE

1 SPIRODELA Schleiden

    1 S. polyrhiza (L.) Schleiden
       Lemna polyrhiza L.

2 LEMNA L.

    1 L. gibba L.

    2 L. minor L.

    3 L. trisulca L.

    4 *L. minuta Kunth
       Lemna minuscula Herter, nom. illegit.; *L. valdiviana* auct., non
       Philippi

3 WOLFFIA Horkel ex Schleiden

    1 W. arrhiza (L.) Horkel ex Wimmer
       Lemna arrhiza L.

149 *COMMELINACEAE

1 *TRADESCANTIA L.
  Zebrina Schnitzl.

    1 *T. virginiana L.

Tradescantia x andersoniana W. Ludw. & Rohw., nom. inval.

2 **T. fluminensis* Vell. Conc.
   Tradescantia albiflora hort., ? an Kunth

150 ERIOCAULACEAE

1   **ERIOCAULON** L.

    1   **E. aquaticum** (Hill) Druce
    Cespa aquatica Hill
    Eriocaulon septangulare With.

151 JUNCACEAE

1   **JUNCUS** L.

    1   **J. squarrosus** L.

    2   **J. tenuis* Willd.
    Juncus dudleyi Wieg.; *J. macer* Gray

    3   **J. compressus** Jacq.

    4   **J. gerardii** Lois.

    5   **J. trifidus** L.

    6   **J. foliosus** Desf.

    7   **J. bufonius** L.
    Juncus bufonius L. subsp. *minutulus* (V. Krecz. & Gontch.) Soó;
    J. minutulus V. Krecz. & Gontch.

    8   **J. ambiguus** Guss.
    Juncus ranarius Nees ex Song. & Perrier

    9   **J. planifolius* R. Br.

    10   **J. capitatus** Weigel
    Juncus mutabilis Lam.

11 **J. subnodulosus** Schrank
Juncus obtusiflorus Ehrh. ex Hoffm.

12 **J. alpinoarticulatus** Chaix
Juncus alpinus Villars, nom. illegit.; *J. marshallii* Pugsley; *J. nodulosus* sensu Beeby et auct., non Wahlenb.

12 x 13 **J. alpinoarticulatus** x **J. articulatus** = **J. x buchenaui** Doerfler

13 **J. articulatus** L.
Juncus lampocarpus Ehrh. ex Hoffm.

13 x 14 **J. articulatus** x **J. acutiflorus** = **J. x surrejanus** Druce ex Stace & Lambinon

14 **J. acutiflorus** Ehrh. ex Hoffm.

15 **J. bulbosus** L.
Juncus bulbosus L. subsp. *kochii* (F. Schultz) Reichg.; *J. kochii* F. Schultz; *J. supinus* Moench

16 **J. pygmaeus** Rich.
Juncus mutabilis auct., non Lam.

17 **J. biglumis** L.

18 **J. triglumis** L.

19 **J. castaneus** Smith

20 **J. maritimus** Lam.

21 **J. acutus** L.

22 *****J. subulatus** Forsskål

23 **J. balticus** Willd.

23 x 25 **J. balticus** x **J. inflexus**

23 x 26 **J. balticus** x **J. effusus** = **J. x obotritorum** Rothm.
Juncus x scalovicus auct., non Asch. & Graebner

24 **J. filiformis** L.

25   J. inflexus L.
Juncus glaucus Sibth.

25 x 26   J. inflexus x J. effusus = J. x diffusus Hoppe

26   J. effusus L.

26 x 27   J. effusus x J. conglomeratus = J. x kern-reichgeltii Jansen &
Wachter ex Reichg.

27   J. conglomeratus L.

28   *J. pallidus R. Br.

2   **LUZULA** DC.

1   **L. forsteri** (Smith) DC.
Juncus forsteri Smith

1 x 2   **L. forsteri** x **L. pilosa** = **L. x borreri** Bromf. ex Bab.

2   **L. pilosa** (L.) Willd.
Juncus pilosus L.

3   **L. sylvatica** (Hudson) Gaudin
Juncus sylvaticus Hudson

4   ***L. luzuloides** (Lam.) Dandy & Wilm.
Juncus luzuloides Lam.

5   **L. campestris** (L.) DC.
Juncus campestris L.

6   **L. multiflora** (Ehrh.) Lej.
Juncus campestris L. var. *multiflorus* Ehrh.

    a   subsp. **multiflora**

    b   subsp. **congesta** (Thuill.) Arcang.
       Juncus congestus Thuill.

7   **L. pallidula** Kirschner
Luzula pallescens auct., non Sw.

8   **L. arcuata** Sw.

9   **L. spicata** (L.) DC.
    Juncus spicatus L.

152 CYPERACEAE

1   **ERIOPHORUM** L.

   1   **E. angustifolium** Honck.

   2   **E. latifolium** Hoppe

   3   **E. gracile** Koch ex Roth

   4   **E. vaginatum** L.
    Eriophorum brachyantherum sensu Tutin, non Trautv. & C.
    Meyer

2   **TRICHOPHORUM** Pers.

   1   **†T. alpinum** (L.) Pers.
    Eriophorum alpinum L.
    Baeothryon alpinum (L.) T. Egor.; *B. hudsonianum* (Michaux)
    Soják

   2   **T. cespitosum** (L.) Hartman
    Scirpus cespitosus L.

       a   subsp. **germanicum** (Palla) Hegi
    Trichophorum germanicum Palla
    Baeothryon cespitosum (L.) D. Dietr. subsp. *germanicum*
    (Palla) Á. Löve & D. Löve; *B. germanicum* (Palla)
    Holub; *Scirpus cespitosus* L. subsp. *germanicus* (Palla)
    Brodd.

3   **ELEOCHARIS** R. Br.

   1   **E. palustris** (L.) Roemer & Schultes
    Scirpus palustris L.

    a   subsp. **vulgaris** Walters
        Eleocharis vulgaris (Walters) Á. Löve & D. Löve

    b   subsp. **palustris**
        Eleocharis palustris (L.) Roemer & Schultes subsp.
        microcarpa Walters

1 x 3   **E. palustris** x **E. uniglumis**

    2   **E. austriaca** Hayek

    3   **E. uniglumis** (Link) Schultes
        Scirpus uniglumis Link

    4   **E. multicaulis** (Smith) Desv.
        Scirpus multicaulis Smith

    5   **E. quinqueflora** (F. Hartmann) O. Schwarz
        Scirpus quinqueflorus F. Hartmann
        Eleocharis pauciflora (Light.) Link

    6   **E. acicularis** (L.) Roemer & Schultes
        Scirpus acicularis L.

    7   **E. parvula** (Roemer & Schultes) Link ex Bluff, Nees & Schauer
        Scirpus parvulus Roemer & Schultes

4 **BOLBOSCHOENUS** (Asch.) Palla
Schoenus taxon *Bolboschoenus* Asch.

    1   **B. maritimus** (L.) Palla
        Scirpus maritimus L.
        Schoenoplectus maritimus (L.) Lye

5 **SCIRPUS** L.

    1   **S. sylvaticus** L.

6 **SCIRPOIDES** Séguier
Holoschoenus Link

    1   **S. holoschoenus** (L.) Soják

Scirpus holoschoenus L.
Holoschoenus vulgaris Link

7   SCHOENOPLECTUS (Reichb.) Palla
Scirpus subgen. *Schoenoplectus* Reichb.

1   S. lacustris (L.) Palla
Scirpus lacustris L.

1 x 3   S. lacustris x S. triqueter = S. x carinatus (Smith) Palla
Scirpus x carinatus Smith

2   S. tabernaemontani (C. Gmelin) Palla
Scirpus tabernaemontani C. Gmelin
Schoenoplectus lacustris (L.) Palla subsp. *glaucus* Bech.; *S.*
lacustris (L.) Palla subsp. *tabernaemontani* (C. Gmelin) Á.
Löve & D. Löve; *Scirpus lacustris* L. subsp. *tabernaemontani*
(C. Gmelin) Syme

2 x 3   S. tabernaemontani x S. triqueter = S. x kuekenthalianus (P.
Junge) D.H. Kent
Scirpus x kuekenthalianus P. Junge
Schoenoplectus x scheuchzeri Palla ex Janchen; *Scirpus x*
scheuchzeri Bruegger, non Vitman

3   S. triqueter (L.) Palla
Scirpus triqueter L.

4   S. pungens (Vahl) Palla
Scirpus pungens Vahl
Schoenoplectus americanus auct., non (Pers.) Volkart; *Scirpus*
americanus auct., non Pers.

8   ISOLEPIS R. Br.

1   I. setacea (L.) R. Br.
Scirpus setaceus L.

2   I. cernua (Vahl) Roemer & Schultes
Scirpus cernuus Vahl

9 ELEOGITON Link

    1 E. fluitans (L.) Link
      Scirpus fluitans L.
      Isolepis fluitans (L.) R. Br.

10 BLYSMUS Panzer ex Schultes

    1 B. compressus (L.) Panzer ex Link
      Schoenus compressus L.
      Scirpus compressus (L.) Pers., non Moench

    2 B. rufus (Hudson) Link
      Schoenus rufus Hudson
      Scirpus rufus (Hudson) Schrader

11 CYPERUS L.

    1 C. longus L.

    2 *C. eragrostis Lam.
      Cyperus vegetus Willd.

    3 C. fuscus L.

12 SCHOENUS L.

    1 S. nigricans L.

    2 S. ferrugineus L.

13 RHYNCHOSPORA Vahl

    1 R. alba (L.) Vahl
      Schoenus albus L.

    2 R. fusca (L.) W.T. Aiton
      Schoenus fuscus L.

14   **CLADIUM** P. Browne

    1   **C. mariscus** (L.) Pohl
        Schoenus mariscus L.

15   **KOBRESIA** Willd.

    1   **K. simpliciuscula** (Wahlenb.) Mackenzie
        Carex simpliciuscula Wahlenb.

16   **CAREX** L.

    1   **C. paniculata** L.

  1 x 2   **C. paniculata** x **C. appropinquata** = **C. x rotae** De Notaris
        Carex x solstitialis Figert

  1 x 3   **C. paniculata** x **C. diandra** = **C. x beckmannii** K. Keck ex F.
        Schultz
        Carex x beckmanniana Figert; *C. x germanica* K. Richter

  1 x 15   **C. paniculata** x **C. remota** = **C. x boenninghausiana** Weihe

  1 x 22   **C. paniculata** x **C. curta** = **C. x ludibunda** Gay

    2   **C. appropinquata** Schum.
        Carex paradoxa Willd., non J. Gmelin

    3   **C. diandra** Schrank
        Carex teretiuscula Gooden.

    4   **C. vulpina** L.
        Carex otrubae auct., non Podp.

    5   **C. otrubae** Podp.
        Carex cuprina (Sándor ex Heuffel) Nendtv. ex Kerner, nom.
        inval.; *C. nemorosa* Rebent., non Schrank nec Lumn. ex
        Honck.

  5 x 9   **C. otrubae** x **C. divulsa**

  5 x 15   **C. otrubae** x **C. remota** = **C. x pseudoaxillaris** K. Richter
        Carex x axillaris Gooden., non L.

6 *C. vulpinoidea** Michaux

7 C. spicata Hudson
Carex contigua Hoppe; *C. muricata* auct., non L.

8 C. muricata L.

    a   subsp. **muricata**
       Carex echinata sensu Kük. et auct., non Murray; *C. pairii*
       F. Schultz subsp. *borealis* N. Hylander

    b   subsp. **lamprocarpa** Celak.
       Carex bullockiana Nelmes; *C. muricata* L. subsp. *pairii* (F.
       Schultz) Celak.; *C. pairii* F. Schultz

9 C. divulsa Stokes

    a   subsp. **divulsa**

    b   subsp. **leersii** (Kneucker) W. Koch
       Carex muricata L. var. *leersii* Kneucker
       Carex leersiana Rauschert; *C. leersii* F. Schultz, non
       Willd.; *C. pairii* F. Schultz subsp. *leersii* (Kneucker) O.
       Schwarz; *C. polyphylla* Karelin & Kir.

9 x 15   C. divulsa x C. remota = C. x emmae L. Gross

10   C. arenaria L.
     Carex ligerica auct., non Gay

11   C. disticha Hudson

12   C. chordorrhiza L.f.

13   C. divisa Hudson

14   C. maritima Gunnerus
     Carex incurva Light.

15   C. remota L.

16   C. ovalis Gooden.
     Carex leporina sensu L.(1754) et auct., non L.(1753)

17   **C. echinata** Murray
      Carex stellulata Gooden.

17 x 18   **C. echinata** x **C. dioica** = **C. x gaudiniana** Guthnick

17 x 22   **C. echinata** x **C. curta** = **C. x biharica** Simonkai
      Carex x tetrastachya Traunst. ex Sauter, non Scheele

18   **C. dioica** L.

19   †**C. davalliana** Smith

20   **C. elongata** L.

21   **C. lachenalii** Schk.

21 x 22   **C. lachenalii** x **C. curta** = **C. x helvola** Blytt ex Fries

22   **C. curta** Gooden.
      Carex canescens sensu Light. et auct., non L.

23   **C. hirta** L.

23 x 29   **C. hirta** x **C. vesicaria** = **C. x grossii** Fiek

24   **C. lasiocarpa** Ehrh.
      Carex filiformis sensu Gooden. et auct., non L.; *C. tomentosa*
      sensu Light. et auct., non L.

24 x 26   **C. lasiocarpa** x **C. riparia** = **C. x evoluta** Hartman

25   **C. acutiformis** Ehrh.

25 x 29   **C. acutiformis** x **C. vesicaria** = **C. x ducellieri** Beauverd

25 x 65   **C. acutiformis** x **C. acuta** = **C. x subgracilis** Druce

26   **C. riparia** Curtis
      Carex acuta auct., non L.

26 x 29   **C. riparia** x **C. vesicaria** = **C. x csomadensis** Simonkai

27   **C. pseudocyperus** L.

27 x 28   **C. pseudocyperus** x **C. rostrata** = **C. x justi-schmidtii** Junge

28   **C. rostrata** Stokes
Carex ampullacea Gooden.

28 x 29   **C. rostrata** x **C. vesicaria** = **C. x involuta** (Bab.) Syme
Carex vesicaria L. var. *involuta* Bab.
Carex x pannewitziana Figert

29   **C. vesicaria** L.
Carex inflata Hudson

29 x 30   **C. vesicaria** x **C. saxatilis** = **C. x grahamii** Boott
Carex x stenolepis auct., non Less.

30   **C. saxatilis** L.

31   **C. pendula** Hudson

32   **C. sylvatica** Hudson

33   **C. capillaris** L.

34   **C. strigosa** Hudson

35   **C. flacca** Schreber
Carex glauca Murray

36   **C. panicea** L.

37   **C. vaginata** Tausch
Carex sparsiflora (Wahlenb.) Lilj. ex Steudel

38   **C. depauperata** Curtis ex With.

39   **C. laevigata** Smith
Carex helodes Link

39 x 40   **C. laevigata** x **C. binervis** = **C. x deserta** Merino

39 x 46   **C. laevigata** x **C. viridula**

39 x 47   **C. laevigata** x **C. pallescens**

40   **C. binervis** Smith

40 x 42   **C. binervis** x **C. punctata**

40 x 46   C. binervis x C. viridula = C. x corstorphinei Druce

   41   C. distans L.

41 x 43   C. distans x C. extensa = C. x tornabenii Chiov.
Carex x gotlandica Englund

41 x 44   C. distans x C. hostiana = C. x muelleriana F. Schultz

41 x 46   C. distans x C. viridula = C. x binderi Podp.

   42   C. punctata Gaudin

   43   C. extensa Gooden.

   44   C. hostiana DC.
Carex hornschuchiana Hoppe

44 x 46   C. hostiana x C. viridula = C. x fulva Gooden.
Carex x appeliana Zahn; *C. x leutzii* Kneucker

   45   C. flava L.

45 x 46   C. flava x C. viridula = C. x alsatica Zahn
Carex x pieperiana Junge; *C. x ruedtii* Kneucker

   46   C. viridula Michaux

      a   subsp. **brachyrrhyncha** (Celak.) B. Schmid
Carex flava L. subsp. *brachyrrhyncha* Celak.
Carex lepidocarpa Tausch; *C. lepidocarpa* Tausch subsp.
scotica E. Davies; *C. viridula* Michaux var. *elatior*
(Schldl.) Crins; *C. viridula* Michaux var. *lepidocarpa*
(Tausch) B. Schmid; *C. viridula* Michaux var. *scotica*
(E. Davies) B. Schmid

      b   subsp. **oedocarpa** (Andersson) B. Schmid
Carex oederi Retz. var. *oedocarpa* Andersson
Carex demissa Hornem.; *C. flava* L. subsp. *demissa*
(Hornem.) O. Bolòs, Massales & Vigo, nom. inval.;
C. oederi Retz. subsp. *demissa* (Hornem.) C. Vicioso,
nom. inval.; *C. serotina* auct., non Mérat; *C.*
tumidicarpa Andersson

c   subsp. **viridula**
   Carex bergrothii Palmgren; *C. oederi* Retz.; *C. pulchella*
   (Lönnr.) Lindman, non S. Berggren; *C. scandinavica*
   E. Davies; *C. serotina* Mérat; *C. serotina* Mérat subsp.
   pulchella (Lönnr.) Ooststr.; *C. viridula* Michaux var.
   pulchella (Lönnr.) B. Schmid

47   **C. pallescens** L.

48   **C. digitata** L.

49   **C. ornithopoda** Willd.

50   **C. humilis** Leysser

51   **C. caryophyllea** Latour.
   Carex praecox Jacq., non Schreber

52   **C. filiformis** L.
   Carex tomentosa L.

53   **C. ericetorum** Pollich

54   **C. montana** L.

55   **C. pilulifera** L.

56   **C. atrofusca** Schk.
   Carex ustulata Wahlenb., nom. illegit.

57   **C. limosa** L.

58   **C. rariflora** (Wahlenb.) Smith
   Carex limosa L. var. *rariflora* Wahlenb.

59   **C. magellanica** Lam.

   a   subsp. **irrigua** (Wahlenb.) Hiit.
      Carex limosa L. var. *irrigua* Wahlenb.
      Carex irrigua (Wahlenb.) Smith ex Hoppe; *C. paupercula*
         Michaux; *C. paupercula* Michaux subsp. *irrigua*
         (Wahlenb.) Á. Löve & D. Löve

60   **C. atrata** L.

61　**C. buxbaumii** Wahlenb.

62　**C. norvegica** Retz.
Carex vahlii Schk.

63　**C. recta** Boott

63 x 64　**C. recta** x **C. aquatilis** = **C. x grantii** A. Bennett

64　**C. aquatilis** Wahlenb.

64 x 67　**C. aquatilis** x **C. nigra** = **C. x hibernica** A. Bennett

64 x 69　**C. aquatilis** x **C. bigelowii** = **C. x limula** Fries
Carex x epigejos auct., non (Laest.) Fries

65　**C. acuta** L.
Carex gracilis Curtis

65 x 67　**C. acuta** x **C. nigra**
Carex ? x elytroides Fries

65 x 68　**C. acuta** x **C. elata** = **C. x prolixa** Fries

66　†**C. trinervis** Degl.

67　**C. nigra** (L.) Reichard
Carex acuta L. var. *nigra* L.
Carex goodenowii Gay, nom. illegit.; *C. vulgaris* Fries

67 x 68　**C. nigra** x **C. elata** = **C. x turfosa** Fries

67 x 69　**C. nigra** x **C. bigelowii** = **C. x decolorans** Wimmer

68　**C. elata** All.
Carex hudsonii A. Bennett ex F. Hanb.; *C. stricta* Gooden., non
Lam.

69　**C. bigelowii** Torrey ex Schwein.
Carex bigelowii Torrey ex Schwein. subsp. *nardeticola* Holub; *C.
bigelowii* Torrey ex Schwein. subsp. *rigida* (Raf.) Schultze-
Motel; *C. rigida* Gooden., non Schrank

70　**C. microglochin** Wahlenb.

71 **C. pauciflora** Light.

72 **C. rupestris** All.

73 **C. pulicaris** L.

153 POACEAE
Gramineae

1 ***SINARUNDINARIA** Nakai

    1 ***S. anceps** (Mitf.) C.S. Chao & Renvoize
      Arundinaria anceps Mitf.
      Arundinaria jaunsarensis Gamble

2 ***PLEIOBLASTUS** Nakai

    1 ***P. pygmaeus** (Miq.) Nakai
      Bambusa pygmaea Miq.
      Arundinaria pygmaea (Miq.) Asch. & Graebner

3 ***SASA** Makino & Shib.

    1 ***S. palmata** (Burb.) Camus
      Bambusa palmata Burb.
      Arundinaria palmata (Burb.) Bean

    2 ***S. veitchii** (Carrière) Rehder
      Bambusa veitchii Carrière

4 ***SASAELLA** Makino

    1 ***S. ramosa** (Makino) Makino & Shib.
      Sasa ramosa Makino
      Arundinaria vagans Gamble

5 ***PSEUDOSASA** Makino ex Nakai

    1 ***P. japonica** (Siebold & Zucc. ex Steudel) Makino ex Nakai

Arundinaria japonica Siebold & Zucc. ex Steudel

6 *CHIMONOBAMBUSA Makino

1 *C. quadrangularis (Fenzi) Makino
Bambusa quadrangularis Fenzi
Arundinaria quadrangularis (Fenzi) Makino

7 LEERSIA Sw.

1 L. oryzoides (L.) Sw.
Phalaris oryzoides L.

8 NARDUS L.

1 N. stricta L.

9 *STIPA L.

1 *S. neesiana Trin. & Rupr.

10 *ORYZOPSIS Michaux
Piptatherum P. Beauv.

1 *O. miliacea (L.) Benth. & J.D. Hook. ex Asch. & Schweinf.
Agrostis miliacea L.
Piptatherum miliaceum (L.) Cosson

11 MILIUM L.

1 M. effusum L.

2 M. vernale M. Bieb.
Milium scabrum Rich.

a subsp. sarniense D. McClint.

12   FESTUCA L.

1   **F. pratensis** Hudson
Festuca elatior auct., non L.

1 x 2   **F. pratensis** x **F. arundinacea** = **F. x aschersoniana** Doerfler
Festuca x intermedia Asch. & Graebner, non Roemer & Schultes

1 x 3   **F. pratensis** x **F. gigantea** = **F. x schlickumii** Grantzow

2   **F. arundinacea** Schreber
Festuca elatior L.

2 x 3   **F. arundinacea** x **F. gigantea** = **F. x fleischeri** Rohlena
Festuca x gigas O. Holmb.

3   **F. gigantea** (L.) Villars
Bromus giganteus L.

4   **F. altissima** All.

5   *****F. heterophylla** Lam.

6   **F. arenaria** Osbeck
Festuca juncifolia St.-Amans; *F. rubra* L. subsp. *arenaria*
(Osbeck) F. Aresch.

7   **F. rubra** L.

a   subsp. **rubra**

b   subsp. **juncea** (Hackel) K. Richter
Festuca rubra L. subvar. *juncea* Hackel
Festuca rubra L. subsp. *pruinosa* (Hackel) Piper

c   subsp. **litoralis** (G. Meyer) Auq.
Festuca rubra L. var. *litoralis* G. Meyer

d   subsp. **commutata** Gaudin
Festuca nigrescens Lam.; *F. rubra* L. subsp. *caespitosa*
Hackel; *F. rubra* L. var. *fallax* sensu Tutin, non
(Thuill.) Hackel

e   subsp. **arctica** (Hackel) Govoruchin
Festuca rubra L. forma *arctica* Hackel

Festuca richardsonii Hook.

f   subsp. **scotica** S. Cunn. ex Al-Bermani

g   subsp. **megastachys** Gaudin
Festuca diffusa Dumort.; *F. fallax* Thuill.; *F. heteromalla*
Pourret; *F. rubra* L. subsp. *fallax* (Thuill.) Nyman; *F.
rubra* L. subsp. *multiflora* Piper; *F. rubra* L. var. *fallax*
(Thuill.) Hackel

8   **F. ovina** L.

a   subsp. **ovina**

b   subsp. **hirtula** (Hackel ex Travis) M. Wilkinson
Festuca ovina L. subvar. *hirtula* Hackel ex Travis
Festuca filiformis Pourret subsp. *hirtula* (Hackel ex
Travis) Kerguélen; *F. hirtula* (Hackel ex Travis)
Kerguélen; *F. ophioliticola* Kerguélen subsp. *hirtula*
(Hackel ex Travis) Auq.; *F. tenuifolia* Sibth. var.
hirtula (Hackel ex Travis) Howarth

c   subsp. **ophioliticola** (Kerguélen) M. Wilk.
Festuca ophioliticola Kerguélen
Festuca ? guestfalica Boenn. ex Reichb.; *F. ophioliticola*
Kerguélen subsp. *calaminaria* Auq.; *F. ovina* L. subsp.
? guestfalica (Boenn. ex Reichb.) K. Richter

8 x 10   **F. ovina** x **F. filiformis**

9   **F. vivipara** (L.) Smith
Festuca ovina L. var. *vivipara* L.

10   **F. filiformis** Pourret
Festuca capillata Lam., nom. illegit.; *F. ovina* L. subsp. *tenuifolia*
(Sibth.) Dumort.; *F. tenuifolia* Sibth.

11   **F. armoricana** Kerguélen
Festuca ophioliticola Kerguélen subsp. *armoricana* (Kerguélen)
Auq.

12   **F. huonii** Auq.

13 F. lemanii Bast.
Festuca bastardii Kerguélen & Plonka; *F. longifolia* sensu
Howarth et auct., non Thuill.

14 F. longifolia Thuill.
Festuca caesia Smith; *F. glauca* Villars var. *caesia* (Smith)
Howarth; *F. glauca* auct., non Villars

15 F. brevipila Tracey
Festuca cinerea Villars var. *trachyphylla* (Hackel) Stohr; *F.
longifolia* sensu C.E. Hubb. et auct., non Thuill.; *F. stricta*
Host subsp. *trachyphylla* (Hackel) Patzke, nom. inval.; *F.
trachyphylla* (Hackel) Kraj., non Hackel ex Druce

12 x 13   FESTUCA x LOLIUM = X FESTULOLIUM Asch. & Graebner

1 x 1   F. pratensis x **L. perenne = X F. loliaceum** (Hudson) P. Fourn.
Festuca x loliacea Hudson

1 x 2   F. pratensis x **L. multiflorum = X F. braunii** (K. Richter) A.
Camus
Festuca x braunii K. Richter

2 x 1   F. arundinacea x **L. perenne = X F. holmbergii** (Doerfler) P.
Fourn.
Festuca x holmbergii Doerfler

2 x 2   F. arundinacea x **L. multiflorum**

3 x 1   F. gigantea x **L. perenne = X F. brinkmannii** (A. Braun) Asch.
& Graebner
Festuca x brinkmannii A. Braun

12 x 14   FESTUCA x VULPIA = X FESTULPIA Meld. ex Stace & R. Cotton

6 x 1   F. arenaria x **V. fasciculata = X F. melderisii** Stace & R.
Cotton

7 x 1   F. rubra x **V. fasciculata = X F. hubbardii** Stace & R. Cotton

7 x 2   F. rubra x **V. bromoides**

7 x 3   F. rubra x **V. myuros**

13 LOLIUM L.

    1 L. perenne L.

    1 x 2 L. perenne x **L. multiflorum** = **L. x boucheanum** Kunth
       Lolium x hybridum Hausskn.

    2 *L. multiflorum Lam.
      Lolium perenne L. subsp. *multiflorum* (Lam.) Husnot

14 VULPIA C. Gmelin
Nardurus (Bluff, Nees & Schauer) Reichb.

    1 V. fasciculata (Forsskål) Fritsch
      Festuca fasciculata Forsskål
      Vulpia membranacea auct., non (L.) Dumort.

    2 V. bromoides (L.) Gray
      Festuca bromoides L.

    3 V. myuros (L.) C. Gmelin
      Festuca myuros L.
      Vulpia megalura (Nutt.) Rydb.

    4 V. ciliata Dumort.

      a *subsp. **ciliata**

      b subsp. **ambigua** (Le Gall) Stace & Auq.
        Festuca ambigua Le Gall
        Vulpia ambigua (Le Gall) More

    5 V. unilateralis (L.) Stace
      Triticum unilaterale L.
      Nardurus maritimus (L.) Murb.; *Vulpia hispanica* (Reichard)
        Kerguélen, nom. inval.

15 CYNOSURUS L.

    1 C. cristatus L.

    2 *C. echinatus L.

16 PUCCINELLIA Parl.

1 **P. maritima** (Hudson) Parl.
Poa maritima Hudson
Glyceria maritima (Hudson) Wahlenb.

1 x 2 **P. maritima** x **P. distans** = **P. x hybrida** O. Holmb.

1 x 4 **P. maritima** x **P. rupestris** = **P. x krusemaniana** Jansen & Wachter

2 **P. distans** (Jacq.) Parl.
Poa distans Jacq.
Glyceria distans (Jacq.) Wahlenb.

    a subsp. **distans**

    b subsp. **borealis** (O. Holmb.) W.E. Hughes
      Poa retroflexa Curtis subsp. *borealis* O. Holmb.
      Puccinellia capillaris (Lilj.) Jansen

2 x 3 **P. distans** x **P. fasciculata**

2 x 4 **P. distans** x **P. rupestris** = **P. x pannonica** (Hackel) O. Holmb.
Atropis x pannonica Hackel

3 **P. fasciculata** (Torrey) E. Bickn.
Poa fasciculata Torrey
Puccinellia pseudodistans (Crépin) Jansen & Wachter

4 **P. rupestris** (With.) Fern. & Weath.
Poa rupestris With.
Glyceria rupestris (With.) E. Marshall

17 BRIZA L.

1 **B. media** L.

2 *****B. minor** L.

3 *****B. maxima** L.

18   POA L.
Parodiochloa C.E. Hubb.

1   **P. infirma** Kunth

2   **P. annua** L.

3   **P. trivialis** L.

4   **P. humilis** Ehrh. ex Hoffm.
   Poa pratensis L. subsp. *alpigena* sensu Tutin, non (Fries) Hiit.;
   P. pratensis L. subsp. *caerulea* (Smith) Tutin; *P. pratensis* L.
   subsp. *irrigata* (Lindman) Lindb.f.; *P. subcaerulea* Smith

5   **P. pratensis** L.

6   **P. angustifolia** L.
   Poa pratensis L. subsp. *angustifolia* (L.) Dumort.

7   *****P. chaixii** Villars

8   **P. flexuosa** Smith

8 x 14   **P. flexuosa** x **P. alpina** = **P. x jemtlandica** (S. Almq.) K.
   Richter
   Poa alpina L. subsp. *jemtlandica* S. Almq.

9   **P. compressa** L.

10   *****P. palustris** L.

11   **P. glauca** Vahl
   Poa balfourii Parnell

12   **P. nemoralis** L.

13   **P. bulbosa** L.

14   **P. alpina** L.

15   *****P. flabellata** (Lam.) Rasp.
   Festuca flabellata Lam.
   Parodiochloa flabellata (Lam.) C.E. Hubb.

19 DACTYLIS L.

1 D. glomerata L.

2 *D. polygama Horvátovszky
Dactylis aschersoniana Graebner; *D. glomerata* L. subsp.
aschersoniana (Graebner) Thell.; *D. glomerata* L. subsp. *lobata*
(Drejer) Lindb.f.

20 CATABROSA P. Beauv.

1 C. aquatica (L.) P. Beauv.
Aira aquatica L.
Catabrosa aquatica (L.) P. Beauv. subsp. *minor* (Bab.) Perring &
Sell

21 CATAPODIUM Link

1 C. rigidum (L.) C.E. Hubb.
Poa rigida L.
Catapodium rigidum (L.) C.E. Hubb. subsp. *majus* (C. Presl)
Perring & Sell; *Desmazeria rigida* (L.) Tutin; *Festuca rigida*
(L.) Rasp., non Roth

1 x 2 C. rigidum x **C. marinum**

2 C. marinum (L.) C.E. Hubb.
Festuca marina L.
Desmazeria marina (L.) Druce

22 SESLERIA Scop.

1 S. caerulea (L.) Ard.
Cynosurus caeruleus L.
Sesleria albicans Kittel ex Schultes; *S. caerulea* (L.) Ard. subsp.
calcarea (Celak.) Hegi

23 PARAPHOLIS C.E. Hubb.

1 P. strigosa (Dumort.) C.E. Hubb.
Lepturus strigosus Dumort.

2   **P. incurva** (L.) C.E. Hubb.
Aegilops incurva L.

24   **GLYCERIA** R. Br.

   1   **G. maxima** (Hartman) O. Holmb.
Molinia maxima Hartman

   2   **G. fluitans** (L.) R. Br.
Festuca fluitans L.

2 x 3   **G. fluitans** x **G. declinata**

2 x 4   **G. fluitans** x **G. notata** = **G. x pedicellata** F. Towns.

   3   **G. declinata** Bréb.

   4   **G. notata** Chevall.
Glyceria plicata (Fries) Fries

25   **MELICA** L.

   1   **M. nutans** L.

   2   **M. uniflora** Retz.

26   **HELICTOTRICHON** Besser ex Schultes & Schultes f.
Avenochloa Holub; *Avenula* (Dumort.) Dumort.

   1   **H. pubescens** (Hudson) Pilger
Avena pubescens Hudson
Avenochloa pubescens (Hudson) Holub; *Avenula pubescens*
   (Hudson) Dumort.

   2   **H. pratense** (L.) Besser
Avena pratensis L.
Avenochloa pratensis (L.) Holub; *Avenula pratensis* (L.) Dumort.

27   **ARRHENATHERUM** P. Beauv.

   1   **A. elatius** (L.) P. Beauv. ex J.S. Presl & C. Presl

Avena elatior L.
Arrhenatherum elatius (L.) P. Beauv. ex J.S. Presl & C. Presl
   subsp. *bulbosum* (Willd.) N. Hylander

28 *AVENA L.

1 *A. barbata Pott ex Link

2 *A. strigosa Schreber

3 *A. fatua L.

4 *A. sterilis L.

   a *subsp. ludoviciana (Durieu) Gillet & Magne
      Avena ludoviciana Durieu

5 *A. sativa L.

29 *GAUDINIA P. Beauv.

1 *G. fragilis (L.) P. Beauv.
   Avena fragilis L.

30 TRISETUM Pers.

1 T. flavescens (L.) P. Beauv.
   Avena flavescens L.

31 KOELERIA Pers.

1 K. vallesiana (Honck.) Gaudin
   Poa vallesiana Honck.

1 x 2 K. vallesiana x K. macrantha

2 K. macrantha (Ledeb.) Schultes
   Aira macrantha Ledeb.
   Koeleria albescens auct., non DC.; *K. britannica* (Domin ex
      Druce) Ujh.; *K. cristata* auct., non (L.) Pers.; *K. glauca* auct.,
      non (Sprengel) DC.; *K. gracilis* Pers., nom. illegit.

32   DESCHAMPSIA P. Beauv.

1   D. cespitosa (L.) P. Beauv.
    Aira cespitosa L.

    a   subsp. **cespitosa**

    b   subsp. **parviflora** (Thuill.) Dumort.
        Aira parviflora Thuill.

    c   subsp. **alpina** (L.) J.D. Hook.
        Aira alpina L.
        Deschampsia alpina (L.) Roemer & Schultes; *D. laevigata*
        (Smith) Smith ex Roemer & Schultes

2   D. setacea (Hudson) Hackel
    Aira setacea Hudson

3   D. flexuosa (L.) Trin.
    Aira flexuosa L.

33   HOLCUS L.

1   H. lanatus L.

1 x 2   H. lanatus x **H. mollis** = **H. x hybridus** Wein

2   H. mollis L.

34   CORYNEPHORUS P. Beauv.

1   C. canescens (L.) P. Beauv.
    Aira canescens L.

35   AIRA L.

1   A. caryophyllea L.
    Aira armoricana Albers; *A. caryophyllea* L. subsp. *armoricana*
        (Albers) Kerguélen; *A. caryophyllea* L. subsp. *multiculmis*
        (Dumort.) Bonnier & Layens; *A. caryophyllea* L. subsp.
        plesiantha (Jordan ex Boreau) K. Richter; *A. multiculmis*
        Dumort.; *A. plesiantha* Jordan ex Boreau

2   **A. praecox** L.

36   **HIEROCHLOE** R. Br.

1   **H. odorata** (L.) P. Beauv.
Holcus odoratus L.
Anthoxanthum nitens (G. Weber) Schouten & Veldk.

37   **ANTHOXANTHUM** L.

1   **A. odoratum** L.
Anthoxanthum alpinum auct., non Á. Löve & D. Löve; *A. odoratum* L. subsp. *alpinum* auct., non (Á. Löve & D. Löve) B. Jones & Meld.

2   *****A. aristatum** Boiss.
Anthoxanthum puelii Lecoq & Lamotte

38   **PHALARIS** L.

1   **P. arundinacea** L.

2   *****P. aquatica** L.
Phalaris bulbosa sensu L.(1759), non L.(1755)

3   *****P. canariensis** L.

4   *****P. minor** Retz.

5   *****P. paradoxa** L.

39   **AGROSTIS** L.

1   **A. capillaris** L.
Agrostis tenuis Sibth.

1 x 2   **A. capillaris** x **A. gigantea** = **A. x bjoerkmanii** Widén

1 x 3   *****A. capillaris** x **A. castellana** = **A. x fouilladei** P. Fourn.

1 x 4   **A. capillaris** x **A. stolonifera** = **A. x murbeckii** Fouill. ex P.
Fourn.
Agrostis x intermedia C. Weber, non Balbis

1 x 8   **A. capillaris** x **A. vinealis** = **A. ? x sanionis** Asch. & Graebner

2   **A. gigantea** Roth
Agrostis stolonifera L. var. *ramosa* Veldk.

2 x 4   **A. gigantea** x **A. stolonifera**

3 ***A. castellana** Boiss. & Reuter

4   **A. stolonifera** L.

4 x 8   **A. stolonifera** x **A. vinealis**

5 ***A. avenacea** J. Gmelin

6   **A. curtisii** Kerguélen
Agrostis setacea Curtis, non Villars

7   **A. canina** L.

8   **A. vinealis** Schreber
Agrostis canina L. subsp. *montana* (Hartman) Hartman; *A.
coarctata* Ehrh. ex Hoffm.; *A. stricta* J. Gmelin

9 ***A. scabra** Willd.
Agrostis hyemalis sensu Philipson et auct., non (Walter) Britton,
Sterns & Poggenb.

9 x 46   **AGROSTIS** x **POLYPOGON** = **X AGROPOGON** P. Fourn.

4 x 1   **A. stolonifera** x **P. monspeliensis** = **X A. littoralis** (Smith)
C.E. Hubb.
Polypogon x littoralis Smith
Agrostis x littoralis sensu Smith, non With.; *X Agropogon lutosus*
auct., non (Poiret) P. Fourn.

4 x 2   **A. stolonifera** x **P. viridis** = **X A. robinsonii** (Druce) Meld. &
D. McClint.
Agrostis x robinsonii Druce

40   CALAMAGROSTIS Adans.

1   C. epigejos (L.) Roth
Arundo epigejos L.

2   C. canescens (Wigg.) Roth
Arundo canescens Wigg.

2 x 4   C. canescens x **C. stricta** = **C. x gracilescens** (Blytt) Blytt
Calamagrostis halleriana Fries var. *gracilescens* Blytt

3   C. purpurea (Trin.) Trin.
Arundo purpurea Trin.

   a   subsp. phragmitoides (Hartman) Tzvelev
   Calamagrostis phragmitoides Hartman

4   C. stricta (Timm) Koeler
Arundo stricta Timm
Calamagrostis neglecta P. Gaertner, Meyer & Scherb., nom.
   illegit. subsp. *stricta* (Timm) Tzvelev

5   C. scotica (Druce) Druce
Deyeuxia neglecta Kunth, nom. illegit. var. *scotica* Druce
Calamagrostis neglecta auct., non P. Gaertner, Meyer & Scherb.

40 x 41   CALAMAGROSTIS x **AMMOPHILA** = **X CALAMMOPHILA**
Brand
X Ammocalamagrostis P. Fourn.

1 x 1   C. epigejos x **A. arenaria** = **X C. baltica** (Fluegge ex Schrader)
Brand
Arundo baltica Fluegge ex Schrader
Ammophila baltica (Fluegge ex Schrader) Dumort.; *X*
   Ammocalamagrostis baltica (Fluegge ex Schrader) P. Fourn.

41   AMMOPHILA Host

1   A. arenaria (L.) Link
Arundo arenaria L.

2 *A. breviligulata Fern.
Ammophila arenaria (L.) Link subsp. breviligulata (Fern.) Maire & Weiller

42 GASTRIDIUM P. Beauv.

1 G. ventricosum (Gouan) Schinz & Thell.
Agrostis ventricosa Gouan

43 *LAGURUS L.

1 *L. ovatus L.

44 APERA Adans.

1 A. spica-venti (L.) P. Beauv.
Agrostis spica-venti L.

2 A. interrupta (L.) P. Beauv.
Agrostis interrupta L.

45 MIBORA Adans.

1 M. minima (L.) Desv.
Agrostis minima L.

46 POLYPOGON Desf.

1 P. monspeliensis (L.) Desf.
Alopecurus monspeliensis L.
Polypogon paniceus (L.) Lagasca

2 *P. viridis (Gouan) Breistr.
Agrostis viridis Gouan
Agrostis semiverticillata (Forsskål) C. Chr.; Polypogon semiverticillatus (Forsskål) N. Hylander

47 ALOPECURUS L.

1 **A. pratensis** L.

1 x 2 **A. pratensis** x **A. geniculatus** = **A. x brachystylus** Peterm.
Alopecurus x hybridus Wimmer

2 **A. geniculatus** L.

2 x 3 **A. geniculatus** x **A. bulbosus** = **A. x plettkei** Mattf.

2 x 4 **A. geniculatus** x **A. aequalis** = **A. x haussknechtianus** Asch.
& Graebner

3 **A. bulbosus** Gouan

4 **A. aequalis** Sobol.
Alopecurus fulvus Smith

5 **A. borealis** Trin.
Alopecurus ? glaucus Less.; *A. alpinus* Smith, non Villars; *A. occidentalis* Scribner & Tweedy; *A. ovatus* Knapp, non G. Forster

6 **A. myosuroides** Hudson

48 *BECKMANNIA Host

1 *****B. syzigachne** (Steudel) Fern.
Panicum syzigachne Steudel

49 PHLEUM L.

1 **P. pratense** L.

2 **P. bertolonii** DC.
Phleum hubbardii D. Kováts; *P. nodosum* auct., non L.; *P. pratense* L. subsp. *bertolonii* (DC.) Bornm.; *P. pratense* L. subsp. *hubbardii* (D. Kováts) Soó; *P. pratense* L. subsp. *serotinum* (Jordan) Berher

3 **P. alpinum** L.
Phleum commutatum Gaudin

4   **P. phleoides** (L.) Karsten
     Phalaris phleoides L.

5   **P. arenarium** L.

50   **BROMUS** L.

1   ***B. arvensis** L.

2   **B. commutatus** Schrader
     Bromus pratensis Ehrh. ex Hoffm., non Lam.; *B. racemosus* L.
     subsp. *commutatus* (Schrader) Syme

2 x 3   **B. commutatus** x **B. racemosus**

3   **B. racemosus** L.

4   **B. hordeaceus** L.

     a   subsp. **hordeaceus**
          Bromus mollis L.

     b   subsp. **ferronii** (Mabille) P.M. Smith
          Bromus ferronii Mabille

     c   subsp. **thominei** (Hardouin) Braun-Blanquet
          Bromus thominei Hardouin

4 x 5   **B. hordeaceus** x **B. lepidus** = **B. x pseudothominei** P.M.
        Smith
        Bromus hordeaceus L. subsp. *pseudothominei* (P.M. Smith) H.
        Scholz; *B. x thominei* sensu Tutin et auct., non Hardouin

5   ***B. lepidus** O. Holmb.
     Bromus ? oostachys Bornm.; *B. britannicus* I.A. Williams; *B.
     gracilis* Krösche, non Leysser & Weigel

6   †**B. interruptus** (Hackel) Druce
     Bromus mollis L. var. *interruptus* Hackel

7   ***B. secalinus** L.

8   ***B. pseudosecalinus** P.M. Smith

51 BROMOPSIS (Dumort.) Fourr.
Bromus sect. *Bromopsis* Dumort.
Bromus sect. *Pnigma* Dumort.; *Zerna* auct., non Panzer

    1 B. ramosa (Hudson) Holub
    Bromus ramosus Hudson
    Zerna ramosa (Hudson) Lindman

    2 B. benekenii (Lange) Holub
    Schedonorus benekenii Lange
    Bromopsis ramosa (Hudson) Holub subsp. *benekenii* (Lange)
        Tzvelev; *Bromus benekenii* (Lange) Trimen; *Zerna benekenii*
        (Lange) Lindman; *Z. ramosa* (Hudson) Lindman subsp.
        benekenii (Lange) Tzvelev

    3 B. erecta (Hudson) Fourr.
    Bromus erectus Hudson
    Zerna erecta (Hudson) Gray

    4 *B. inermis (Leysser) Holub
    Bromus inermis Leysser
    Zerna inermis (Leysser) Lindman

        a *subsp. **inermis**

        b *subsp. **pumpelliana** (Scribner) W.A. Weber
            Bromus pumpellianus Scribner
            Bromopsis pumpelliana (Scribner) Holub; *Bromus inermis*
                Leysser subsp. *pumpellianus* (Scribner) Wagnon

52 ANISANTHA K. Koch
Bromus sect. *Genea* Dumort.

    1 *A. diandra (Roth) Tutin ex Tzvelev
    Bromus diandrus Roth
    Anisantha gussonei (Parl.) Nevski

    2 *A. rigida (Roth) N. Hylander
    Bromus rigidus Roth
    Bromus diandrus Roth subsp. *rigidus* (Roth) Laínz; *B. maximus*
        Desf., non Gilib.

    3 A. sterilis (L.) Nevski
    Bromus sterilis L.

Zerna sterilis (L.) Panzer

4 **A. tectorum* (L.) Nevski
   Bromus tectorum L.
   Zerna tectorum (L.) Lindman

5 **A. madritensis* (L.) Nevski
   Bromus madritensis L.
   Bromus diandrus sensu Curtis, non Roth; *Zerna madritensis* (L.)
      Gray

53 ***CERATOCHLOA** DC. & P. Beauv.
   Bromus sect. *Ceratochloa* (DC. & P. Beauv.) Griseb.

   1 **C. carinata* (Hook. & Arn.) Tutin
      Bromus carinatus Hook. & Arn.
      Bromus marginatus auct., non Nees ex Steudel

   2 **C. marginata* (Nees ex Steudel) B.D. Jackson
      Bromus marginatus Nees ex Steudel

   3 **C. cathartica* (Vahl) Herter
      Bromus catharticus Vahl
      Bromus unioloides (Willd.) Kunth; *B. willdenowii* Kunth

54 **BRACHYPODIUM** P. Beauv.

   1 **B. pinnatum** (L.) P. Beauv.
      Bromus pinnatus L.

   1 x 2 **B. pinnatum** x **B. sylvaticum** = **B. x cugnacii** A. Camus

   2 **B. sylvaticum** (Hudson) P. Beauv.
      Festuca sylvatica Hudson

55 **ELYMUS** L.
   Agropyron auct., non Gaertner

   1 **E. caninus** (L.) L.
      Triticum caninum L.
      Agropyron caninum (L.) P. Beauv.; *A. donianum* F.B. White;
         Elymus donianus (F.B. White) Á. Löve & D. Löve; *E.*

trachycaulus (Link) Hoover subsp. *donianus* (F.B. White) Á.
Löve; *Roegneria canina* (L.) Nevski; *R. doniana* (F.B. White)
Meld.

56   ELYTRIGIA Desv.
Agropyron auct., non Gaertner; *Thinopyrum* Á. Löve

   1   E. repens (L.) Desv. ex Nevski
        Triticum repens L.
        Agropyron repens (L.) P. Beauv.; *Elymus repens* (L.) Gould

        a   subsp. **repens**

        b   subsp. **arenosa** (Spenner) Á. Löve
            Triticum repens L. var. *arenosum* Spenner
            Agropyron maritimum (Koch & Ziz) Jansen & Wachter,
            non (L.) P. Beauv.; *Elymus repens* (L.) Gould subsp.
            arenosus (Spenner) Meld.

1 x 2   E. repens x **E. atherica = E. x oliveri** (Druce) Kerguélen ex
        Carreras Martinez
        Agropyron x oliveri Druce
        Agropyron x campestre auct., non Gren. & Godron; *Elymus x
        oliveri* (Druce) Meld. & D. McClint.

1 x 3   E. repens x **E. juncea = E. x laxa** (Fries) Kerguélen
        Triticum x laxum Fries
        Agropyron x laxum (Fries) Tutin; *Elymus x laxus* (Fries) Meld. &
        D. McClint.

   2   E. atherica (Link) Kerguélen ex Carreras Martinez
        Triticum athericum Link
        Agropyron pungens auct., non (Pers.) Roemer & Schultes; *A.
        pycnanthum* (Godron) Godron; *Elymus athericus* (Link)
        Kerguélen; *E. pungens* auct., non (Pers.) Meld.; *E.
        pycnanthus* (Godron) Meld.; *Elytrigia pungens* auct., non
        (Pers.) Tutin; *E. pycnantha* (Godron) Á. Löve

2 x 3   E. atherica x **E. juncea = E. x obtusiuscula** (Lange) N.
        Hylander
        Agropyron x obtusiusculum Lange
        Elymus x obtusiusculus (Lange) Meld. & D. McClint.

3 **E. juncea** (L.) Nevski
Triticum junceum L.
Agropyron junceum (L.) P. Beauv.; *Elymus farctus* (Viv.) Runem.
ex Meld.; *Elytrigia farcta* (Viv.) Holub; *Thinopyrum junceum*
(L.) Á. Löve

a subsp. **boreoatlantica** (Simonet & Guinochet) N.
Hylander
Agropyron junceum (L.) P. Beauv. subsp. *boreoatlanticum*
Simonet & Guinochet
Agropyron junceiforme (Á. Löve & D. Löve) Á. Löve &
D. Löve, nom. inval.; *Elymus farctus* (Viv.) Runem. ex
Meld. subsp. *boreoatlanticus* (Simonet & Guinochet)
Meld.; *Elytrigia junceiformis* Á. Löve & D. Löve;
Thinopyrum junceiforme (Á. Löve & D. Löve) Á. Löve

56 x 59 **ELYTRIGIA** x **HORDEUM** = **X ELYTRORDEUM** N. Hylander

1 x 4 **E. repens** x **H. secalinum** = **X E. langei** (K. Richter) N.
Hylander
Agropyron x langei K. Richter
X *Agrohordeum langei* (K. Richter) Camus ex A. Camus; X
Elyhordeum langei (K. Richter) Meld.

57 **LEYMUS** Hochst.
Elymus auct., non L.

1 **L. arenarius** (L.) Hochst.
Elymus arenarius L.

58 **HORDELYMUS** (Jessen) Jessen
Hordeum subgen. *Hordelymus* Jessen

1 **H. europaeus** (L.) Jessen
Elymus europaeus L.

59 **HORDEUM** L.
Critesion Raf.

1 *H. distichon L.

2 H. murinum L.
Critesion murinum (L.) Á. Löve

   a subsp. **murinum**

   b *subsp. **leporinum** (Link) Arcang.
   Hordeum leporinum Link
   Critesion murinum (L.) Á. Löve subsp. *leporinum* (Link)
   Á. Löve

3 *H. jubatum L.

4 H. secalinum Schreber
Critesion secalinum (Schreber) Á. Löve; *Hordeum nodosum* auct.,
non L.

5 H. marinum Hudson
Critesion marinum (Hudson) Á. Löve

60 *TRITICUM L.

   1 *T. aestivum L.

61 DANTHONIA DC.
Sieglingia Bernh.

   1 D. decumbens (L.) DC.
   Festuca decumbens L.
   Sieglingia decumbens (L.) Bernh.

62 *CORTADERIA Stapf

   1 *C. selloana (Schultes & Schultes f.) Asch. & Graebner
   Arundo selloana Schultes & Schultes f.

63 MOLINIA Schrank

   1 M. caerulea (L.) Moench
   Aira caerulea L.

      a subsp. **caerulea**

b   subsp. **arundinacea** (Schrank) K. Richter
     Molinia arundinacea Schrank
     Molinia caerulea (L.) Moench subsp. *altissima* (Link)
          Domin; *M. caerulea* (L.) Moench subsp. *litoralis* (Host)
          Paul

64   PHRAGMITES Adans.

1   **P. australis** (Cav.) Trin. ex Steudel
     Arundo australis Cav.
     Phragmites communis Trin.

65   *ERAGROSTIS Wolf

1   ***E. curvula** (Schrader) Nees
     Poa curvula Schrader

2   ***E. minor** Host

66   *CYNODON Rich.

1   ***C. dactylon** (L.) Pers.
     Panicum dactylon L.

2   ***C. incompletus** Nees

67   SPARTINA Schreber

1   **S. maritima** (Curtis) Fern.
     Dactylis maritima Curtis

1 x 3   **S. maritima** x **S. alterniflora** = **S. x townsendii** Groves & J.
         Groves

2   **S. anglica** C.E. Hubb.
     Spartina townsendii auct., non Groves & J. Groves

3   ***S. alterniflora** Lois.
     Spartina glabra Muhlenb. ex Bigelow

4   ***S. pectinata** Bosc ex Link

68 *ECHINOCHLOA P. Beauv.

    1 *E. crusgalli (L.) P. Beauv.
       Panicum crusgalli L.

69 *PASPALUM L.

    1 *P. distichum L.
       Paspalum paspalodes (Michaux) Scribner

70 *SETARIA P. Beauv.

    1 *S. viridis (L.) P. Beauv.
       Panicum viride L.

71 *DIGITARIA Haller

    1 *D. ischaemum (Schreber ex Schweigger) Muhlenb.
       Panicum ischaemum Schreber ex Schweigger

72 *SORGHUM Moench

    1 *S. halepense (L.) Pers.
       Holcus halepensis L.

154 SPARGANIACEAE

1 SPARGANIUM L.

    1 S. erectum L.

       a subsp. **erectum**
          Sparganium ramosum Hudson, nom. illegit.

       b subsp. **microcarpum** (Neuman) Domin
          Sparganium ramosum Hudson, nom. illegit. forma
            microcarpa Neuman

c   subsp. **neglectum** (Beeby) Schinz & Thell.
Sparganium neglectum Beeby

d   subsp. **oocarpum** (Celak.) Domin
Sparganium neglectum Beeby var. *oocarpum* Celak.
Sparganium x tardivum Topa

2   **S. emersum** Rehmann
Sparganium simplex Hudson, nom. illegit.

2 x 3   **S. emersum x S. angustifolium = S. x diversifolium**
Graebner
Sparganium x zetlandicum Druce, nom. nud.

3   **S. angustifolium** Michaux

4   **S. natans** L.
Sparganium minimum Wallr.

155 TYPHACEAE

1   **TYPHA** L.

1   **T. latifolia** L.

1 x 2   **T. latifolia x T. angustifolia = T. x glauca** Godron

2   **T. angustifolia** L.

156 *BROMELIACEAE

1 *FASCICULARIA Mez

1   *F. pitcairniifolia** (Verlot) Mez
Hechtia pitcairniifolia Verlot

2 *OCHAGAVIA Philippi

1   *O. carnea** (Beer) Lyman B. Smith & Looser
Bromelia carnea Beer

Fascicularia litoralis auct., non (Philippi) Mez

157 *PONTEDERIACEAE

1 *PONTEDERIA L.

    1 *P. cordata L.

158 LILIACEAE
Alliaceae; Amaryllidaceae; Trilliaceae

1 TOFIELDIA Hudson

    1 T. pusilla (Michaux) Pers.
    Narthecium pusillum Michaux

2 NARTHECIUM Hudson

    1 N. ossifragum (L.) Hudson
    Anthericum ossifragum L.

3 *ASPHODELUS L.

    1 *A. albus Miller

4 SIMETHIS Kunth

    1 S. planifolia (L.) Gren.
    Anthericum planifolium L.

5 *HEMEROCALLIS L.

    1 *H. fulva (L.) L.
    Hemerocallis lilioasphodelus L. var. *fulva* L.

    2 *H. lilioasphodelus L.
    Hemerocallis flava L., nom. illegit.

6 *KNIPHOFIA Moench

    1 *K. uvaria (L.) Oken
      Aloe uvaria L.
      Kniphofia aloides Moench

    2 *K. praecox Baker

7 COLCHICUM L.

    1 C. autumnale L.

8 LLOYDIA Salisb. ex Reichb.

    1 L. serotina (L.) Reichb.
      Bulbocodium serotinum L.

9 GAGEA Salisb.

    1 G. lutea (L.) Ker Gawler
      Ornithogalum luteum L.

    2 G. bohemica (Zauschner) Schultes & Schultes f.
      Ornithogalum bohemicum Zauschner
      Gagea saxatilis auct., non (Mert. & Koch) Schultes & Schultes f.

10 *TULIPA L.

    1 *T. sylvestris L.

    2 *T. saxatilis Sieber ex Sprengel

    3 *T. gesneriana L.

11 *FRITILLARIA L.

    1 *F. meleagris L.

12 *LILIUM L.

    1 *L. martagon L.

    2 *L. pyrenaicum Gouan

13 CONVALLARIA L.

    1 C. majalis L.

14 POLYGONATUM Miller

    1 P. multiflorum (L.) All.
    Convallaria multiflora L.

    1 x 2 P. multiflorum x P. odoratum = P. x hybridum Bruegger
    Polygonatum x intermedium Boreau, non Dumort.

    2 P. odoratum (Miller) Druce
    Convallaria odorata Miller

    3 P. verticillatum (L.) All.
    Convallaria verticillata L.

15 MAIANTHEMUM Wigg.

    1 M. bifolium (L.) F.W. Schmidt
    Convallaria bifolia L.

16 *REINECKEA Kunth

    1 *R. carnea (Andrews) Kunth
    Sansevieria carnea Andrews

17 PARIS L.

    1 P. quadrifolia L.

18 ORNITHOGALUM L.

    1 O. pyrenaicum L.

    2 O. angustifolium Boreau
       Ornithogalum umbellatum auct., non L.

    3 *O. nutans L.

19 SCILLA L.

    1 *S. bifolia L.

    2 *S. messeniaca Boiss.

    3 *S. siberica Haw.

    4 S. verna Hudson

    5 *S. lilio-hyacinthus L.

    6 *S. peruviana L.

    7 S. autumnalis L.

20 HYACINTHOIDES Heister ex Fabr.
Endymion Dumort.

    1 *H. italica (L.) Rothm.
       Scilla italica L.

    2 H. non-scripta (L.) Chouard ex Rothm.
       Hyacinthus non-scriptus L.
       Endymion non-scriptus (L.) Garcke; *Scilla non-scripta* (L.)
          Hoffsgg. & Link

  2 x 3 H. non-scripta x **H. hispanica**
       Scilla ? x patula Lam. ex DC.

    3 *H. hispanica (Miller) Rothm.
       Scilla hispanica Miller
       Endymion hispanicus (Miller) Chouard

21 *HYACINTHUS L.

1 *H. orientalis L.

22 *CHIONODOXA Boiss.

1 *C. forbesii Baker
Chionodoxa luciliae sensu Baker, non Boiss.; *Scilla forbesii* (Baker) Speta; *S. siehii* (Stapf) Speta

2 *C. sardensis Drude

23 *MUSCARI Miller

1 *M. neglectum Guss. ex Ten.
Muscari atlanticum Boiss. & Reuter

2 *M. armeniacum Leichtlin ex Baker

3 *M. botryoides (L.) Miller
Hyacinthus botryoides L.

4 *M. comosum (L.) Miller
Hyacinthus comosus L.

24 ALLIUM L.

1 A. schoenoprasum L.

2 *A. unifolium Kellogg

3 *A. roseum L.
Allium roseum L. subsp. *bulbiferum* (DC.) E. Warb.

4 *A. neapolitanum Cirillo

5 *A. subhirsutum L.

6 *A. moly L.

7 *A. triquetrum L.

8 *A. pendulinum Ten.

9 *A. paradoxum (M. Bieb.) Don
    Scilla paradoxa M. Bieb.

10 A. ursinum L.

11 A. oleraceum L.

12 *A. carinatum L.

13 A. ampeloprasum L.
    Allium babingtonii Borrer

14 A. scorodoprasum L.

15 A. sphaerocephalon L.

16 A. vineale L.

17 *A. nigrum L.

25 *NECTAROSCORDUM Lindley

1 *N. siculum (Ucria) Lindley
    Allium siculum Ucria

    a *subsp. siculum

    b *subsp. bulgaricum (Janka) Stearn
        Nectaroscordum bulgaricum Janka

26 *NOTHOSCORDUM Kunth

1 *N. borbonicum Kunth
    Allium gracile auct., non Aiton
    Allium inodorum auct., non Aiton; *Nothoscordum inodorum*
        auct., non (Aiton) Nicholson; *N. gracile* sensu Stearn, non
        (Aiton) Stearn

27 *AGAPANTHUS L'Hér.

1 *A. praecox Willd.

    a *subsp. **orientalis** (F.M. Leighton) F.M. Leighton
    Agapanthus orientalis F.M. Leighton

28 *TRISTAGMA Poeppig
Ipheion Raf.

1 *T. uniflorum (Lindley) Traub
Triteleia uniflora Lindley
Ipheion uniflorum (Graham) Raf.; *Milla uniflora* Graham

29 *AMARYLLIS L.

1 *A. belladonna L.

30 *STERNBERGIA Waldst. & Kit.

1 *S. lutea (L.) Ker Gawler ex Sprengel
Amaryllis lutea L.

31 LEUCOJUM L.

1 L. aestivum L.

    a subsp. **aestivum**

    b *subsp. **pulchellum** (Salisb.) Briq.
    Leucojum pulchellum Salisb.

2 L. vernum L.

32 GALANTHUS L.

1 G. nivalis L.

1 x 2 G. nivalis x G. elwesii

1 x 3 *G. nivalis x G. plicatus

2 *G. elwesii J.D. Hook.

3 *G. caucasicus (Baker) Grossh.
  Galanthus nivalis L. subsp. *caucasicus* Baker

4 *G. plicatus M. Bieb.

   a *subsp. plicatus

   b *subsp. byzantinus (Baker) D. Webb
     Galanthus byzantinus Baker

33 NARCISSUS L.

1 *N. tazetta L.

1 x 3 *N. tazetta x N. poeticus = N. x medioluteus Miller
  Narcissus x biflorus Curtis; *N. x poeticus* auct., non L.

2 *N. papyraceus Ker Gawler

3 *N. poeticus L.

   a *subsp. poeticus
     Narcissus majalis Curtis, nom. illegit.; *N. ornatus* Haw.

   b *subsp. radiiflorus (Salisb.) Baker
     Narcissus radiiflorus Salisb.

3 x 5 *N. poeticus x N. pseudonarcissus = N. x incomparabilis
  Miller

4 *N. bulbocodium L.

5 N. pseudonarcissus L.

   a subsp. pseudonarcissus
     Narcissus gayii (Hénon) Pugsley

   b *subsp. obvallaris (Salisb.) Fernandes
     Narcissus obvallaris Salisb.

c *subsp. **major** (Curtis) Baker
   Narcissus major Curtis
   Narcissus hispanicus Gouan

5 x jon *N. **pseudonarcissus** x N. **jonquilla** L. = N. x **odorus** L.
   Narcissus x infundibulum Poiret

6 *N. **cyclamineus** DC.

34 ASPARAGUS L.

1 A. **officinalis** L.

a subsp. **prostratus** (Dumort.) Corbière
   Asparagus prostratus Dumort.

b *subsp. **officinalis**

35 RUSCUS L.

1 R. **aculeatus** L.

2 *R. **hypoglossum** L.

36 *ALSTROEMERIA L.

1 *A. **aurea** Graham
   Alstroemeria aurantiaca D. Don

159 IRIDACEAE

1 *LIBERTIA Sprengel

1 *L. **formosa** Graham
   Libertia chilensis (Molina) Klotzsch ex Baker, nom. inval.

2 *L. **elegans** Poeppig

2 SISYRINCHIUM L.

1 **S. bermudiana** L.
Sisyrinchium graminoides Bickn.; *S. hibernicum* Á. Löve & D. Löve

2 ***S. montanum** E. Greene
Sisyrinchium bermudiana auct., non L.

3 ***S. californicum** (Ker Gawler) Dryander
Marica californica Ker Gawler
Hydastylis borealis Bickn.; *Sisyrinchium boreale* (Bickn.) J.K. Henry

4 ***S. laxum** Otto ex Sims
Sisyrinchium chilense Hook. var. *urambabense* Vargas; *S. iridifolium* Kunth subsp. *valdivianum* (Philippi) Ravenna

5 ***S. striatum** Smith

3 *ARISTEA Sol. ex Aiton

1 ***A. ecklonii** Baker

4 *HERMODACTYLUS Miller

1 ***H. tuberosus** (L.) Miller
Iris tuberosa L.

5 IRIS L.

1 ***I. germanica** L.

2 ***I. sibirica** L.

3 **I. pseudacorus** L.

4 ***I. versicolor** L.

4 x vir ***I. versicolor** x I. virginica L. = I. x robusta E.S. Anderson

5 *I. ensata Thunb.
   Iris kaempferi Siebold ex Lemaire

6 *I. spuria L.

7 *I. orientalis Miller
   Iris ochroleuca L.; *I. spuria* L. subsp. *ochroleuca* (L.) Dykes

8 I. foetidissima L.

9 *I. latifolia (Miller) Voss
   Xiphion latifolia Miller
   Iris xiphioides Ehrh.

10 *I. xiphium L.
   Iris variabilis Jacq.

fil x tin *I. filifolia Boiss. x I. tingitana Boiss. & Reuter = I. x
   hollandica hort.

6 *WATSONIA Miller

   1 *W. borbonica (Pourret) Goldblatt
     Lomenia borbonica Pourret

      a *subsp. ardernei (Sander) Goldblatt
        Watsonia ardernei Sander
        Watsonia meriana auct., non (L.) Miller

7 ROMULEA Maratti

   1 R. columnae Sebast. & Mauri

   2 *R. rosea (L.) Ecklon
     Ixia rosea L.

8 *CROCUS L.

   1 *C. vernus (L.) Hill
     Crocus sativus L. var. *vernus* L.
     Crocus purpureus Weston

2 *C. tommasinianus Herbert

3 *C. nudiflorus Smith

4 *C. kotschyanus K. Koch

5 *C. sieberi Gay

6 *C. chrysanthus (Herbert) Herbert
   Crocus annulatus Herbert var. *chrysanthus* Herbert

7 *C. flavus Weston
   Crocus aureus Smith

8 *C. speciosus M. Bieb.

9 *C. pulchellus Herbert

9 GLADIOLUS L.

1 G. illyricus Koch

2 *G. communis L.

    a *subsp. communis

    b *subsp. byzantinus (Miller) A.P. Ham.
       Gladiolus byzantinus Miller

10 *IXIA L.

1 *I. campanulata Houtt.
   Ixia speciosa Andrews

2 *I. paniculata Delaroche

11 *SPARAXIS Ker Gawler

1 *S. grandiflora (Delaroche) Ker Gawler
   Ixia grandiflora Delaroche

12 *FREESIA Ecklon ex Klatt

> **1 *F. x hybrida** L. Bailey
> *Freesia x refracta* auct., non (Jacq.) Ecklon ex Klatt

13 *CROCOSMIA Planchon
Curtonus N.E. Br.; *Montbretia* DC.

> **1 *C. paniculata** (Klatt) Goldblatt
> *Antholyza paniculata* Klatt
> *Curtonus paniculatus* (Klatt) N.E. Br.

> **2 *C. masoniorum** (L. Bolus) N.E. Br.
> *Tritonia masoniorum* L. Bolus

> **3 *C. pottsii** (Macnab ex Baker) N.E. Br.
> *Montbretia pottsii* Macnab ex Baker
> *Tritonia pottsii* (Macnab ex Baker) Baker

> **3 x aur *C. pottsii** x **C. aurea** (Hook.) Planchon = **C. x crocosmiiflora**
> (Lemoine ex Burb. & Dean) N.E. Br.
> *Montbretia x crocosmiiflora* Lemoine ex Burb. & Dean
> *Tritonia x crocosmiiflora* (Lemoine ex Burb. & Dean) Nicholson

14 *CHASMANTHE N.E. Br.

> **1 *C. bicolor** (Gasp. ex Ten.) N.E. Br.
> *Antholyza bicolor* Gasp. ex Ten.
> *Antholyza aethiopica* L. var. *bicolor* (Gasp. ex Ten.) Baker

160 *AGAVACEAE

1 *YUCCA L.

> **1 *Y. recurvifolia** Salisb.

2 *AGAVE L.

> **1 *A. americana** L.

3 *CORDYLINE Comm. ex Adr. Juss.

    1 *C. australis (G. Forster) Endl.
      Dracaena australis G. Forster

4 *PHORMIUM Forster & G. Forster

    1 *P. tenax Forster & G. Forster

    2 *P. cookianum Le Jolis
      Phormium colensoi J.D. Hook.

161 DIOSCOREACEAE

1 TAMUS L.

    1 T. communis L.

162 ORCHIDACEAE
Cypripediaceae

1 CYPRIPEDIUM L.

    1 C. calceolus L.

2 CEPHALANTHERA Rich.

    1 C. damasonium (Miller) Druce
      Serapias damasonium Miller

  1 x 2 C. damasonium x C. longifolia = C. x schulzei Camus,
      Bergon & A. Camus
      Cephalanthera x salaevensis Rouy

    2 C. longifolia (L.) Fritsch
      Serapias helleborine L. var. *longifolia* L.

    3 C. rubra (L.) Rich.
      Serapias rubra L.

3 EPIPACTIS Zinn

1 E. palustris (L.) Crantz
Serapias helleborine L. var. *palustris* L.

2 E. atrorubens (Hoffm.) Besser
Serapias atrorubens Hoffm.

2 x 4 E. atrorubens x **E. helleborine** = **E. x schmalhausenii** K. Richter

3 E. purpurata Smith
Epipactis helleborine (L.) Crantz praesp. *purpurata* (Smith) Sunderm., nom. inval.; *E. sessilifolia* Peterm.; *E. violacea* (Dur.-Duq.) Boreau

3 x 4 E. purpurata x **E. helleborine** = **E. x schulzei** P. Fourn.

4 E. helleborine (L.) Crantz
Serapias helleborine L.

5 E. youngiana A. Richards & A. Porter

6 E. leptochila (Godfery) Godfery
Epipactis viridiflora (Hoffm.) Reichb. var. *leptochila* Godfery
Epipactis cleistogama C. Thomas; *E. dunensis* (Stephenson & T.A. Stephenson) Godfery; *E. helleborine* (L.) Crantz praesp. *leptochila* (Godfery) Sunderm., nom. inval.

7 E. phyllanthes G.E. Smith
Epipactis cambrensis C. Thomas; *E. confusa* D.P. Young; *E. helleborine* (L.) Crantz praesp. *phyllanthes* (G.E. Smith) Sunderm., nom. inval.; *E. helleborine* (L.) Crantz subsp. *phyllanthes* (G.E. Smith) Sunderm., nom. inval.; *E. pendula* C. Thomas, non A.A. Eaton; *E. vectensis* (Stephenson & T.A. Stephenson) Brooke & F. Rose

4 EPIPOGIUM Gmelin ex Borkh.

1 E. aphyllum Sw.

5   **NEOTTIA** Guett.

   1   **N. nidus-avis** (L.) Rich.
     Ophrys nidus-avis L.

6   **LISTERA** R. Br.

   1   **L. ovata** (L.) R. Br.
     Ophrys ovata L.

   2   **L. cordata** (L.) R. Br.
     Ophrys cordata L.

7   **SPIRANTHES** Rich.

   1   **S. spiralis** (L.) Chevall.
     Ophrys spiralis L.

   2 †**S. aestivalis** (Poiret) Rich.
     Ophrys aestivalis Poiret

   3   **S. romanzoffiana** Cham.
     Spiranthes romanzoffiana Cham. subsp. *gemmipara* (Smith)
       Clapham; *S. romanzoffiana* Cham. subsp. *stricta* (Rydb.)
       Clapham

8   **GOODYERA** R. Br.

   1   **G. repens** (L.) R. Br.
     Satyrium repens L.

9   **LIPARIS** Rich.

   1   **L. loeselii** (L.) Rich.
     Ophrys loeselii L.

10   **HAMMARBYA** Kuntze

   1   **H. paludosa** (L.) Kuntze
     Ophrys paludosa L.

Malaxis paludosa (L.) Sw.

11   CORALLORRHIZA Ruppius ex Gagnebin
Corallorhiza Châtel.

   1   C. trifida Châtel.

12   HERMINIUM L.

   1   H. monorchis (L.) R. Br.
   Ophrys monorchis L.

13   PLATANTHERA Rich.

   1   P. chlorantha (Custer) Reichb.
   Orchis chlorantha Custer

   1 x 2   P. chlorantha x **P. bifolia** = **P. x hybrida** Bruegger

   2   P. bifolia (L.) Rich.
   Orchis bifolia L.

13 x 15   PLATANTHERA x **PSEUDORCHIS** = **X PSEUDANTHERA**
McKean

   1 x 1   P. chlorantha x **P. albida** = **X P. breadalbanensis** McKean

14   ANACAMPTIS Rich.

   1   A. pyramidalis (L.) Rich.
   Orchis pyramidalis L.

14 x 16   ANACAMPTIS x **GYMNADENIA** = **X GYMNANACAMPTIS**
Asch. & Graebner

   1 x 1   A. pyramidalis x **G. conopsea** = **X G. anacamptis** (Wilms)
   Asch. & Graebner
   Gymnadenia x anacamptis Wilms

15 **PSEUDORCHIS** Séguier
Leucorchis E. Meyer

    1 **P. albida** (L.) Á. Löve & D. Löve
       Satyrium albidum L.
       Leucorchis albida (L.) E. Meyer

15 x 16 **PSEUDORCHIS x GYMNADENIA = X PSEUDADENIA** P. Hunt

    1 x 1 **P. albida x G. conopsea = X P. schweinfurthii** (Hegelm. ex A.
       Kerner) P. Hunt
       Gymnadenia x schweinfurthii Hegelm. ex A. Kerner
       X *Gymleucorchis schweinfurthii* (Hegelm. ex A. Kerner)
       Stephenson & T.A. Stephenson, nom. inval.

15 x 18 **PSEUDORCHIS x DACTYLORHIZA = X PSEUDORHIZA** P. Hunt

    1 x 2 **P. albida x D. maculata = X P. bruniana** (Bruegger) P. Hunt
       Orchis x bruniana Bruegger

16 **GYMNADENIA** R. Br.

    1 **G. conopsea** (L.) R. Br.
       Orchis conopsea L.

       a subsp. **conopsea**

       b subsp. **densiflora** (Wahlenb.) Camus, Bergon & A.
         Camus
         Orchis conopsea L. var. *densiflora* Wahlenb.

       c subsp. **borealis** (Druce) F. Rose
         Habenaria gymnadenia Druce var. *borealis* Druce
         Gymnadenia conopsea (L.) R. Br. var. *borealis* (Druce)
           Godfery; *G. conopsea* (L.) R. Br. var. *insulicola* Heslop-
           Harrison; *G. odoratissima* sensu Pamplin et auct., non
           (L.) Rich.

16 x 17 **GYMNADENIA** x **COELOGLOSSUM** = **X GYMNAGLOSSUM**
Rolfe

    1 x 1 **G. conopsea** x **C. viride** = **X G. jacksonii** (Quirk) Rolfe
    X Gymplatanthera jacksonii Quirk

16 x 18 **GYMNADENIA** x **DACTYLORHIZA** = **X DACTYLODENIA** Garay
& H. Sweet

    1 x 1 **G. conopsea** x **D. fuchsii** = **X D. st-quintinii** (Godfery) J.
    Duvign.
    X Orchigymnadenia st-quintinii Godfery
    X Dactylodenia ? heinzeliana (Reichhardt) Garay & H. Sweet; *X
    D. cookei* (Heslop-Harrison) Peitz; *X Dactylogymnadenia
    cookei* (Heslop-Harrison) Soó

    1 x 2 **G. conopsea** x **D. maculata** = **X D. legrandiana** (Camus) Peitz
    Gymnadenia x legrandiana Camus
    X Dactylodenia evansii (Druce) Averyanov, nom. inval.; *X D.
    souppensis* (Camus) Peitz; *X Dactylogymnadenia legrandiana*
    (Camus) Soó

    1 x 3 **G. conopsea** x **D. incarnata** = **X D. vollmannii** (Schulze) Peitz
    X Orchigymnadenia vollmanii Schulze
    X Dactylogymnadenia vollmannii (Schulze) Soó

    1 x 4 **G. conopsea** x **D. praetermissa** = **X D. wintoni** (Druce) Peitz
    Habenaria x wintoni Druce
    X Dactylogymnadenia wintoni (Druce) Soó

    1 x 5 **G. conopsea** x **D. purpurella** = **X D. varia** (Stephenson & T.A.
    Stephenson) Averyanov
    X Orchigymnadenia varia Stephenson & T.A. Stephenson
    X Dactylogymnadenia varia (Stephenson & T.A. Stephenson)
    Soó

17 **COELOGLOSSUM** Hartman

    1 **C. viride** (L.) Hartman
    Satyrium viride L.

17 x 18 **COELOGLOSSUM x DACTYLORHIZA = X DACTYLOGLOSSUM** P. Hunt & Summerh.

1 x 1 **C. viride x D. fuchsii = X D. mixtum** (Asch. & Graebner) Rauschert
X Orchicoeloglossum mixtum Asch. & Graebner

1 x 2 **C. viride x D. maculata = X D. dominianum** (Camus, Bergon & A. Camus) Soó
Orchis x dominiana Camus, Bergon & A. Camus
Orchis x mixta Domin, non Retz.

1 x 5 **C. viride x D. purpurella = X D. viridella** (J. Heslop-Harrison) Soó
Orchis x viridella J. Heslop-Harrison

18 **DACTYLORHIZA** Necker ex Nevski
Dactylorchis (Klinge) Vermeulen

1 **D. fuchsii** (Druce) Soó
Orchis fuchsii Druce
Dactylorchis fuchsii (Druce) Vermeulen; *D. fuchsii* (Druce)
Vermeulen subsp. *hebridensis* (Wilm.) J. Heslop-Harrison;
D. fuchsii (Druce) Vermeulen subsp. *okellyi* (Druce)
Vermeulen; *D. okellyi* (Druce) Butcher, nom. inval.;
Dactylorhiza hebridensis (Wilm.) Averyanov; *D. longebracteata*
sensu Holub, non (F.W. Schmidt) Holub; *D. maculata* (L.)
Soó praesp. *fuchsii* (Druce) Sunderm., nom. inval.; *D.*
maculata (L.) Soó subsp. *fuchsii* (Druce) N. Hylander; *D.*
maculata (L.) Soó subsp. *okellyi* (Druce) H. Baumann &
Kunkele; *D. okellyi* (Druce) Averyanov; *Orchis ? meyeri*
Reichb.; *O. longebracteata* sensu Holub, non F.W. Schmidt

1 x 2 **D. fuchsii x D. maculata = D. x transiens** (Druce) Soó
Orchis x transiens Druce
Dactylorhiza x corylensis (Heslop-Harrison) Soó

1 x 3 **D. fuchsii x D. incarnata = D. x kerneriorum** (Soó) Soó
Orchis x kerneriorum Soó
Dactylorhiza x engadinensis (Cif. & Giacom.) Soó, nom. inval.;
Orchis x engadinensis Cif. & Giacom., nom. nud.; *D. x*
variabilis (J. Heslop-Harrison) Soó

1 x 4 **D. fuchsii** x **D. praetermissa** = **D. x grandis** (Druce) P. Hunt
Orchis x grandis Druce
Dactylorhiza x mortonii (Druce) Soó

1 x 5 **D. fuchsii** x **D. purpurella** = **D. x venusta** (Stephenson & T.A. Stephenson) Soó
Orchis x venusta Stephenson & T.A. Stephenson
Dactylorhiza x hebridella (Wilm.) Soó

1 x 6 **D. fuchsii** x **D. majalis** = **D. x braunii** (Hal.) Borsos & Soó
Orchis x braunii Hal.

1 x 7 **D. fuchsii** x **D. traunsteineri**
Dactylorhiza x kelleriana P. Hunt, nom. inval.; *D. x robertsii*
Averyanov, nom. inval.

2 **D. maculata** (L.) Soó
Orchis maculata L.
Dactylorchis maculata (L.) Vermeulen

   a subsp. **ericetorum** (E.F. Linton) P. Hunt & Summerh.
   Orchis maculata L. subsp. *ericetorum* E.F. Linton
   Dactylorchis maculata (L.) Vermeulen subsp. *ericetorum*
   (E.F. Linton) Vermeulen; *D. maculata* (L.) Vermeulen
   subsp. *rhoumensis* (J. Heslop-Harrison) J. Heslop-
   Harrison; *Dactylorhiza ericetorum* (E.F. Linton)
   Averyanov; *D. maculata* (L.) Soó subsp. *rhoumensis* (J.
   Heslop-Harrison) Soó; *D. maculata* (L.) Soó subsp.
   cornubiensis (Pugsley) Soó; *D. maculata* (L.) Soó var.
   praecox (A. Webster) Soó; *Orchis elodes* auct., non
   Griseb.; *O. fuchsii* Druce subsp. *rhoumensis* J. Heslop-
   Harrison

2 x 3 **D. maculata** x **D. incarnata** = **D. x carnea** (Camus) Soó
Orchis x carnea Camus
Dactylorhiza x ampolai Hautzinger; *D. x claudiopolitana*
(Simonkai) Borsos & Soó; *D. x maculatiformis* (Rouy) Borsos
& Soó

2 x 4 **D. maculata** x **D. praetermissa** = **D. x hallii** (Druce) Soó
Orchis x hallii Druce
Dactylorhiza ? x townsendiana (Rouy) Soó

2 x 5 **D. maculata** x **D. purpurella** = **D. x formosa** (Stephenson &
T.A. Stephenson) Soó
Orchis x formosa Stephenson & T.A. Stephenson

2 x 6 **D. maculata** x **D. majalis** = **D. x dinglensis** (Wilm.) Soó
Orchis x dinglensis Wilm.
Dactylorhiza x townsendiana auct., non (Rouy) Soó

2 x 7 **D. maculata** x **D. traunsteineri** = **D. x jenensis** (Brand) Soó
Orchis x jenensis Brand
Orchis x schulzei K. Richter, non Hausskn. & Nyman

3 **D. incarnata** (L.) Soó
Orchis incarnata L.
Dactylorchis incarnata (L.) Vermeulen

    a subsp. **incarnata**
Dactylorchis incarnata (L.) Vermeulen subsp. *gemmana*
(Pugsley) J. Heslop-Harrison; *Dactylorhiza gemmana*
(Pugsley) Averyanov; *D. incarnata* (L.) Soó subsp.
gemmana (Pugsley) Sell; *Orchis strictifolia* Opiz

    b subsp. **coccinea** (Pugsley) Soó
Orchis latifolia L. var. *coccinea* Pugsley
Dactylorchis incarnata (L.) Vermeulen subsp. *coccinea*
(Pugsley) J. Heslop-Harrison; *Dactylorhiza coccinea*
(Pugsley) Averyanov; *Orchis strictifolia* Opiz subsp.
coccinea (Pugsley) Clapham

    c subsp. **pulchella** (Druce) Soó
Orchis incarnata L. var. *pulchella* Druce
Dactylorchis incarnata (L.) Vermeulen subsp. *pulchella*
(Druce) J. Heslop-Harrison; *Dactylorhiza pulchella*
(Druce) Averyanov

    d subsp. **cruenta** (Mueller) Sell
Orchis cruenta Mueller
Dactylorchis incarnata (L.) Vermeulen subsp. *cruenta*
(Mueller) Vermeulen; *Dactylorhiza cruenta* (Mueller)
Soó; *D. incarnata* (L.) Soó praesp. *cruenta* (Mueller)
Sunderm., nom. inval.; *D. incarnata* (L.) Soó var.
cruenta (Mueller) N. Hylander

    e subsp. **ochroleuca** (Boll) P. Hunt & Summerh.
Orchis incarnata L. var. *ochroleuca* Boll

Dactylorchis incarnata (L.) Vermeulen subsp. *ochroleuca*
(Boll) J. Heslop-Harrison; *Dactylorhiza incarnata* (L.)
Soó var. *ochroleuca* (Boll) N. Hylander; *D. ochroleuca*
(Boll) Holub

3 x 4　**D. incarnata** x **D. praetermissa** = **D. x wintoni** (A. Camus) P.
Hunt
Orchis x wintoni A. Camus

3 x 5　**D. incarnata** x **D. purpurella** = **D. x latirella** (P. Hall) Soó
Orchis x latirella P. Hall

3 x 6　**D. incarnata** x **D. majalis** = **D. x aschersoniana** (Hausskn.)
Soó
Orchis x aschersoniana Hausskn.

3 x 7　**D. incarnata** x **D. traunsteineri** = **D. x dufftii** (Hausskn.)
Peitz
Orchis x dufftii Hausskn.
Dactylorhiza x lehmanii (Klinge) Soó; *D. x thellungiana* (Braun-
Blanquet) Soó

4　**D. praetermissa** (Druce) Soó
Orchis praetermissa Druce
Dactylorchis praetermissa (Druce) Vermeulen; *D. praetermissa*
(Druce) Vermeulen var. *junialis* (Vermeulen) Vermeulen;
Dactylorhiza majalis (Reichb.) P. Hunt & Summerh. subsp.
pardalina (Pugsley) E. Nelson, nom. inval.; *D. majalis*
(Reichb.) P. Hunt & Summerh. subsp. *praetermissa* (Druce)
David Moore & Soó; *D. majalis* (Reichb.) P. Hunt &
Summerh. var. *junialis* (Vermeulen) Senghas; *D. pardalina*
(Pugsley) Averyanov; *Orchis pardalina* Pugsley

4 x 5　**D. praetermissa** x **D. purpurella** = **D. x insignis** (Stephenson
& T.A. Stephenson) Soó
Orchis x insignis Stephenson & T.A. Stephenson
Dactylorhiza x salteri (Stephenson) Soó

4 x 7　**D. praetermissa** x **D. traunsteineri**

5　**D. purpurella** (Stephenson & T.A. Stephenson) Soó
Orchis purpurella Stephenson & T.A. Stephenson
Dactylorchis purpurella (T. & T.A. Stephenson) Vermeulen;
Dactylorhiza majalis (Reichb.) P. Hunt & Summerh. praesp.
purpurella (Stephenson & T. A. Stephenson) Sunderm., nom.

inval.; *D. majalis* (Reichb.) P. Hunt & Summerh. subsp.
purpurella (Stephenson & T.A. Stephenson) David Moore &
Soó; *D. occidentalis* (Pugsley) Soó var. *muculosa* (Stephenson)
Bateman & Denholm

5 x 6   **D. purpurella** x **D. majalis**

6   **D. majalis** (Reichb.) P. Hunt & Summerh.
Orchis majalis Reichb.
Dactylorchis majalis (Reichb.) Vermeulen; *Dactylorhiza ?*
fistulosa (Moench) H. Baumann & Kunkele

   a   subsp. **occidentalis** (Pugsley) Sell
   Orchis majalis Reichb. var. *occidentalis* Pugsley
   Dactylorchis occidentalis (Pugsley) Vermeulen;
      Dactylorhiza kerryensis (Wilm.) P. Hunt & Summerh.;
      D. kerryensis (Wilm.) P. Hunt & Summerh. subsp.
      occidentalis (Pugsley) H.Baumann & Kunkele; *D.*
      latifolia (L.) Soó subsp. *occidentalis* (Pugsley) Soó; *D.*
      majalis (Reichb.) P. Hunt & Summerh. subsp.
      kerryensis (Wilm.) Senghas, nom. illegit.; *D. majalis*
      (Reichb.) P. Hunt & Summerh. subsp. *scotica* E.
      Nelson; *D. majalis* (Reichb.) P. Hunt & Summerh.
      var. *kerryensis* (Wilm.) Bateman & Denholm; *D.*
      majalis (Reichb.) P. Hunt & Summerh. var. *scotica*
      (Nelson) Bateman & Denholm; *D. occidentalis*
      (Pugsley) Soó

   b   subsp. **cambrensis** (Roberts) Roberts
   Dactylorchis majalis (Reichb.) Vermeulen subsp.
      cambrensis Roberts
   Dactylorhiza cambrensis (Roberts) Averyanov; *D. latifolia*
      (L.) Soó subsp. *cambrensis* (Roberts) Soó; *D. majalis*
      (Reichb.) P. Hunt & Summerh. var. *cambrensis*
      (Roberts) Bateman & Denholm; *D. purpurella*
      (Stephenson & T.A. Stephenson) Soó subsp.
      majaliformis E. Nelson ex Ljtnant

7   **D. traunsteineri** (Sauter ex Reichb.) Soó
   Orchis traunsteineri Sauter ex Reichb.
   Dactylorchis traunsteinerioides (Pugsley) Vermeulen; *D.*
      traunsteineri (Sauter ex Reichb.) Vermeulen; *Dactylorhiza*
      francis-drucei (Wilm.) Averyanov; *D. majalis* (Reichb.) P.
      Hunt & Summerh. subsp. *traunsteineri* (Sauter ex Reichb.)
      D. Webb, nom. inval.; *D. majalis* (Reichb.) P. Hunt &

Summerh. subsp. *traunsteinerioides* (Pugsley) Bateman &
Denholm; *D. majalis* (Reichb.) P. Hunt & Summerh. var.
eborensis (Godfery) Bateman & Denholm; *D. majalis*
(Reichb.) P. Hunt & Summerh. var. *francis-drucei* (Wilm.)
Bateman & Denholm; *D. traunsteineri* (Sauter ex Reichb.)
Soó subsp. *francis-drucei* (Wilm.) Soó; *D. traunsteineri*
(Sauter ex Reichb.) Soó subsp. *hibernica* Landw.; *D.*
traunsteineri (Sauter ex Reichb.) Soó subsp. *traunsteinerioides*
(Pugsley) Soó; *D. traunsteinerioides* (Pugsley) Landw., nom.
inval.

8 D. lapponica (Hartman) Soó
Orchis angustifolia M. Bieb. var. *lapponica* Hartman
Dactylorhiza pseudocordigera (Neumann) Soó; *D. traunsteineri*
(Sauter ex Reichb.) Soó subsp. *lapponica* (Hartman) Soó

19 NEOTINEA Reichb.f.

1 N. maculata (Desf.) Stearn
Satyrium maculatum Desf.
Neotinea intacta (Link) Reichb.f.

20 ORCHIS L.

1 O. laxiflora Lam.

1 x 3 O. laxiflora x **O. morio** = **O. x alata** Fleury

2 O. mascula (L.) L.
Orchis morio L. var. *mascula* L.

2 x 3 O. mascula x **O. morio** = **O. x morioides** Brand
Orchis x wilmsii Camus, non K. Richter

3 O. morio L.

4 O. ustulata L.

5 O. purpurea Hudson

6 O. militaris L.

6 x 7 O. militaris x **O. simia** = **O. x beyrichii** A. Kerner

7   **O. simia** Lam.

0 x 21   ORCHIS x **ACERAS** = **X ORCHIACERAS** Camus

7 x 1   **O. simia** x **A. anthropophorum** = **X O. bergonii** (Nanteuil)
Camus
Orchis x bergonii Nanteuil
Orchis x weberi Chodat

21   ACERAS R. Br.

1   **A. anthropophorum** (L.) W.T. Aiton
Ophrys anthropophora L.

22   HIMANTOGLOSSUM Koch

1   **H. hircinum** (L.) Sprengel
Satyrium hircinum L.
Orchis hircina (L.) Crantz

23   OPHRYS L.

1   **O. insectifera** L.
Ophrys muscifera Hudson

1 x 2   **O. insectifera** x **O. sphegodes** = **O. x hybrida** Pokorny

1 x 3   **O. insectifera** x **O. apiferà**
Ophrys x pietzschii Kumpel ex Rauschert, nom. inval.

2   **O. sphegodes** Miller

3   **O. apifera** Hudson
Ophrys apifera Hudson subsp. *jurana* Ruppert; *O. apifera*
Hudson subsp. *trollii* (Hegetschw.) K. Richter; *O. holoserica*
(Burm.f.) Greuter; *O. trollii* Hegetschw.

3 x 4   **O. apifera** x **O. fuciflora** = **O. x albertiana** Camus

4   **O. fuciflora** (Crantz) Moench
Orchis fuciflora Crantz
Orchis holoserica auct., non (Burm.f.) Greuter

Index

The names of families and genera, and in the genera *Carex*, *Hieracium*, *Rubus* and *Taraxacum* the names of species, are indexed. Page-references to accepted names are in Roman, to synonyms in italics.